PHOTOGRAPHIC G
to the • wildflowers
of South Africa

Supported by the
National Botanical Institute

Supported by the UK
Darwin Initiative (Department for
Environment, Food and Rural Affairs)

PHOTOGRAPHIC GUIDE
to the wildflowers
of South Africa

JOHN MANNING

BRIZA

Photographs by John Manning and Colin Paterson-Jones

Published by

BRIZA

BRIZA PUBLICATIONS
CK 90/11690/23

PO Box 56569
Arcadia 0007
Pretoria
South Africa

First edition, first impression, 2003

ISBN 1 875093 42 7

Managing editor   Reneé Ferreira
Production coordinator   Douglas van der Horst
Copy-editor   David Pearson
Proofreader   Tessa Kennedy
Cover and inside design   Lyndall du Toit
Typesetting   Gerhardt van Rooyen
Distribution maps   Gavin Swingewood
Reproduction   Unifoto, Cape Town
Printed and bound by   Tien Wah Press (Pte.) Ltd, Singapore

Acknowledgements

I would like to thank Hester Steyn of the National Herbarium for providing the distribution maps, Prof. Gideon Smith for his support of this project, Cornelia Clack and Pascale Chesselet for their help in identifying the Aizoaceae, and Julian Lloyd for very kindly checking the spelling of the vernacular names. These have been largely derived from two incomparable sources: Elsa Pooley's *A Field Guide to Wildflowers: KwaZulu-Natal and the Eastern Region*, published by the Natal Flora Publications Trust, and Auriol Batten & Hertha Bokelman's *Wild Flowers of the Eastern Cape Province*, originally published by Books of Africa and subsequently rewritten by myself as *South African Wild Flower Guide 11: Eastern Cape*, published by the Botanical Society of South Africa in association with the National Botanical Institute. I am especially grateful to Colin Paterson-Jones, who did not hesitate in associating himself with this project, thereby making an impossible task feasible, and finally, it is with great pleasure that I thank all the friends and colleagues who shared their knowledge and field experience with me.

The map of the biomes is derived from Rutherford, M.C. (1997) 'Categorization of biomes', in Cowling, R.M., Richardson, D.M., Pierce, S.M. (eds) *Vegetation of Southern Africa*, Cambridge University Press, Cambridge, pp. 91–98. I am very grateful to Les Powrie of the National Botanical Institute for providing it in electronic format.

The Briza production team are to be complimented on their patience and professionalism. It has been a pleasure to work with them all.

Page 1:   *Brilliant orange* Arctotis fastuosa *brightens the granite hills around Springbok* (JCM)

Pages 2–3:   *A pink froth of* Brunsvigia bosmaniae *foams about the dolerite outcrops near Nieuwoudtville in autumn* (JCM)

Page 6:   *Golden rivulets of* Didelta carnosa *among the dunes fringing Table Bay* (JCM)

Page 8:   *Bright yellow* Rhynchopsidium pumilum *and magenta mesembs near Calvinia* (JCM)

Page 20:   *Damp grassland in the KwaZulu-Natal Drakensberg* (JCM)

Page 120:   *Arid fynbos in the Olifants River Mountains* (JCM)

Page 262:   *Spring annuals among the granite outcrops in Namaqualand* (JCM)

Contents

Introduction

SOUTH AFRICA IS A wildflower paradise, home to a rich flora of around 19 000 different species of flowering plants. These range from diminutive succulents little more than a centimetre high to towering forest giants. Many are extremely beautiful. The country has a long history of interest in its plants but the sheer number of species makes their identification difficult, even for professional botanists. The number of wildflower guides available in bookstores is eloquent testimony to this. Traditionally, and with good reason, these guides have concentrated on the plants from a more or less well-defined geographical area, possibly a region, province or even a single reserve.

To buy all the guides covering the country is expensive, and the alternative is to try to provide a single guide to all or most of the country. At first sight it would seem impossible to achieve even passable coverage of the whole country in a single volume but the task, although daunting, is not impossible, for two main reasons.

Firstly, not all of the flowering plants are likely to attract the attention of a passer-by. Among such is the group that comprises grasses, sedges and reeds. Although they are the dominant vegetation group over much of the country, and of the first importance in its ecology, grasses seldom draw attention except en masse. Another group that can be excluded comprises trees and larger shrubs. The small flowers that characterise many of these plants, combined with the difficulty in reaching them, means that their identification is a highly specialised discipline that relies on features of the leaves, stem and bark. In addition, there are several first-class identification manuals available about the trees of southern Africa. Of the remaining wildflowers, many are either very inconspicuous, in which case they are unlikely to attract attention, or they are rare or very localised in their distribution, which means that they are unlikely to be seen at all. By excluding trees, grasses and other grass-like families, as well as those plants that are not readily noticed or encountered, the number of wildflowers is substantially reduced. Of this smaller number, even less are common enough or interesting enough to attract attention. Quite which species fulfil these requirements can only be established by extensive field knowledge and I sincerely hope that mine proves equal to the task.

The second reason that such a guide is possible is that not all parts of the country are equally rich in wildflowers and therefore not equally likely to be visited by those interested in seeing them. The greater part of the western interior of the country, for instance, is arid and relatively poor in wildflowers. This is not to say that wildflowers cannot be found in the Karoo and Kalahari; some very striking species occur there but they are few and far between in comparison to the rest of the country. Excluding certain groups of plants, concentrating on those that are most likely to be seen, and focusing on those parts of the country in which one is most likely to see them, reduces the coverage necessary for a successful field guide. This reasoning has led to this book.

It illustrates nearly 900 of the most common and conspicuous wildflowers in South Africa and concentrates on those that are most likely to attract the attention of the average traveller in the more popularly visited parts of the country. These are particularly the Drakensberg of Mpumalanga, KwaZulu-Natal and the Eastern Cape, the eastern seaboard, the Western Cape and Namaqualand. Within these areas three main wildflower regions have been identified that coincide in broad terms with one or more of the main vegetation types that occur across the country. These three regions are Grassland and Savannah, Fynbos, and Namaqualand. The floras of these three regions are largely complementary, with little overlap, and the few common species that stretch across more than one region are featured in each.

Symbols used in this guide

The distribution maps for each species have been generated from specimens housed in the collections of the National Botanical Institute in Pretoria and the Compton Herbarium in Cape Town. As such they represent the recorded occurrence of each species and not necessarily the total actual distribution, although in most instances these will coincide. It is therefore very unlikely that the species will be found much outside of the ranges shown. Flowering time is illustrated by a bar with the main months of flowering highlighted in  and months in which sporadic flowering can be expected coloured in ▣ . For example:

Abbreviations used in vernacular names

(A) Afrikaans
(E) English
(N) Nama and related Khoisan languages
(SS) South Sotho
(Sw) Swazi
(X) Xhosa
(Z) Zulu

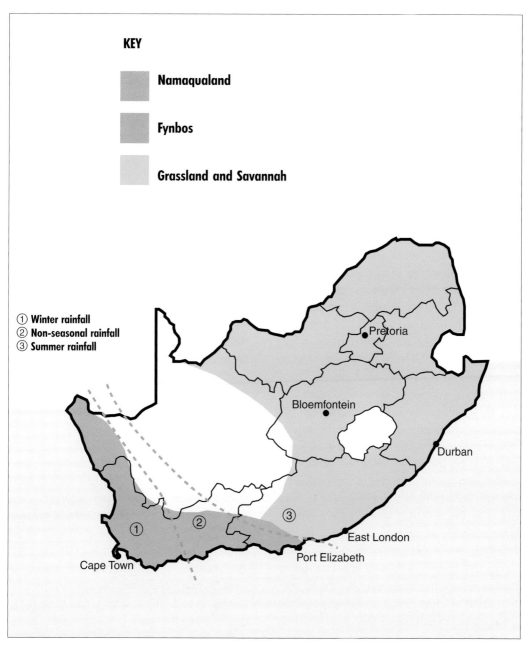

THE THREE WILDFLOWER REGIONS RECOGNISED IN THIS BOOK. THE SPECIES TREATED ARE GROUPED IN THESE THREE REGIONS.

Wildflower regions and climate

THE NATURAL VEGETATION of southern Africa can be divided into seven broad classes based on the dominant types of plants that occur in them, including such groups as trees, grasses and other herbaceous perennials, or annual herbs. The classes are termed biomes and each is defined by the dominant lifestyle found among its component plants. These lifestyles are a direct response to climatic factors, especially the average annual rainfall, the season in which most of it falls and the degree of summer aridity. The biomes are defined, therefore, on the structure of the vegetation rather than on the identity of the individual species. No less than eight different biomes occur in South Africa alone (although the Desert Biome is largely restricted to the Namibian coast and enters South Africa only along the lower reaches of the Orange, or Gariep, River). The large number of biomes that occur in South Africa is a reflection of the great variation in climate that occurs across the country. Climate is the prime determinant for the diversity of wildflowers that characterise a region and is, in turn, determined by its geography, latitude (and therefore the weather systems associated with it), and the ocean currents that pass along its coasts.

The eastern and western shores of southern Africa are washed by two very different currents, with dissimilar effects on their rainfall. In the east the Agulhas current flows southwards, bringing warm tropical water with it and raising the humidity of the air above it to levels that sustain the lush, subtropical vegetation that characterises the eastern seaboard. The west coast, in sharp contrast, is an arid desert, the result of the cold Benguela current that sweeps northwards from the southern polar region, lowering the humidity and reducing rainfall. Here the vegetation is dominated by a dwarf succulent shrubland. Between these two different coasts is the central plateau, which supports temperate grassland in the east and a semi-arid scrubland in the west. This plateau drops dramatically along the Drakensberg to the coastal plain in the east; to the west it slopes gently and then drops gradually to the coast.

To the south the coastal forelands have been folded into the parallel ranges of sandstone rock that form the towering ramparts of the Cape Fold mountains, which are the bastion of fynbos shrubland. Compounding the differences in the coastal currents is the influence of two distinct weather systems. The bulk of the country comes under the sway of a tropical high-pressure system that prevents warm, moisture-laden air from the Indian Ocean reaching the interior in winter. The result is that the central and eastern parts of the country receive the bulk of their rain during the summer months, in the form of thunderstorms and showers carried from the Indian Ocean by north-easterly winds. In contrast, the south-western part of the country receives the bulk of its rain in winter,

when it comes under the influence of a low-pressure system that moves north at this time of the year. From April to September westerly winds drive a series of cold fronts across the southern part of the country, depositing rain in their wake. Sandwiched between these two regions is a narrow band that receives relatively little rain throughout the year.

South Africa's biomes are the result of the interplay between these geographical and climatological influences.

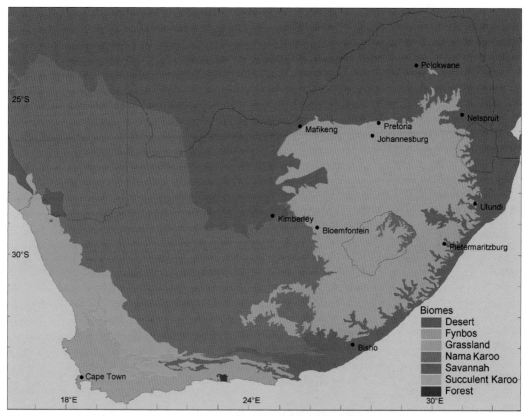

THE MAJOR VEGETATION CLASSES, OR BIOMES, RECOGNISED IN SOUTHERN AFRICA

Forest Biome

Forests are restricted to frost-free areas with a mean annual rainfall of more than 525 mm in the winter rainfall region and more than 725 mm in the summer rainfall region. They are sensitive to fire and persist only in places where fires are rare or absent, in humid coastal areas or protected valleys.

Forests cover only around 0,5% of South Africa's surface. They occur mainly as patches along the southern and eastern coast of the country, and inland along the eastern edge of the escarpment up to 2 100 m above sea level. They comprise a continuous canopy of mostly evergreen trees, beneath which is a multi-layered understorey of smaller trees and shrubs. The dense shade beneath the canopy prevents a distinct ground layer of plants from developing. Some 650 different woody plant species and almost as many herbaceous ones have been recorded from the forests of South Africa.

Scadoxus multiflorus *in coastal swamp forest*

Thicket Biome

Thicket replaces forest where the rainfall is too low to support true forest but where the absence of fires still allows the development of a vegetation type dominated by woody plants.

Thicket occurs as a series of narrow strips along the southern and especially eastern coasts, interdigitated among other vegetation types, mainly along river valleys. It covers just over 3% of the land area of the country. Thicket is a closed shrubland or low forest dominated by evergreen, small-leaved or succulent trees, shrubs and vines, many of which are armed with spines on their stems. It is often impenetrable and is not obviously layered, with little herbaceous cover on the ground.

Savannah Biome

The Savannah Biome is the largest in southern Africa, occupying around 46% of the land area. It is best developed in the northern and north-eastern parts of the country where it covers large areas of land, but small patches have also developed in the south-east. It is delimited largely by an average summer rainfall of 235–1 000 mm, which is insufficient to prevent the development of a woody canopy but enough to allow a grass layer to persist. Frost is a relatively uncommon occurrence.

Savannah is characterised by a grassy ground layer overtopped by a distinct upper layer of woody plants. The shrub or tree layer varies greatly in height, from 1 to 20 m, giving rise to a variety of different vegetation types, known variously as shrubveld, bushveld or woodland. Frequent fires are an important factor in maintaining them and almost all species in the biome are adapted to survive fires.

Grassland Biome

Grassland is found chiefly on the high central plateau and inland areas in the eastern part of the country, where it covers around 26% of the area, from near the coast to 2 850 m above sea level. The Grassland Biome is delimited by a combination of mean annual rainfall between 400–2 000 mm and low winter temperatures that prevent the development of a layer of woody plants.

Grassland is dominated by a single layer of grasses, and trees are absent except in a few localised habitats, such as rock outcrops. Fires are a frequent occurrence and the majority of associated plants are adapted to them, often flowering only after a fire has removed the grassy canopy. These plants form a class known as forbs, protecting their renewal buds and shoots from damage by fire and frost by keeping them underground, either in bulbs or other woody rootstocks. These underground organs also store nutrients and enable the forbs to sprout rapidly in the

Gerbera viridifolia *in high grassland*

spring before the grass cover can re-grow after a fire. The combination of fire, frost and grazing ensures the dominance of grasses and other herbaceous perennials by preventing the establishment of trees.

Nama Karoo Biome

Nama Karoo covers around 23% of the country in the drier, western half of the central plateau between 500–2 000 m above sea level. The distribution of this biome is determined primarily by a low annual summer rainfall of 100–520 mm per year.

The vegetation is dominated by an open, grassy, dwarf shrubland and the relatively sparse cover means that fires are rare. In historical times large nomadic or migratory herds of springbok and other game traversed the area following patches of rainfall occurrences.

Succulent Karoo Biome

The Succulent Karoo occurs in a band below the western and southern edges of the central escarpment north of the Cape Fold Belt, mainly below 800 m but up to 1 500 m above sea level in the east, covering 6,5% of the land area. The biome is delimited essentially by a low winter rainfall of below 200 mm and extreme summer aridity. Fog is common near the coast but frost is rare.

The vegetation of the Succulent Karoo is dominated by a unique assemblage of dwarf, succulent shrubs of which the mesembs and stonecrops are especially prominent. Annuals are also common and provide mass displays in the spring but grasses are rare. The number of plant species, mainly succulents, is high and unparalleled elsewhere in the world for an arid area of this size. Around half of the biome falls within the area known as Namaqualand.

Fynbos Biome

Fynbos covers just over 6% of the land area in the extreme south and south-west of southern Africa but supports something less than half of all the species recorded in southern Africa. The distribution of the biome is determined by moderate to high winter rainfall, between 210–3 000 mm with moderate to high summer aridity.

Fynbos is an open or closed shrubland dominated by leathery and often fine-leaved woody shrubs and perennials together with a high representation (around 16%) of bulbous and cormous plants. Although seldom more than 3 m in height, it is more or less distinctly three-layered, with a canopy of medium or tall shrubs, especially members of the protea and erica families, a median layer of grasses, restios and small shrubs, and an understorey of herbaceous perennials. This basic structure is subject to the age of the vegetation as determined by the interval between successive fires, which affects the relative contribution that each of these classes makes.

Fire is an essential element in the biome, serving to rejuvenate the vegetation. The frequency normally varies between 4 and 25 years. Many of the plant species in fynbos are highly localised in their distribution.

Desert Biome

The Desert Biome in southern Africa comprises the Namib Desert, which forms a broad belt along the west coast of Namibia. The climate is characterised by low summer rainfall of between 13–70 mm, resulting in extreme summer aridity. Coastal fogs are frequent and some strand plants are adapted to make use of this additional source of moisture, absorbing it through their leaves. The plant diversity is lowest of all the biomes.

The vegetation is dominated by annuals, which avoid water stress in the form of seeds. They include several grasses. North of the Swakop River is a narrow belt, no more than 200 m wide, of dwarf shrubs that depend on the coastal fogs for their survival.

JCM

Erica inflata *in montane fynbos*

Recommended regional wildflower guides

Grassland and Savannah

FABIAN, A. & G. GERMISHUIZEN. 1997. *Wildflowers of northern South Africa.* Fernwood Press, Cape Town.

MANNING, J.C. 2001. *Eastern Cape. South African Wildflower Guide 11.* Botanical Society of S.A. and the National Botanical Institute, Cape Town.

ONDERSTAL, J. 1984. *Transvaal lowveld and escarpment. South African Wildflower Guide 4.* Botanical Society of S.A. and the National Botanical Institute, Cape Town.

POOLEY, E. 1998. *A field guide to wildflowers: KwaZulu-Natal and the Eastern Region.* Natal Flora Publications Trust, Durban.

SHEARING, D. 1994. *Karoo. South African Wildflower Guide 6.* Botanical Society of S.A. and the National Botanical Institute, Cape Town.

VAN ROOYEN, N. 2001. *Flowering plants of the Kalahari dunes.* Ekotrust cc, Pretoria.

Fynbos

BURMAN, L. & A. BEAN. 1985. *Hottentots Holland to Hermanus. South African Wildflower Guide 5.* Botanical Society of S.A. and the National Botanical Institute, Cape Town.

MANNING, J. & P. GOLDBLATT. 2000. *West Coast. South African Wildflower Guide 7.* Botanical Society of S.A. and the National Botanical Institute, Cape Town.

MAYTHAM KIDD, M. 1996. *Cape Peninsula. South African Wildflower Guide 3.* Botanical Society of S.A. and the National Botanical Institute, Cape Town.

MORIARTY, A. 1996. *Outeniqua, Tsitsikamma and eastern Little Karoo. South African Wildflower Guide 2.* Botanical Society of S.A. and the National Botanical Institute, Cape Town.

MUSTART, P., R. COWLING & J. ALBERTYN. 1997. *Southern Overberg. South African Wildflower Guide 8.* Botanical Society of S.A. and the National Botanical Institute, Cape Town.

VANDERPLANK, H. J. 1998. *Wildflowers of the Port Elizabeth area: Swartkops to Sundays Rivers.* Bluecliff Publishing, Hunters Retreat.

VANDERPLANK, H. J. 1999. *Wildflowers of the Port Elizabeth area: Gamtoos to Swartkops Rivers.* Bluecliff Publishing, Hunters Retreat.

VAN ROOYEN, G. & H. STEYN. 1999. *Cedarberg, Clanwilliam and Biedouw valley. South African Wildflower Guide 10.* Botanical Society of S.A. and the National Botanical Institute, Cape Town.

Namaqualand

LE ROUX, A. & T. SCHELPE. 1988. *Namaqualand. South African Wildflower Guide 1.* Botanical Society of S.A. and the National Botanical Institute, Cape Town.

MANNING, J. & P. GOLDBLATT. 1997. *Nieuwoudtville, Bokkeveld Plateau and Hantam. South African Wildflower Guide 9.* Botanical Society of S.A. and the National Botanical Institute, Cape Town.

Quick guide to

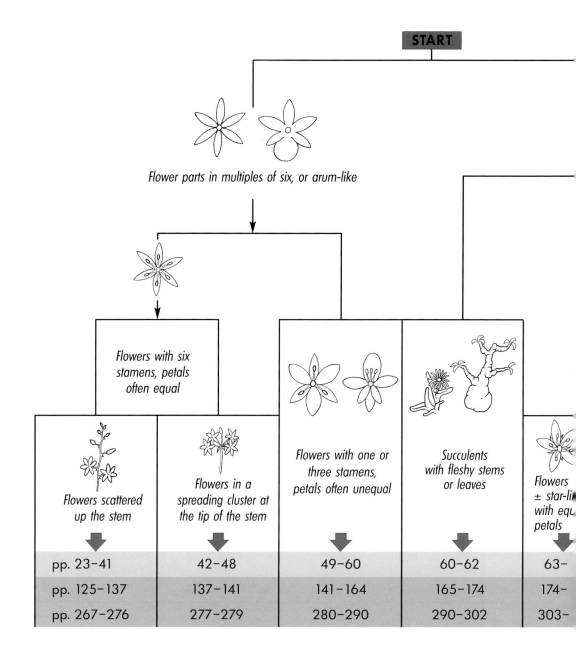

START

Flower parts in multiples of six, or arum-like

Flowers with six stamens, petals often equal		Flowers with one or three stamens, petals often unequal	Succulents with fleshy stems or leaves	Flowers ± star-li♦ with equ♦ petals
Flowers scattered up the stem	Flowers in a spreading cluster at the tip of the stem			
pp. 23–41	42–48	49–60	60–62	63–
pp. 125–137	137–141	141–164	165–174	174–
pp. 267–276	277–279	280–290	290–302	303–

wildflower groups

Use this pictorial guide to narrow down your options. Select the features shown by your plant from each successive pair of characteristics offered in the guide until you reach the group of species that displays this combination of features. Then turn to the relevant pages and match your plant to the illustrations. Read the descriptions carefully for details, especially colour variations.

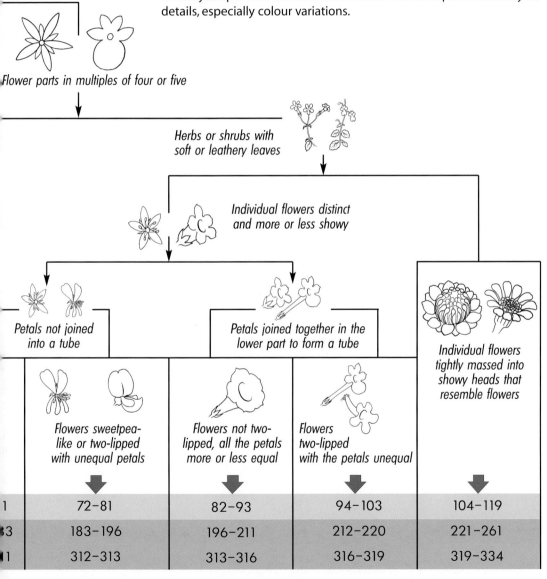

Flower parts in multiples of four or five

Herbs or shrubs with soft or leathery leaves

Individual flowers distinct and more or less showy

Petals not joined into a tube

Petals joined together in the lower part to form a tube

Individual flowers tightly massed into showy heads that resemble flowers

Flowers sweetpea-like or two-lipped with unequal petals

Flowers not two-lipped, all the petals more or less equal

Flowers two-lipped with the petals unequal

	72–81	82–93	94–103	104–119
3	183–196	196–211	212–220	221–261
1	312–313	313–316	316–319	319–334

Grassland and Savannah

GRASSLAND AND SAVANNAH are the most common vegetation types in South Africa and together they cover a little under two-thirds of the country. Along the eastern seaboard they are interpolated by fingers of thicket running up the river valleys, while patches of coastal and mistbelt forest are dotted along the east coast or form a discontinuous arc along the seaward side of the eastern escarpment. In the south-western interior the grassy vegetation gives way to a more arid scrubland called the Karoo. Together these various vegetation types cover almost 90% of the land area of South Africa and account for something in the region of 10 000 species of flowering plants, or around half of the total number found in the country.

These diverse vegetation types are all characteristic of the summer rainfall part of South Africa, unlike the Cape Region and Namaqualand, which occupy the winter rainfall portion of the country. The grasslands of South Africa are home to many of its most lovely wildflowers. The flowering season is lengthy, stretching throughout the rainy season from early spring through summer and into early autumn. There are two peaks in flowering over this period, one in spring and the other in late summer, with a slight dip in midsummer.

Blooming of wildflowers associated with grasslands, known to ecologists as forbs, is greatly stimulated by burning off the grass cover in winter. These forbs typically have tuberous large, woody rootstocks that burst into growth after the first rains, quickly sending up annual shoots that flower before the grass cover can re-establish itself and choke the smaller and more delicate species. In late October the burned grasslands of the KwaZulu-Natal Midlands and Mpumalanga present a colourful spectacle of daisies, milkweeds, wild peas, pelargoniums and other wildflowers. Among the daisies, the most conspicuous are several species of gerbera in various colours, purple vernonias, and yellow thistles in the genus *Berkheya*. The most spectacular of the gerberas are undoubtedly the orange-flowered *G. aurantiaca*, which is now rather rare, and the red-flowered *G. jamesonii*, which is fortunately quite common in bushveld around Lydenburg and Nelspruit. Other wonderful spring-flowering wildflowers are the several species of crinum and arum lily, especially the glorious golden *Zantedeschia pentlandii*. The jewels of the summer months are two lovely members of the Gloriosa family, *Littonia* and *Sandersonia*, bearing elegant orange bells.

By late summer many of the more robust bulbous plants have grown up and are coming into flower. These include several species of gladiolus, watsonia, agapanthus and pineapple flowers. At this time of the year the most profitable areas to visit are the higher-lying grasslands along the edge of the Mpumalanga escarpment, especially around Wakkerstroom and Graskop, and the KwaZulu-Natal Drakensberg. Here the climate is cooler and moister and numerous montane and alpine wildflowers can be seen in bloom. All of the mountain resorts are worth visiting at this time of the year. In the north the slopes of The Sentinel are an alpine garden while to the south the hillsides around the remote mountain village of Rhodes are studded with the almost impossibly large, scarlet flowers of *Gladiolus saundersii*.

Along the coast the flame-like flowers of *Gloriosa* can be seen shimmering in the coastal scrub while several species of orchid can be found in flower in the damper grasslands. One of the most breathtaking sights, however, must be the scarlet heads of the fireball lily, *Scadoxus multiflorus*, glowing like embers in the gloom of coastal forests. These glorious plants grow only in the dankest, darkest parts of the forest and the sight of a colony in full bloom is a magical experience. At this time of the year, too, the magnificent, balloon-sized flower heads of the brunsvigias can be seen in suitable grasslands. Their spherical heads bear the flowers on long spokes that stiffen in fruit to form a rigid ball that breaks free from the bulb and bowls along in the wind, scattering seeds along its path.

Any relatively pristine area of grassland will contain numerous wildflowers but over-grazing rapidly reduces the diversity, and plantations are the ultimate disaster for much of the richest grasslands along the eastern escarpment. Road verges and railway preserves, which are protected from grazing, can be rich refuges for wildflowers. The more arid western parts of the country are rather less rewarding although various annuals appear rapidly after rain and some lovely shrubs, such as the brilliant yellow *Rhigozum obovatum*, also burst into flower then.

Papaver aculeatum *growing in roadside scree in the KwaZulu-Natal Drakensberg*

Stylochiton natalensis

ARUM FAMILY

Bushveld arum (E), umFana-nkomo (Z)

(Latin *natalensis*, from Natal)

Tuberous perennial, 10–40 cm
high. Leaves arrow-shaped with netted vena-
tion. Flowers solitary at ground level, crowded
in a narrow spike which is enclosed by a flask-
shaped, leathery, creamy yellow bract.
Habitat: Stony grassland and open woodland.
Notes: Roots and leaves used medicinally for
earache and chest complaints.

Zantedeschia rehmannii

ARUM FAMILY

Dwarf arum lily (E), pienkvarkoor (A),

umFana-kamacejane (Sw)

(Named after Polish botanist Anton

Rehmann who first collected the species)

Tuberous perennial, 20–60 cm high. Leaves
narrowly elliptical. Flowers crowded in a
narrow yellow spike 3–4 cm long which is
enclosed by a narrowly funnel-shaped,
leathery, white or pinkish bract.
Habitat: Rocky grassland and bush margins.

Zantedeschia albomaculata

ARUM FAMILY

Spotted-leaved arum lily (E), witvlek-

varkoor (A), inTebe (Z)

(Latin *albomaculatus*, white-spotted,

referring to the leaves)

Tuberous perennial, 40–60 cm high. Leaves
arrow-shaped and usually flecked or spotted
with white. Flowers crowded in a narrow
yellow spike 4–8 cm long which is enclosed
by a narrowly funnel-shaped, leathery, white
to cream-coloured bract with a purple blotch
in the base.
Habitat: Damp grassland, among rocks or in
vleis.
Notes: *Zantedeschia aethiopica* has plain
green leaves, a more flaring floral bract and
fruiting stalks that remain erect instead of
bending down.

Zantedeschia pentlandii

ARUM FAMILY

Yellow arum lily (E), geelvarkoor (A)
(Named after R. Whyte, Pentland House,
who introduced it into cultivation in
Britain in 1892)

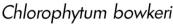

Tuberous perennial, 40–60 cm high. Leaves
arrow-shaped. Flowers crowded in a narrow
yellow spike 8–9 cm long which is enclosed by
a flaring, leathery, yellow or rarely a cream-
coloured bract with a purple blotch in the base.
Habitat: Rocky grassland and open woodland
among dolerite boulders.

Chlorophytum bowkeri

ANTHERICUM FAMILY

Bowker's chlorophytum (E)
(Named for Col. James Bowker, who first
collected the species)

Robust rhizomatous perennial to 1 m. Leaves
narrow and channelled, rather fibrous in
texture. Flowers clustered in a long spike
with more than one flower per bract, star
shaped, white, each lasting a single day,
20 mm diameter.
Habitat: Damp grassland.

Drimia altissima

HYACINTH FAMILY

Tall white squill (E), jeukbol (A),
umGulube (Z)
(Latin altissumus, very tall)

Bulbous perennial to 1 m, with large, pinkish
bulb. Leaves dry or just emerging at flowering,
lance-shaped in a large tuft. Flowers in a cylindrical raceme on long, spreading pedicels,
white or greenish, lasting a single day, 10 mm
diameter.
Habitat: Hot bushveld and open thicket.
Notes: Leaves used as a soap and although
poisonous traditionally used to treat colds and
backaches.

Drimia macrocentra

HYACINTH FAMILY

Large snake-head (E), slangkop (A), inJoba (X, Z)

(Greek *macrocentron*, large spur)

Bulbous perennial to 1 m. Leaf solitary, cylindrical and hollow, not present in flowering plants. Flowers in a dense raceme, white or greenish, lasting a single day, 10 mm diameter, the lowermost bracts with a long, flat spur.
Habitat: Damp or marshy grassland near streams.
Notes: Poisonous and used traditionally as a vermifuge.

Schizocarphus nervosus

HYACINTH FAMILY

(= *Scilla nervosa*)

White squill (E), maGagana (X), iNgcolo (Z)

(Latin *nervosus*, veined, alluding to the fibrous leaves)

Bulbous perennial to 40 cm high, the bulb covered with fibrous sheaths. Leaves narrow or broader, stiff and often twisted with thickened margins. Flowers on long pedicels, white to cream with a green or blackish ovary, 5–8 mm diameter.
Habitat: Stony or open grassland.
Notes: Used to treat rheumatic fever and dysentery.

Ornithogalum tenuifolium

HYACINTH FAMILY

Common ornithogalum (E), bosui (A)

(Latin *tenuifolius*, slender-leaved)

Bulbous perennial 30–80 cm high. Leaves narrow and channelled, rather drooping. Flowers in a long raceme, usually with long bracts, white or greenish with a green band on the petals, 10 mm diameter.
Habitat: Rough grassland or thicket, often along streams or roadsides.
Notes: Sap is an irritant on sensitive skin.

Ornithogalum longibracteatum
HYACINTH FAMILY
Pregnant onion, devil's onion (E),
maxabana (X), umBabaza (Z)
(Latin *longibracteatus*, with long bracts)

Bulbous perennial 1–1,5 m high, with a smooth, green bulb exposed above the ground and producing numerous bulbils. Leaves strap-shaped and usually with a tail-like tip, rather drooping. Flowers in a long raceme with very long bracts, white with a green band on the petals, 10 mm diameter.
Habitat: Shaded slopes and forest margins.
Notes: Well known as a houseplant and widely used in traditional medicine.

Albuca abyssinica
HYACINTH FAMILY
Bushveld slime lily (E), bosveld
slymlelie (A)
(Latin *abyssinicus*, from Ethiopia,
formerly Abyssinia)

Bulbous perennial to 1 m high. Leaves strap-shaped and rather sappy, hairy on the underside towards the base. Flowers in slender spikes, spreading on short pedicels, green with darker keels, *c.*20 mm long.
Habitat: Rocky slopes on forest margins and shaded cliffs.

Albuca humilis
HYACINTH FAMILY
Drakensberg slime lily (E)
(Latin *humilis*, low-growing)

Deciduous bulbous perennial to 50 cm high, solitary. Leaves narrow, channelled and rather sappy. Flowers in slender spikes, held erect on long pedicels, white with green keels, scented of spicy vanilla, 15–20 mm long.
Habitat: Damp montane grassland and cliffs.
Notes: Common in the KwaZulu-Natal Drakensberg. *Albuca setosa* is similar but the bulb is topped with stout bristles and it occupies drier grassland and savannah.

Albuca nelsonii

HYACINTH FAMILY

Nelson's slime lily (E)

(Named for British nurseryman, William Nelson, who first collected the species)

Evergreen bulbous perennial to 1 m high, growing in clumps. Leaves strap-shaped and rather sappy. Flowers in stout spikes, held erect on long pedicels, white with green keels, 25–35 mm long.

Habitat: Grassland, especially near the coast.

Ornithogalum saundersiae

HYACINTH FAMILY

Giant white ornithogalum (E), Transvaalse tjienk (A)

(Named for Victorian flower artist, Katherine Saunders, who lived near Durban)

Bulbous perennial 1–1,5 m high. Leaves tongue-shaped. Flowers in rather flat-topped racemes, erect on conspicuous pedicels, petals rather thick-textured, white with a blackish ovary, 15 mm diameter.

Habitat: Localised on rocky banks and out-crops in thicket.

Notes: Bulbs very poisonous. An elegant and sophisticated cut flower.

Galtonia candicans

HYACINTH FAMILY

White berg lily (E), berglelie (A)

(Latin *candicans*, becoming pure white)

Bulbous perennial to 1,5 m high. Leaves strap- or tongue-shaped and chan-nelled. Flowers in a conical raceme, nodding and bell-shaped, white or cream-coloured, 30–45 mm long, stamens 18–19 mm long.

Habitat: Rough grassland along streams and forest margins.

Notes: A statuesque plant popular in British gardens.

Galtonia regalis

HYACINTH FAMILY

Royal berg lily (E), berglelie (A)

(Latin *regalis*, regal, from the type locality in Royal Natal National Park)

Bulbous perennial to 80 cm high. Leaves strap- or tongue-shaped and channelled. Flowers in a conical raceme, nodding and bell-shaped, greenish, 25–40 mm long, stamens 9–10 mm long.

Habitat: Wet basalt cliffs at high altitude.

Eucomis autumnalis

HYACINTH FAMILY

Common pineapple lily (E)

(Latin *autumnalis*, autumnal)

Bulbous perennial, 6–30 cm high. Leaves spreading in a basal cluster, tongue-shaped with undulate or crisped margins, uniformly green. Flowers tightly clustered on a plain green peduncle on pedicels 3–9 mm long, white to greenish, 13–25 mm diameter.

Habitat: Rocky, grassy slopes.

Notes: A decoction of the bulb is used for various ailments, including infections of the bowel and urinary tract.

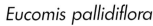

Eucomis pallidiflora

HYACINTH FAMILY

Giant pineapple lily (E)

(Latin *pallidiflorus*, pale-flowered)

Bulbous perennial, 45–120 cm high. Leaves sub-erect in a basal cluster, tongue-shaped with undulate or crisped margins, uniformly green. Flowers more or less loosely clustered on a plain green peduncle on pedicels 15–50 mm long, white to greenish, 13–25 mm diameter.

Habitat: Marshy grassland, often along streams.

Notes: *Eucomis comosa* is another large species, with purple-spotted flower stalks that tend to lean sideways.

Eucomis bicolor

HYACINTH FAMILY

Bicoloured pineapple lily (E), bontpynappel-
lelie (A), umBola (Z)

(Latin *bicolor*, bicoloured)

Bulbous perennial, 20–60 cm high. Leaves sub-
erect in a basal cluster, tongue-shaped with
undulate or crisped margins, spotted with
purple beneath. Flowers more or less drooping,
clustered on a spotted peduncle on pedicels
15–50 mm long, white with purple margins and
speckling, 13–25 mm diameter.
Habitat: Montane grassland along streams and
wet cliffs.

Pseudogaltonia clavata

HYACINTH FAMILY

Desert hyacinth (E)

(Latin *clavatus*, club-like, alluding to the
flower shape)

Bulbous perennial, 50–100 cm high. Leaves
usually emerging or present at flowering, sub-
erect in a basal cluster. Flowers nodding in a
dense, globose raceme, tubular and curved,
white with pale green banding, 30–45 mm long.
Habitat: Stony and sandy flats.
Notes: Most often seen in the Kalahari.

Veltheimia bracteata

HYACINTH FAMILY

Forest sandlily (E), sandui (A)

(Latin *bracteatus*, with bracts, alluding to
the conspicuous floral bracts)

Bulbous perennial, 20–40 cm high. Leaves
glossy green, lanceolate or tongue-shaped.
Flowers crowded in an ovoid or conical
raceme, spreading to nodding, tubular, pink
or pale yellow and finely speckled with red,
25–35 mm long.
Habitat: Coastal scrub and thicket.
Notes: A lovely garden plant for partly shaded
situations.

Ledebouria cooperi

HYACINTH FAMILY

Cooper's ledebouria (E)

(Named after the English plant
collector, Thomas Cooper)

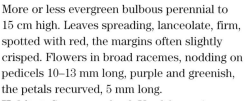

Deciduous bulbous perennial to 15 cm high.
Leaves sub-erect, narrow, more or less
streaked and lined with purple beneath.
Flowers spreading on pedicels 6–12 mm long,
pink, the petals weakly recurved, 5 mm long.
Habitat: Damp grassland and seeps.
Notes: Variable but often distinguished by the
bright pink flowers.

Ledebouria revoluta

HYACINTH FAMILY

Common ledebouria (E), inQwebebane (X),
iCubudwana (Z)

(Latin *revolutus*, rolled back,
referring to the petals)

More or less evergreen bulbous perennial to
15 cm high. Leaves spreading, lanceolate, firm,
spotted with red, the margins often slightly
crisped. Flowers in broad racemes, nodding on
pedicels 10–13 mm long, purple and greenish,
the petals recurved, 5 mm long.
Habitat: Stony grassland. Used for various
ailments.

Ledebouria floribunda

HYACINTH FAMILY

Green ledebouria (E)

(Latin *floribundus*, profusely flowering)

More or less evergreen
bulbous perennial to 20 cm high. Leaves
spreading, lanceolate, firm, spotted with red.
Flowers in broad racemes, nodding on
pedicels 12–16 mm long, usually uniformly
greenish, the petals recurved, 7–9 mm long.
Habitat: Stony slopes, often in bushveld.
Notes: Common around Nelspruit. The heated
leaves are used as a source of eardrops.

Merwilla natalensis

HYACINTH FAMILY

(= *Scilla natalensis*)

Large blue squill (E), blouslangkop (A),
iCitha (Z), kherere (SS)

(Latin *natalensis*, from Natal)

Bulbous perennial to 1 m high, solitary or com-
munal, the bulb covered with papery, brownish
scales. Leaves usually just emerging at flowering, lance-shaped, smooth or velvety. Flowers
in tall racemes, star-shaped, blue to lilac with
white stamens, *c*.10 mm diameter.
Habitat: Damp grassland and cliffs.
Notes: Decoctions are taken as an enema for
internal tumours and to enhance fertility and
performance.

Cyanotis speciosa

COMMELINA FAMILY

Doll's powderpuff (E), uMagoswana (X),
uMakotigoyile (Z)

(Latin *speciosus*, showy)

Perennial herb to 50 cm high. Leaves narrowly
lanceolate with a sheathing petiole, hairy.
Flowers in tight clusters subtended by a
leaf-like bract, fragile, blue to mauve, 10 mm
diameter, lasting a few hours, with prominent
fluffy stamen filaments.
Habitat: Grassland.
Notes: Used to treat infertility and as a love
charm.

Aneilema aequinoctale

COMMELINA FAMILY

Clinging aneilema (E), iDangabane
elikhulu (Z)

(Latin *aequinoctialis*, of the equinox or
midday, when the flowers fade)

Erect or trailing perennial herb to 60 cm high.
Leaves lance-shaped with a sheathing base
covered in hooked hairs. Flowers in branched
clusters, fragile, yellow with two prominent
petals, 10 mm diameter, lasting a single
morning.
Habitat: Coastal forest margins.
Notes: Used as a spinach.

Xerophyta retinervis

VELLOZIA FAMILY

Large black-stick lily (E),
bobbejaanstert (A)

(Latin *retinervis*, net-veined)

Tufted perennial with erect stems to 1 m high covered with the thickly fibrous remains of the leaf bases, usually blackened by fire. Leaves narrow and channelled with stiff hairs along the keel and margins, fibrous. Flowers solitary on slender stalks covered with stiff hairs, pale to deep mauve, 60 mm diameter.

Habitat: Rocky outcrops and hills.

Notes: Flowers after fire.

Xerophyta viscosa

VELLOZIA FAMILY

Small black-stick lily (E), lefiroane (SS)

(Latin *viscosus*, sticky, alluding to the flower stalks)

Tufted rhizomatous perennial to 50 cm high. Leaves narrow and channelled with stiff hairs along the keel and margins, fibrous. Flowers solitary on slender stalks covered with black, glandular hairs, white to pink or mauve, 60 mm diameter.

Habitat: Damp sandstone cliffs.

Notes: Leaves plaited into rope.

Rhodohypoxis baurii

STARGRASS FAMILY

Red star (E), rooisterretjie (A)

(Named for the missionary and plant collector, Rev. Leopold Bauer)

Cormous perennial, 5–10 cm high. Leaves narrow and channelled, covered with conspicuous hairs. Flowers on slender, roughly hairy stalks, white, pink or red, 20–30 mm diameter.

Habitat: Rock sheets and damp ledges in short grassland.

Notes: A popular plant among alpine enthusiasts in the northern hemisphere.

Hypoxis hemerocallidea

STARGRASS FAMILY

Medicinal star-flower (E), sterblom (A), inKomfe (Z)

(Latin *hemerocallideus*, resembling the day-lily, *Hemerocallis*)

Cormous perennial to 30 cm high. Leaves in three ranks, sickle-shaped and channelled with a prominent keel, covered with white hairs on the underside and margins. Flowers several per stem, yellow, 30–40 mm diameter.
Habitat: Grassland and open woodland.
Notes: The leaves are used to make rope and the bulb to blacken floors. Used to treat headaches, dizziness, mental disorders and cancer.

Hypoxis rigidula

STARGRASS FAMILY

Stiff-leaved star-flower (E), inKomfe (Z)

(Latin *rigidulus*, somewhat stiff or rigid)

Erect, cormous perennial, 30–60 cm high. Leaves erect, narrow and strongly ribbed, covered with white hairs and forming a false stem at the base. Flowers several per stem, 30–40 mm diameter.
Habitat: Stony grassland.
Notes: The leaves are used to make ropes.

Hypoxis costata

STARGRASS FAMILY

Ribbed star-flower (E), kharatsa (SS)

(Latin *costatus*, ribbed)

Cormous perennial, 10–15 cm high. Leaves rather broad and ribbed with strongly thickened margins, smooth or hairy, especially on the margins. Flowers several per stem, 30–40 mm diameter.
Habitat: Grassland.

Bulbine capitata

ALOE FAMILY

Narrow-leaved bulbine (E)

(Latin *capitatus*, with a knob-like head, referring to the flower head)

Rhizomatous perennial to 30 cm high. Leaves narrow and sappy, bright green, with broad membranous bases, decaying into membranous strips at the base. Flowers in a head-like raceme, bright yellow, lasting a single day each, with fluffy stamens, 10 mm diameter.

Habitat: Open grassland, conspicuous after a burn.

Notes: *Bulbine abyssinica* is similar but the leaves are pink at the base and decay into long membranous strips and the raceme is conical or cylindrical.

Bulbine narcissifolia

ALOE FAMILY

Strap-leaved bulbine (E), komo-ea-balisa (SS)

(Latin narcissifolius, with leaves like a daffodil, *Narcissus*)

Rhizomatous perennial to 30 cm high. Leaves in a fan, twisted and strap-like, grey and firm, decaying into fine fibres at the base. Flowers in a conical raceme, pale canary yellow, lasting a single day each, with fluffy stamens, 10 mm diameter.

Habitat: Open grassland, common on over-grazed range land.

Notes: Used traditionally to induce pregnancy.

Kniphofia laxiflora

ALOE FAMILY

Slender poker (E), iCacane (Z)

(Latin *laxiflorus*, loosely flowered)

Perennial herb to 1 m, solitary or in small groups. Leaves slender and keeled, grass-like with smooth or minutely toothed margins. Flowers in a lax or loose spike, tubular with the anthers not protruding, orange to reddish or yellowish, 25–35 mm long.

Habitat: Rocky outcrops in grassland.

Kniphofia ichopensis

ALOE FAMILY

Ixopo poker (E)

(Latin *ichopenis,* from Ixopo)

Perennial herb to 80 cm, in colonies. Leaves slender and keeled, grass-like with smooth or minutely toothed margins. Flowers in a lax or loose spike, tubular with the anthers scarcely protruding, yellowish green to orange with yellowish buds, 25–35 mm long.

Habitat: Grassland vleis and marshy places.

Kniphofia triangularis

ALOE FAMILY

Mandarin poker (E),

leloele-le-lenye (SS)

(Latin *triangularis,* triangular, referring to the shape of the flower spike)

Perennial herb to 60 cm high, solitary or in small groups. Leaves narrow and keeled with the margins smooth or toothed, firm or softer in texture. Flowers in a conical head, tubular with the anthers scarcely protruding, coral-red to orange-yellow, 25–35 mm long.

Habitat: Montane grassland in damp places.

Notes: Pieces of the rhizome are threaded onto necklaces worn by pregnant women as protection against lightning.

Kniphofia thodei

ALOE FAMILY

Thode's poker (E)

(Named for the plant collector, Justus Thode)

Perennial herb to 50 cm high, usually solitary. Leaves narrow and keeled with the margins smooth or minutely toothed, soft in texture and greyish. Flowers in a conical head, tubular with the anthers scarcely protruding, reddish in bud opening white, 28–35 mm long.

Habitat: Montane grassland in damp places.

Notes: Easily seen near The Sentinel.

Kniphofia ritualis

ALOE FAMILY
Ritual poker (E)
(Latin *ritualis*, pertaining to the ritual usage
of the plant)

Perennial herb to 80 cm high, solitary or in
small groups. Leaves narrow and keeled with
the margins regularly toothed, soft in texture.
Flowers in an ovoid or cylindrical head,
tubular with the anthers scarcely protruding,
orange-red in bud opening greenish yellow,
25–30 mm long.
Habitat: Montane grassland in damp places,
especially at the base of cliffs.
Notes: Easily seen near The Sentinel. Leaves
used to make rope. Used traditionally during
initiation of young women.

Kniphofia ensifolia

ALOE FAMILY
Pale poker (E)
(Latin *ensifolius*, sword-leaved)

Perennial herb to 1 m, in groups
or colonies. Leaves strap-shaped and keeled
with toothed margins, firm. Flowers in a dense
cylindrical head, tubular with the anthers conspicuously protruding, yellowish to cream with
pinkish buds, 15–20 mm long.
Habitat: Grassy vleis and marshes.

Kniphofia tysonii

ALOE FAMILY
Tyson's poker (E)
(Named for William Tyson, teacher and
plant collector)

Perennial herb to 2 m high, in groups. Leaves
narrow and keeled with smooth or minutely
toothed margins. Flowers in an oblong or
sub-cylindrical head, tubular with the anthers
conspicuously protruding, orange to red
opening yellow or greenish, 20–28 mm long.
Habitat: Vleis or seepage areas on hillsides.
Notes: *Kniphofia linearifolia* is similar but
has slightly longer flowers with the anthers
less conspicuously protruding.

Kniphofia caulescens

ALOE FAMILY

Lesotho poker (E), Basoetoe vuurpyl (A), leloele-la-loti (SS)

(Latin *caulescens*, developing a stem)

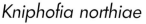

Evergreen perennial herb to 1 m high, with a well-defined stem, in groups or colonies. Leaves narrow and keeled with toothed margins, bluish grey and firm textured. Flowers in a cylindrical head, tubular with the anthers protruding, yellow with orange buds, 25 mm long.

Habitat: Damp mountainsides along streams.

Notes: The persistent, grey leaves are distinctive.

Kniphofia northiae

ALOE FAMILY

Marianne North's poker (E), leloele (SS)

(Named for the Victorian wildflower artist, Marianne North, who discovered the species on her travels)

Evergreen perennial herb to 1,7 m high, solitary or loose colonies. Leaves broad and without a keel, with toothed margins, leathery. Flowers in a cylindrical head, tubular with the anthers protruding, whitish or yellow to orange with reddish buds, 25 mm long.

Habitat: Damp mountainsides along streams and seeps.

Aloe kniphofioides

ALOE FAMILY

Poker aloe (E)

(Resembling a red-hot poker, *Kniphofia*)

Tufted perennial herb to 50 cm high with tuberous roots and swollen, bulb-like leaf bases. Leaves narrow and channelled, sometimes with small white teeth along the margins. Flowers in loose racemes, tubular, red with green tips, 50 mm long.

Habitat: Scattered in moist, stony grassland after fire.

Aloe cooperi

ALOE FAMILY

Cooper's grass aloe (E), isiPhukutwane (Z)

(Named for the English plant collector,

Thomas Cooper)

Tufted rhizomatous perennial herb to 1 m high. Leaves narrow and channelled with small white teeth along the margins and white spots at the base. Flowers in cone-shaped racemes, tubular-tapering, red with green tips, 40 mm long.

Habitat: Rocky grassland.

Notes: Flowers and leaves eaten as a vegetable. Used medicinally to promote easy birth.

Aloe ecklonis

ALOE FAMILY

Ecklon's grass aloe (E)

(Named for nineteenth-century

German plant collector, C.F. Ecklon,

who originally sent seeds of the species to Europe)

Tufted rhizomatous perennial herb to 50 cm. Leaves strap-shaped with white teeth on the margins and white spots at the base. Flowers in head-like racemes, ovoid, orange, red or yellow, 25 mm long.

Habitat: Grassy slopes.

Notes: Flowers and leaves eaten as a vegetable. Used traditionally to treat tuberculosis.

Aloe maculata

ALOE FAMILY

Common soap aloe (E), bontaalwyn (A), amaHlala (Z)

(Latin *maculatus*, blotched)

Stemless succulent perennial to 1 m. Leaves spreading and triangular with the tips usually curved down, densely spotted with white and with sharp, brown teeth on the margins. Flowers in head-like or flat-topped racemes, tubular with a swollen base, red to yellow, 45 mm long.

Habitat: Rocky outcrops, thicket and dry grassland.

Notes: Leaves eaten as a vegetable. Used traditionally for various ailments.

Aloe cryptopoda
ALOE FAMILY

Bushveld aloe (E), geelaalwyn (A)
(Greek *cryptopodus*, hidden foot,
alluding to the large bracts that
conceal the flower pedicels)

Stemless succulent perennial to 1 m. Leaves in
a dense rosette, rather erect and lance-shaped,
greyish green with small reddish teeth along
the margins. Flowers in conical racemes,
tubular and slightly upturned at the mouth,
red to yellow or bicoloured, 30–40 mm long.
Habitat: In bushveld on open flats or rocky
hills.

Aloe greatheadii
ALOE FAMILY

Greathead's aloe (E), Transvaalaalwyn (A)
(Named for Dr J.B. Greathead who
collected the original material with the
botanist, Dr S. Schönland)

Stemless succulent perennial to 1,5 m. Leaves
spreading and triangular to lance-shaped with
the tips often dead, shiny green and densely
marked with pale spots arranged in bands and
with sharp, brown teeth on the margins.
Flowers in ovoid racemes, tubular with a
swollen base, pink to red, 30–35 mm long.
Habitat: Rocky grassland.

Aloe chabaudii
ALOE FAMILY

Chabaud's aloe (E), inKalane (Z)
(Named for John Chabaud, who first
flowered the species in his garden)

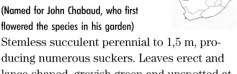

Stemless succulent perennial to 1,5 m, producing numerous suckers. Leaves erect and
lance-shaped, greyish green and unspotted at
maturity, with short, scattered, whitish teeth
on the margins. Flowers in rather loose, ovoid
racemes, tubular with a swollen base, pinkish
to red, 35–40 mm long.
Habitat: Rock outcrops in bushveld.

Aloe marlothii

ALOE FAMILY
Marloth's mountain aloe (E), bergaalwyn (A),
umHlaba (Z)
(Named after the chemist and botanist
H.W. Rudolf Marloth)

Single-stemmed succulent to 5 m high. Leaves broad and dull green with dark brown spines on the margins and especially the lower surface. Flowers in well-branched panicles, each branch often more or less horizontal, the flowers facing upwards, tubular, red to yellow, 25 mm long.
Habitat: Rocky slopes and open bushveld.

Aloe castanea

ALOE FAMILY
Cat's-tail aloe (E), katstertaalwyn (A)
(*Castanea* is the chestnut, an allusion to the
brownish nectar)

Single-stemmed succulent to 5 m high. Leaves narrow and dull green with small brown teeth on the margins. Flowers in dense, rather twisted, brush-like spikes, the flowers facing upwards, shortly tubular with very prominent, protruding stamens, orange-brown, 25 mm long.
Habitat: Rocky slopes and open bushveld.

Aloe ciliaris

ALOE FAMILY
Common rambling aloe (E)
(Latin *ciliaris*, fringed, referring to the leaf
sheaths)

Shrublet with erect or sprawling stems to 6 m long. Leaves scattered along the branches, lanceolate with small white teeth on the margins and clasping bases that are conspicuously fringed at the mouth. Flowers in ovoid racemes, red with yellow and green tips, *c.*25 mm long.
Habitat: Coastal thicket and scrub.

Sandersonia aurantiaca

GLORIOSA FAMILY

Christmas bells (E), geelklokkie (A),
uMagobongwana, uShayabhici (Z)

(Latin *aurantiacus*, orange)

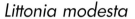

Tuberous perennial to 75 cm high. Leaves
lanceolate with three main veins, sometimes
forming tendrils at the tip. Flowers nodding,
lantern-like, orange, *c*.25 mm long.
Habitat: Damp grassland, often on the
margins of bush.
Notes: Used as an aphrodisiac and a charm
against evil.

Littonia modesta

GLORIOSA FAMILY

Littonia (E), geelklokkie (A), iHlamvu
lehlathi (Z)

(Latin *modestus*, modest, alluding to the
coyly bowed flowers)

Erect or scrambling tuberous perennial to
75 cm high. Leaves lanceolate with three
main veins, sometimes forming tendrils at
the tip. Flowers nodding, cup-shaped, orange,
20-30 mm diameter.
Habitat: Damp grassland, often on the
margins of bush.
Notes: Used traditionally as a fertility drug.

Gloriosa superba

GLORIOSA FAMILY

Flame lily (E), vlamlelie (A), iHlamvu,
isiMiselo (Z)

(Latin *superbus*, superb)

Tuberous perennial with sprawling or climbing
annual stems to 2 m high. Leaves lanceolate
and tapering to a tendril at the tip. Flowers
nodding, shaped like a turk's-cap lily, yellowish
to orange and yellow with recurved petals
crinkled along the margins, *c*.70 mm long.
Habitat: Coastal dunes and in thicket.
Notes: The whole plant is extremely poisonous but is used as an antiparasitic and remedy
for ascites. The brightly coloured seeds are
used in necklaces.

Androcymbium melanthioides
GLORIOSA FAMILY

Pyjama flower (E), patrysblom (A), khara (SS)
(Resembling the North American bunch-
flower, *Melanthium*, in the form of the
individual flowers)

Cormous perennial, 10–20 cm high. Leaves
narrow and channelled. Flowers clustered
between large creamy-white or lilac bracts
with conspicuous green veins, the stamen
filaments 8–10 mm long.
Habitat: Stony grassland.
Notes: *Androcymbium orienticapense* has
the stamen filaments only 4–5 mm long.

Haemanthus humilis
AMARYLLIS FAMILY

Rabbit's ears, common paintbrush lily (E),
bobbejaanoor (A), sekitla (SS)
(Latin *humilis*, low growing)

Bulbous perennial, 12–20 cm high. Leaves
appearing at flowering, two, tongue-shaped
and usually hairy, curving backward onto the
ground. Flowers in a loose terminal cluster
on a reddish stem, pale pink or white,
25 mm long.
Habitat: Rocky grassland, among boulders.
Notes: Used traditionally for stomachaches,
wounds and asthma.

Scadoxus puniceus
AMARYLLIS FAMILY

Blood lily (E), rooikwas (A), isiPhompo (Z)
(Latin *puniceus*, phoenician purple,
crimson)

Bulbous perennial, 40–50 cm high. Leaves
appearing at flowering, five to eight, soft-
textured and bright green with the bases forming a false stem. Flowers in a dense terminal
cluster subtended by large greenish to
chocolate-brown bracts, red, 25 mm long.
Habitat: Coastal forest and inland bush
clumps, often among rocks.
Notes: Used as a poultice, to treat coughs,
stomach ailments, and headaches. The bulb is
poisonous.

Scadoxus multiflorus

AMARYLLIS FAMILY

Fireball lily, Catherine wheel (E),
isiPhompo (Z)

(Latin *multiflorus*, many-flowered)

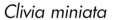

Bulbous perennial, 30–100 cm high. Leaves present at flowering, four or five, soft-textured, the bases forming a false stem. Flowers, many in a dense terminal cluster on a stout stem speckled with purple, borne on fairly long pedicels to form a rounded ball about 20 cm in diameter, pinkish to red, 40 mm long. Fruits fleshy, berry-like, red when ripe.
Habitat: Coastal and inland forests in damp places.

Clivia miniata

AMARYLLIS FAMILY

Clivia, bush lily (E), boslelie (A),
uMayime (Z)

(Latin *miniatus*, saturn-red, flame-red)

Rhizomatous perennial to 60 cm. Leaves strap-like, dark green. Flowers in a terminal cluster, spreading, funnel-shaped, pale orange with a yellow centre, 50–60 mm diameter. Fruits fleshy, berry-like, red when ripe.
Habitat: Coastal and inland forest, sheltered ledges and ravines.
Notes: Used for snakebite and relieving fevers. The leaves are used in delayed pregnancy and to ease childbirth.

Clivia caulescens

AMARYLLIS FAMILY

Transvaal clivia (E)

(Latin *caulescens*, developing a stem)

Rhizomatous perennial to 1 m, with a distinct, often sprawling stem. Leaves strap-like, dark green. Flowers in a terminal cluster, nodding, tubular, deep red with short greenish to yellow-tipped petals, 40 mm long. Fruits fleshy, berry-like, red when ripe.
Habitat: Forest floors along the Mpumalanga escarpment.

Cyrtanthus tuckii
AMARYLLIS FAMILY

Green-tipped fire lily (E), brandlelie (A),
isiWesa (Z)

(Named for horticulturist and collector,
William Tuck)

Bulbous perennial to 20 cm high. Leaves
usually appearing after the flowers, narrow
and strap-like. Flowers, several in a terminal
cluster, tubular, strongly curved and nodding,
red with yellowish or green tips, 50–60 mm
long.

Habitat: Damp grassland, flowering best after
veld fires.

Cyrtanthus sanguineus
AMARYLLIS FAMILY

Inanda lily, Kei lily (E), isiLawu
esimhlope (X)

(Latin *sanguineus*, blood-red)

Bulbous perennial to 25 cm high. Leaves narrow and strap-like, channelled. Flowers one or
two, funnel-shaped with a long tube, bright red
with paler throat striped with red, 100 mm
long.

Habitat: Riverine bush, shady rocks and cliffs.
Notes: Traditionally used as an emetic.

Cyrtanthus breviflorus
AMARYLLIS FAMILY

Yellow fire lily (E), geelvuurlelie (A),
uVelabahleke (Z)

(Latin *breviflorus*, with short flowers)

Bulbous perennial to 15 cm high. Leaves often
absent or just emerging at flowering time, narrow and strap-like. Flowers, several in a loose
terminal cluster, funnel-shaped, yellow,
20–30 mm long.

Habitat: Marshes and damp grassland, flowering best after veld fires.

Cyrtanthus mackenii

AMARYLLIS FAMILY

Ifafa lily (E), ifafalelie (A)

(Named for Mark McKen, first curator of the Durban Botanic Gardens)

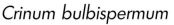

Bulbous perennial to 20 cm high, usually growing in clumps. Leaves shiny, narrow and strap-like, appearing with or after the flowers. Flowers narrowly tubular with short spreading petals, whitish or yellow to creamy-pink or red, c.50 mm long.

Habitat: Grassland, forest margins, stony slopes and along the coast.

Crinum bulbispermum

AMARYLLIS FAMILY

Orange River lily, Vaal River lily (E), vleilelie (A), lelutla (SS), umNduze (Z)

(Greek *bulbispermus*, bulb-seeded, referring to the fact that the seeds develop directly into bulbils)

Bulbous perennial to 1 m high. Leaves spreading, strap-like with wavy margins. Flowers nodding in bud and flower, narrowly funnel-shaped with a long slender tube, pale pink with darker stripes and white to pink anthers, strongly fragrant at night, 150 mm long.

Habitat: Damp grassland near streams and seasonal pans.

Notes: Used traditionally to treat colds and rheumatism and as a poultice for sores.

Crinum macowanii

AMARYLLIS FAMILY

MacOwan's river lily (E), rivierlelie (A), inTelezi (X), umNduze (Z)

(Named for Victorian botanist, Peter MacOwan, who first collected the species)

Bulbous perennial to 80 cm high. Leaves spreading, strap-like with wavy margins. Flowers erect in bud but nodding and funnel-shaped with a long slender tube at flowering, pale pink with black anthers, strongly fragrant at night, 150 mm long.

Habitat: Grassland near rivers.

Notes: Used as a treatment for urinary tract infections, rashes and as a charm.

Crinum moorei

AMARYLLIS FAMILY

Moore's river lily (E), boslelie (A),
umNduze (Z)

(Named for D. Moore, director of Dublin
Botanic Gardens)

Bulbous perennial to 1,2 m high, often growing
in clumps and forming large colonies. Leaves
spreading and strap-like with wavy margins,
forming a false stem at the base. Flowers
nodding and bell-like with a long slender tube,
white to pale pink, sweetly scented, opening
more widely at night and more strongly
scented, 150 mm long.

Habitat: Vleis and marshy sites, in shade or
sun.

Notes: Used traditionally for urinary tract
infections.

Nerine angustifolia

AMARYLLIS FAMILY

Ribbon-leaved nerina (E), lematlana (SS)

(Latin *angustifolius*, narrow-leaved)

Bulbous perennial, 20–50 cm
high. Leaves narrow and strap-like or
channelled. Flowers on shortly hairy pedicels,
flaring with narrow, crisped petals, pink,
30–40 mm diameter.

Habitat: Grassy marshes.

Nerine bowdenii

AMARYLLIS FAMILY

Great nerina (E)

(Named for Mr Cornish-Bowden, a govern-
ment surveyor, who first collected the
species)

Bulbous perennial, 30–70 cm high. Leaves
strap-like and channelled. Flowers on hairless
pedicels, flaring with narrow, crisped petals,
pink, 40–50 mm diameter.

Habitat: Wet cliffs at high altitude.

Notes: Abundant along the path up The
Sentinel.

Boophone disticha

AMARYLLIS FAMILY

Oxbane (E), seerooglelie (A), inCwadi (X, Z)
(Latin *distichus,* arranged in two opposite
rows, alluding to the fan of leaves)

Bulbous perennial to 45 cm high. Leaves dry or
just emerging at flowering, strap-like and often
twisted, many in a two-ranked fan. Flowers in
a dense terminal cluster, borne on stalks that
lengthen with age, funnel-shaped, deep pink,
30 mm diameter. Fruiting head a large tumble-
weed, breaking loose from the plant when dry
and blowing in the wind.

Habitat: Grassland, open bush, and rocky flats.

Notes: A poultice is used for boils and
abscesses while the fresh leaf is applied to cuts
to stop bleeding. The sap is toxic and was used
by the San in the preparation of arrow poison.

Ammocharis coranica

AMARYLLIS FAMILY

Ammocharis (E), seerooglelie (A), isiDiya (Z)
(Name alludes to the tribe Korana San)

Bulbous perennial to 20 cm
high. Leaves several, strap-shaped and spreading, greyish green. Flowers in a rounded terminal cluster, star-like with a slender tube, pink
to crimson, sweetly scented, 40 mm diameter.

Habitat: Dry grassland and flats.

Notes: Paste from the bulbs used to water-
proof clay pots and traditionally used for men's
head rings.

Brunsvigia natalensis

AMARYLLIS FAMILY

Common candelabra (E), misryblom (A),
lematla (SS)
(Latin *natalensis,* from Natal)

Bulbous perennial to 20 cm high. Leaves four
to six, tongue-like and rough, flat on the
ground. Flowers in a rounded terminal cluster
on long pedicels, deep pink to maroon, 40 mm
diameter. Fruiting head a ball-like tumble-
weed, breaking free of the plant when dry and
bowling across the veld in the wind.

Habitat: Grassland.

Brunsvigia grandiflora

AMARYLLIS FAMILY

Giant candelabra (E), kandelaar (A),
isiChwe (X), umQhele-wenkuzi (Z)
(Latin *grandiflorus*, large-flowered)

Bulbous perennial to 60 cm high. Leaves
present at flowering, 10 to 15, oblong and
wavy, more or less erect in a fan. Flowers in
a rounded terminal cluster on long pedicels,
pale to deep pink, 40 mm diameter. Fruiting
head a ball-like tumble-weed, breaking free
of the plant when dry and bowling across
the veld in the wind.
Habitat: Grassland.
Notes: Bulb used traditionally to soothe and
heal wounds, particularly after circumcision.

Agapanthus campanulatus

AGAPANTHUS FAMILY

Bell agapanthus (E), bloulelie (A),
uGebeleweni (X), uBani (Z)
(Latin *campanulatus*, bell-shaped)

Rhizomatous perennial herb, 40–70 cm. Leaves
strap-shaped, deciduous. Flowers spreading in
umbels, widely funnel-shaped with the petals
much longer than the flower tube, blue to
purple, 20–35 mm long.
Habitat: Rocky grassland.

Agapanthus inapertus

AGAPANTHUS FAMILY

Drooping agapanthus (E), bloulelie (A)
(Latin *inapertus*, without an obvious mouth,
alluding to the tubular flowers)

Rhizomatous perennial herb, 40–150 cm.
Leaves strap-shaped, deciduous. Flowers
nodding in umbels, tubular with the petals
shorter than the flower tube, blue to purple,
30–50 mm long.
Habitat: Damp grassland or stream sides.
Notes: Rhizomes used as a purgative ante-
natally and postnatally.

48

Aristea angolensis

IRIS FAMILY

Common branched aristea (E)

(Latin *angolensis*, from Angola, where the original material was collected)

Rhizomatous perennial, 60–100 cm. Leaves narrow and fibrous, in a loose fan. Flowers in small clusters on a branching stem, pale to deep blue, lasting a single morning, 10–15 mm diameter.

Habitat: Damp grassland and margins of bush clumps.

Notes: *Aristea woodii* is similar but the flower clusters are scattered along an unbranched stem.

Dietes iridioides

IRIS FAMILY

Wood iris, dietes (E), inDawo yehlati (Z)

(Resembling the genus *Iris* in its flowers and rhizomatous habit)

Evergreen perennial herb to 60 cm high, with a creeping rhizome. Leaves sword-shaped, in a loose fan, dark green. Flowers subtended by sheathing bracts, each lasting a single morning, white with the inner petals often marked with brown streaks near the base and the style branches lightly flushed with violet, 30–40 mm diameter.

Habitat: Evergreen forest or clearings in bush.

Notes: *Dietes grandiflora* has larger flowers that last for several days each.

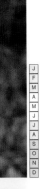

Moraea brevistyla

IRIS FAMILY

Partridge moraea (E)

(Latin *brevistylus*, short-styled)

Cormous perennial, 20–50 cm high, usually branched. Leaf solitary, slender and channelled. Flowers white, the outer three petals speckled with brown at the base, the inner petals three-lobed and coiled at the tips, 20–25 mm diameter.

Habitat: Montane grassland, often in damper places.

Moraea inclinata

IRIS FAMILY

Common blue moraea (E)

(Latin *inclinatus*, inclined, alluding to the stem)

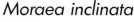

Cormous perennial, 30–90 cm high, the stem sharply inclined above the leaf. Leaves solitary and inserted well up on the stem, narrow and channelled. Flowers mauve, the outer petals marked with yellow and purple at the base, the inner petals tongue-shaped and spreading, 30–40 mm diameter.

Habitat: Montane grassland.

Moraea polystachya

IRIS FAMILY

Karoo iris (E)

(Latin *polystachyus*, many-spiked, alluding to the branched inflorescence)

Cormous perennial, 40–90 cm high, branched. Leaves several, narrow and channelled, trailing. Flowers blue, the outer petals marked with yellow at the base, the inner petals tongue-shaped and erect, 40–50 mm diameter.

Habitat: Stony slopes in karroid bush.

Notes: Common around Beaufort West. Parts of the plant are poisonous when green, causing death in stock and occasionally humans.

Moraea muddii

IRIS FAMILY

Early yellow moraea (E)

(Named for the English horticulturist, C. Mudd, who first collected the species)

Cormous perennial, 20–50 cm high, solitary. Basal leaf solitary, narrow and channelled, often overtopping the stem. Flowers pale yellow, the outer three petals with a darker yellow eye and the inner tepals tongue-shaped and erect, 40–50 mm diameter.

Habitat: Damp or marshy grassland.

Notes: Distinguished by its small stature. Common around Graskop.

Moraea spathulata

IRIS FAMILY

Large yellow moraea, teele-e-kholo (SS), iHlamvu lentaba (X), iNdlolothi (Z)

(Latin *spathulatus*, spatula-shaped, referring to the petals)

Cormous perennial to about 1 m high, solitary or growing in small clumps. Basal leaf single, leathery, flat or channelled, often bent and trailing above. Flowers bright yellow, the outer three petals with a darker yellow eye and the inner tepals tongue-shaped and erect, 50–60 mm diameter.

Habitat: Grassland, often among rocks.

Notes: *Moraea huttonii* has a brown mark on each style crest and grows in clumps, while *M. moggii* is similar but the leaf is distinctly grey. Poisonous to stock.

Flowering: May to September in the south, November to February in the interior and north.

Dierama floriferum

IRIS FAMILY

Tufted hairbell (E)

(Latin *floriferus*, bearing many flowers)

Cormous perennial, 40–70 cm high, growing in dense clumps. Leaves narrow and fibrous. Flowers rather crowded in a slender, nodding spike, funnel-shaped, mauve, 15–20 mm long, the floral bracts densely speckled with brown in the centre.

Habitat: Well-watered grassland.

Notes: Common around Nottingham Road.

Dierama luteoalbidum

IRIS FAMILY

Large white hairbell (E)

(Latin *luteoalbidus*, yellowish white)

Cormous perennial, 70–100 cm high, solitary. Leaves narrow and fibrous. Flowers, rather few in a slender, nodding spike, funnel-shaped, ivory-white, 30–50 mm long, the floral bracts white.

Habitat: Well-watered grassland.

Notes: Common around Nottingham Road and Karkloof.

Hesperantha baurii
IRIS FAMILY

Common hesperantha (E), khahla-
enyenyane (SS), isiDwa (Z)
(Named for the missionary and plant
collector, Rev. Leopold Bauer)

Cormous perennial, 15–40 cm. Basal leaves
two, slender and sword-like. Flowers with a
tube 6–12 mm long, deep pink, 15–20 mm
diameter.
Habitat: Well-watered grassland.
Notes: Common in the Drakensberg.

Hesperantha coccinea
IRIS FAMILY

(= *Schizostylis coccinea*)
Scarlet river lily (E), khahlana (SS)
(Latin *coccineus*, deep red)

Perennial with a short rhizome, 40–90 cm high.
Leaves narrow and sword-shaped, in a loose
fan. Flowers with a slender tube 30 mm long,
bright red or pink, 30 mm diameter.
Habitat: Stream banks.
Notes: A popular garden plant, better known
under the old name *Schizostylis*.

Freesia laxa
IRIS FAMILY

(= *Anomatheca laxa*)
Small forest freesia (E), bospaletblaar (A)
(Latin *laxus*, loose, not crowded)

Cormous perennial, 15–30 cm high. Leaves
narrowly sword-like and soft-textured, in a
loose fan. Flowers with a long, slender tube
20–40 mm long, red or lilac with darker marks
on the lower petals, 20–25 mm diameter.
Habitat: Forest margins and edges of bush
clumps or thicket.
Notes: The lilac form is found only along the
northern KwaZulu-Natal coast.

Watsonia pillansii

IRIS FAMILY

Pillans' watsonia (E)

(Named for Cape Town botanist, Neville Pillans)

Cormous perennial, 50–120 cm high, growing in colonies. Leaves sword-shaped, leathery, mostly 10–18 mm wide. Flowers in a two-ranked spike, scarlet to orange, trumpet-shaped, the floral tube 35–50 mm long, the petals 20–26 mm long.

Habitat: Rocky outcrops in grassland.

Watsonia densiflora

IRIS FAMILY

Natal watsonia (E), khahla (SS), inCembuzane (Z)

(Latin *densiflorus*, densely flowered)

Cormous perennial, 60–120 cm high, growing in clumps. Leaves sword-shaped, leathery, mostly 10–18 mm wide. Flowers in inclined, two-ranked spike, pink, funnel-shaped, the floral tube 20–40 mm long, the petals 18–24 mm long.

Habitat: Well-watered grassland.

Notes: Distinguished from related species by its clumped growth habit and pale greenish-straw bracts with dark margins and pale veins.

Watsonia lepida

IRIS FAMILY

Drakensberg watsonia (E), khahla (SS)

(Latin *lepidus*, attractive)

Cormous perennial, 25–60 cm high, solitary. Leaves sword-shaped, leathery, mostly 5–15 mm wide, the lower leaves dry and brown or burned off. Flowers in erect, two-ranked spike, pink, funnel-shaped, the floral tube 20–35 mm long, the petals 20 mm long.

Habitat: Well-watered, montane grassland.

Notes: Distinguished by its solitary growth habit and dry lower leaves.

Crocosmia paniculata

IRIS FAMILY

Zigzag crocosmia, Aunt-Eliza (E),
uDwendweni, umLunge (Z)
(Latin *paniculatus,* a branched
inflorescence)

Cormous perennial, 1–2 m high, growing in large clumps. Leaves sword-like and longitudinally pleated, in a loose fan. Flowers in a one-sided, branched inflorescence, on zigzag branches, trumpet-shaped, orange and yellow with darker petals, 70 mm long.
Habitat: Rock outcrops in grassland and along road verges.
Notes: Used traditionally to treat dysentery and infertility.

Crocosmia aurea

IRIS FAMILY

Falling stars, Forest montbretia (E),
umLunge (Z)
(Latin *aureus,* golden-yellow)

Cormous geophyte to about 1 m high. Leaves narrowly sword-like, in a loose fan. Flowers nodding, star-like with a slender, curved tube, bright orange, 40 mm diameter. Fruits yellow-orange on the inside with dark brown or black seeds.
Habitat: Forest margins and clearings and light bush.
Notes: Used traditionally to treat dysentery.

Gladiolus woodii

IRIS FAMILY

Wood's gladiolus (E)
(Named for John Medley Wood, first
curator of the Durban Botanic Gardens,
who collected the species)

Cormous perennial, 30–50 cm high. Leaves few and scattered up the stem with at most a short blade, with scattered soft hairs. Flowers in an angled, one-sided spike, funnel-shaped, yellow, dark brown or lilac, 25 mm long.
Habitat: Stony grassland.

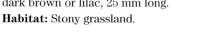

Gladiolus longicollis

IRIS FAMILY

Moth gladiolus (E), aandblom (A), khala-enyenyane (SS), umBejo (Z)

(Latin *longicollis*, long-necked, referring to the slender floral tube)

Cormous perennial to 60 cm high. Leaves three, narrow, almost grass-like, X-shaped in section. Flowers often solitary, cream, often mottled with light to dark brown, somewhat closed during the day but opening and sweetly scented at night, trumpet-shaped with a long slender floral tube 50–100 mm long.
Habitat: Moist grassland.
Notes: Pollinated by hawkmoths.

Gladiolus crassifolius

IRIS FAMILY

Thick-leaved gladiolus (E), khala-enyenyane (SS), iGulusha (Z)

(Latin *crassifolius*, thick leaved)

Cormous perennial, mostly 50–100 cm high. Leaves narrow and fibrous with pale, thickened margins and midrib, in a loose fan, the bases often forming a stem. Flowers in a one-sided spike, funnel-shaped, cream flushed pink or orange and with darker marks on the lower lip, 25–40 mm long.
Habitat: Well-watered grassland.

Gladiolus papilio

IRIS FAMILY

Butterfly gladiolus (E), sidvwana (SS), iButha (Z)

(Latin *papilio*, butterfly)

Cormous perennial, mostly 50–100 cm high. Leaves narrow and relatively short, in a loose fan. Flowers few in an angled, one-sided spike, nodding, bell-shaped, yellowish green or cream, often flushed purple, with large dark marks on the lower lip, 50 mm long.
Habitat: Marshy or damp grassland.

Gladiolus ecklonii
IRIS FAMILY
Speckled gladiolus (E), khahla (SS)
(Named for nineteenth-century German
plant collector, C.F. Ecklon)

Cormous perennial, mostly 25–40 cm high.
Leaves sword-shaped with pale, thickened
margins, in a tight fan. Flowers in a short, one-
sided spike, in the axils of large, green bracts,
funnel-shaped, mottled purple, red or brown
on a cream to pink background, the floral tube
15–20 mm long, the petals 25–35 mm long.
Habitat: Marshy or well-watered grassland.
Notes: The corm may be eaten raw or cooked
and is used for treatment of rheumatic pain.

Gladiolus sericeovillosus
IRIS FAMILY
Large speckled gladiolus (E), isiDwa (Z)
(Latin *sericeo-*, *villosus*, silky, shaggy)

Cormous perennial, 50–150 cm.
Leaves narrow and fibrous with prominent
margins, in a loose fan with the bases forming
a stem, smooth or finely hairy. Flowers in a
two-ranked spike on a woolly stem, funnel-
shaped with a rather closed mouth, whitish or
pink to greenish, 30 mm long.
Habitat: Rough grassland and edges of bush.
Notes: Used traditionally to treat dysentery
and for sprains and swollen joints.

Gladiolus oppositiflorus
IRIS FAMILY
Large pink gladiolus (E)
(Latin *oppositiflorus*, with flowers in
opposite ranks)

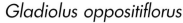

Cormous geophyte to 100 cm or more. Leaves
narrow and fibrous, in a loose fan, often
minutely velvety. Flowers several to many in a
more or less two-ranked spike, narrowly tubular below, pink to salmon, the lower petals
with darker streaks in the midline, floral tube
30–55 mm long, petals 40–40 mm long.
Habitat: Stony open grassland and mountain
slopes.

Gladiolus dalenii

IRIS FAMILY

Parrot lily (E), khala-e-kholo (SS), isiDwi
esibomvu (Z)

(Named in 1828 for Cornelius Dalen,
director of the Rotterdam Botanical Gardens)

Cormous perennial, 70–100 cm high. Leaves
sword-shaped, in a loose fan. Flowers in a one-
sided spike, funnel-shaped, orange or greenish,
sometimes flushed purple, the lower petals
often yellow, the floral tube 30–50 mm long
and the upper petals 20–50 mm long.
Habitat: Open grassland, rocky slopes and
ledges.

Gladiolus saundersii

IRIS FAMILY

Saunders' gladiolus, Lesotho lily (E), khala
ea maloti (SS)

(Named for the English grower, W. Wilson
Saunders, who employed the collector Thomas Cooper)

Cormous perennial, 50–90 cm high. Leaves
sword-shaped, in a tight fan. Flowers in a one-
sided spike, drooping, funnel-shaped with the
petals curled back, red with white speckles on
the lower lip, the floral tube 35–40 mm long
and the upper petals 50–70 mm long.
Habitat: Open grassland, rocky slopes and
ledges.
Notes: Common near Rhodes.

Strelitzia reginae

CRANE FLOWER FAMILY

Crane flower (E), geel piesang (A)

(Latin *reginae*, queen, alluding to its regal
appearance)

Evergreen stemless perennial to 1,5 m high.
Leaves on long petioles with large, elliptical
blades. Flowers enclosed in a leathery,
boat-shaped bract, orange with blue styles,
*c.*200 mm long. Fruit a woody capsule containing black, pea-like seeds bearing a tuft of
bright orange hairs.
Habitat: River banks, in coastal bush and
thicket.

Eulophia clavicornis
ORCHID FAMILY

Early fire eulophia (E), imFeyamasele
eluhlaza (Z)
(Latin *clavicornis*, club-horned, alluding to
the spur)

Rhizomatous perennial to 30 cm high. Leaves
produced on a separate shoot, partly to fully
developed at flowering, narrow and pleated.
Flowers in a loose spike, white or lilac and
purplish or yellow and brown, *c.*20 mm long,
the lip covered with slender papillae and bearing a narrow spur 2–9 mm long.
Habitat: Grassland, especially after fire.

Eulophia ensata
ORCHID FAMILY

Yellow cluster eulophia (E), iPhamba
lentaba (Z)
(Latin *ensatus*, sword-shaped, alluding to
the leaves)

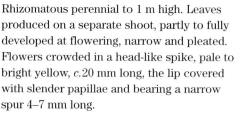

Rhizomatous perennial to 1 m high. Leaves
produced on a separate shoot, partly to fully
developed at flowering, narrow and pleated.
Flowers crowded in a head-like spike, pale to
bright yellow, *c.*20 mm long, the lip covered
with slender papillae and bearing a narrow
spur 4–7 mm long.
Habitat: Grassland and open bushveld, often
coastal.

Eulophia foliosa
ORCHID FAMILY

Green cluster eulophia (E), lekholela (SS)
(Latin *foliosus*, leafy)

Rhizomatous perennial to
60 cm high. Leaves produced on a separate
shoot, partly to fully developed at flowering,
narrow and pleated. Flowers crowded in a
dense spike, green with a purple lip, 20 mm
long, the lip covered with stout papillae and
without a spur.
Habitat: Grassland.

Eulophia angolensis

ORCHID FAMILY

Yellow marsh eulophia (E)

(Latin *angolensis*, from Angola, where it was first collected)

Stout rhizomatous perennial, 60–120 cm. Leaves produced on a separate shoot, stiff and pleated. Flowers in a loose spike, yellow with the upper tepals folded over the flower, fragrant, 25 mm diameter, the lip covered with rough crests and with a very short conical spur.

Habitat: Marshy grassland, often coastal.
Notes: Used traditionally as a love charm.

Eulophia streptopetala

ORCHID FAMILY

Bushveld harlequin orchid (E), amaBelejongosi (Z)

(Latin *streptopetalus*, with striped petals)

Stout perennial with partly exposed pseudo-bulbs. Leaves produced on a separate shoot, thin-textured. Flowers in a loose spike, thick-textured, yellow and brown with the upper tepals held like a roof over the flower, 30 mm diameter, the lip folded and with a short conical spur.

Habitat: Bushveld and open scrub.
Notes: Used traditionally as a love charm.

Eulophia speciosa

ORCHID FAMILY

Yellow harlequin orchid (E), umLunge omhlope (Z)

(Latin *speciosus*, showy)

Stout perennial with subterranean or partly exposed pseudobulbs. Leaves produced on a separate shoot, leathery and channelled. Flowers in a loose spike, thick-textured, bright yellow and green with purple streaks on the lip, 30 mm diameter, the lip bearing shallow ridges and with a short conical spur.

Habitat: Bushveld and open scrub.
Notes: Used traditionally as an emetic and charm against storms.

Brownleea macroceras
ORCHID FAMILY

Large false disa (E)

(Greek *macroceras*, large horned i.e. spurred)

Tuberous perennial, 6–20 cm high. Leaves one to three, narrow. Flowers few, pale to deep lilac, upper petals with a long, slender spur 25–40 mm long, lip vestigial.

Habitat: Damp montane grassland and wet ledges.

Disperis stenoplectron
ORCHID FAMILY

Purple granny's bonnet (E), moederkappie (A)

(Greek *stenoplectron*, narrow spur)

Tuberous perennial, 15–30 cm high. Leaves two to four, lanceolate. Flowers in a two-sided spike, dull pink to purple and greenish, with a sac-like hood, 20 mm diameter.

Habitat: Moist montane grassland.

Notes: One of several similar species. *Disperis fanniniae*, with larger, white flowers, is not uncommon on inland forest floors. Most species are pollinated by specialised oil-collecting bees.

Delosperma obtusum
MESEMB FAMILY

Mountain vygie (E), kransvygie (A)

(Latin *obtusus*, blunt, referring to the leaves)

Creeping, succulent dwarf shrub, to 5 cm high, with papillate branches. Leaves three-angled, succulent. Flowers in small clusters, brilliant magenta, 20 mm diameter.

Habitat: Rock sheets and outcrops at high altitude.

Notes: Easily seen at Witzieshoek.

Carpobrotus dimidiatus

MESEMB FAMILY

Sourfig (E), perdevy (A), gaukum (N)

(Latin *dimidiatus*, halved, alluding to the leaf pairs)

Robust succulent perennial with trailing stems that root along their length and form dense mats. Leaves succulent and three-sided, almost straight. Flowers solitary, purple, pink or white, 60–80 mm diameter, rounded at the base and narrowed abruptly into the flower stalk.
Habitat: Sand dunes and rocks along the seashore, and rocky coastal grassland.
Notes: The fruits are used for jam and syrup. The juice of the leaves is highly astringent and mildly antiseptic and is useful for burns, wounds and eczema. It is used as a gargle and is also taken internally for a variety of stomach ailments.

Portulacaria afra

PORTULACA FAMILY

Elephant bush (E), spekboom (A)

(Latin *afra*, from Africa)

Succulent shrub or small tree
to 3 m high. Leaves opposite, fleshy, obovate. Flowers in clusters at the branch tips, pink, *c.*5 mm diameter.
Habitat: Dry rocky slopes.
Notes: Dry, powdered leaves used traditionally as a snuff. A valuable fodder plant in dry areas, particularly for the Addo elephants.

Crassula sarcocaulis

STONECROP FAMILY

Bonsai bush (E), uMadinsane (Z)

(Greek *sarcocaulis*, fleshy stemmed)

Succulent shrublet to 60 cm
high, resembling a bonsai in form. Leaves narrow and fleshy. Flowers in dense, rounded clusters, cup-shaped, creamy white and pinkish, unpleasantly scented, 6 mm diameter.
Habitat: Damp or partially shaded rock outcrops, often at high altitudes.
Notes: Used traditionally as an emetic.

Crassula vaginata
STONECROP FAMILY

White stonecrop, yellow crassula (E),
umDumbukane (Z)

(Latin *vaginatus*, sheathing, referring to the
leaves)

Perennial herb with a leafy annual stem to
50 cm high from a tuberous rootstock. Leaves
grading down in size up the stem, lance-shaped
and smooth or hairy with a white-fringed margin. Flowers in a flat-topped, branched cluster,
yellow or white, fragrant, 6 mm diameter.
Habitat: Moist grassland.
Notes: Used traditionally to treat earache and
bruises. The ground roots are added to milk as
a carbohydrate in times of famine.

Kalanchoe thyrsiflora
STONECROP FAMILY

White lady (E), meelplakkie (A), utywAla
bentaka (X), utywAla benyoni (Z)

(Latin *thyrsiflorus*, with the flowers
produced in the arrangement known as a thyrse)

Succulent biennial to 1,5 m in flower,
producing a rosette of leaves in the first year
and flowering in the second. Leaves mainly
in a basal rosette, obovate, greyish with the
margins tinged red. Flowers crowded in
an elongate inflorescence, bright yellow,
fragrant, 12–20 mm long.
Habitat: Dry rocky grassland.
Notes: Used to treat earache and colds, as a
vermifuge and charm.

Cotyledon orbiculata
STONECROP FAMILY

Pig's ears (E), varkoor (A), iPhewula (X, Z)

(Latin *orbiculatus*, circular, referring to the
rounded leaves)

Succulent shrublet to 1 m high. Leaves obovate
to narrowly ovoid, smooth and with a grey
bloom or sometimes velvety. Flowers nodding
in terminal clusters, reddish, 8–30 mm long.
Habitat: Rocky outcrops in scrub.
Notes: Used traditionally to treat warts, corms,
earache, toothache and as a poultice for boils.

Nymphaea nouchali

WATERLILY FAMILY

(= *Nymphaea caerulea*)

Blue waterlily (E)

(Origin of the name obscure)

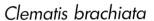

Aquatic perennial with floating leaves. Leaves orbicular and deeply notched at the base with undulate or scalloped margins. Flowers blue to pink, scented, 100–120 mm diameter, closing at night.

Habitat: Pools and sluggish rivers.

Notes: Used traditionally to treat colds and as a love charm.

Clematis brachiata

RANUNCULUS FAMILY

Traveller's joy (E), lemoenbloeisels (A), morarana-oa-mafehlo (SS), iTyolo (X), iHlonzo lezinduli (Z)

(Latin *brachiatus*, with spreading branchlets)

Climber with wiry stems. Leaves opposite, divided into ovate segments with coarsely toothed margins, sparsely hairy on the underside. Flowers in clusters, hairy, white, fragrant, 20 mm diameter. Fruits topped with the feathery style.

Habitat: Scrub and forest margins.

Notes: The dried plant is pounded as a snuff for clearing the head. An infusion of the leaves is taken as a vermifuge.

Knowltonia transvaalensis

RANUNCULUS FAMILY

Transvaal blistering leaves (E), brandblaar (A), umVuthuza (X, Z)

(Latin *transvaalensis*, from the Transvaal)

Slender perennial herb, 40–100 cm. Leaves mostly basal on slender petioles, deeply lobed and coarsely toothed on the margins. Flowers in clusters on slender pedicels, white, often tinged reddish, 15–20 mm diameter.

Habitat: Damp grassy slopes and river banks.

Ranunculus multifidus
RANUNCULUS FAMILY

Common buttercup (E), hlapi (SS), iShasha-
kazane, uXhapozi (Z)

(Latin *multifidus*, divided into many parts,
alluding to the leaves)

Silky, perennial herb, 20–50 cm high. Leaves
divided and celery-like with toothed segments,
hairy. Flowers on branched stems, bright
glossy yellow, 10–15 mm diameter.
Habitat: Damp ground near streams or
marshes.
Notes: The acrid juice from the pounded plant
is used to treat skin irritations.

Ranunculus baurii
RANUNCULUS FAMILY

Nasturtium-leaved buttercup (E), qojoana (SS)

(Named for the missionary and plant
collector, Rev. Leopold Bauer)

Perennial herb, 60–120 cm. Leaves in a basal
tuft on slender petioles, circular and attached
in the centre like an umbrella, finely toothed
on the margin. Flowers on tall, branched
stems, bright glossy yellow, 20–25 mm
diameter.
Habitat: Along waterfalls and stream sides at
high altitude.

Anemone fanninii
RANUNCULUS FAMILY

Giant anemone (E), groot anemoon (A),
uManzamnyama (X)

(Named for George F. Fannin, who first
collected the species)

Tufted perennial herb with annual stems to
1,2 m high from a woody rootstock. Leaves
mostly basal, five- to seven-lobed on long
petioles, leathery and velvety above with long
hairs beneath, the margins with red-tipped
teeth. Flowers on branched stems, creamy
white, 80–100 mm diameter.
Habitat: Moist depressions along drainage
lines and stream sides.

Dianthus basuticus

CARNATION FAMILY

Lesotho carnation (E), hlokoa-la-tsela (SS)
(Latin *basuticus*, growing in Basutoland,
now Lesotho)

Tufted perennial, to 25 cm, often mat-forming.
Leaves narrow and grass-like, greyish. Flowers
on slender stems, white or pink with toothed
or fringed petals, 20–30 mm diameter.
Habitat: Montane and alpine grassland in
rocky places.
Notes: Used traditionally as a love charm.

Oxalis obliquifolia

SORREL FAMILY

Oblique-leaved sorrel (E),
skuinsblaarsuring (A)
(Latin *obliquifolius*, oblique-leaved)

Cormous perennial herb to 10 cm high. Leaves
divided into three spade-shaped, thinly hairy
leaflets. Flowers solitary on slender stalks,
bright pink or white with a yellow or white
centre, 10–20 mm diameter.
Habitat: Stony grassland.
Notes: *Oxalis smithiana* is similar but has
narrow leaflets.

Hypericum aethiopicum

FLAX FAMILY

Small St John's wort (E), vlieëpisbossie (A),
iThalelimpofu (Z)
(Named for the eighteenth-century
Swedish botanist, Carl Thunberg, the father of South African
botany)

Perennial herb with slender annual stems to
50 cm high from a woody base. Leaves narrow
or elliptical with the lower ones opposite.
Flowers in loosely branched clusters, yellow
but reddish in bud, 10 mm diameter.
Habitat: Stony grassland.
Notes: Used traditionally to purify the blood.

Hypericum revolutum
FLAX FAMILY

Curry bush (E), kerriebos (A)

(Latin *revolutus*, rolled back, referring to the leaf margins)

Shrub to 2 m high. Leaves elliptical with translucent glands and the margins rolled under. Flowers solitary, deep yellow, 30–40 mm diameter.

Habitat: Stream banks and forest margins.

Acridocarpus natalitius
MALPIGHIA FAMILY

Moth-fruit (E), uMabopha (X, Z)

(Latin *natalitius*, coming from Natal)

Sprawling shrub or small tree with rust-coloured hairs on the young branches and leaves. Leaves elliptical and leathery. Flowers in loose racemes, bright golden yellow, 20–30 mm diameter.

Habitat: Forest margins and bushveld, often near the coast.

Notes: Roots traditionally used medicinally.

Papaver aculeatum
POPPY FAMILY

Orange poppy (E), doringpapawer (A), sehlolo (SS)

(Latin *aculeatus*, prickly)

Prickly, tufted annual to 1 m high. Leaves deeply lobed and toothed, covered with stiff yellow prickles. Flowers on slender stalks, orange, 50 mm diameter.

Habitat: Disturbed ground.

Notes: Young plants eaten as a spinach. The only poppy native in the southern hemisphere. Apparently allied to certain Mediterranean species.

Tricliceras longipedunculatum

WORMSKIOLDIA FAMILY

Lion's eye (E)

(Latin *longipedunculatus*, with a long peduncle i.e. flowering stalk)

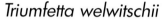

Herb to 20 cm high with stems covered with coarse, purple bristles. Leaves narrow with smooth or somewhat toothed margins, sometimes bristle on the midrib beneath. Flowers on long, slender peduncles, velvety reddish orange, 20 mm diameter.

Habitat: Open grassland and savannah.

Triumfetta welwitschii

LINDEN FAMILY

Maagbossie (A)

(Named after the nineteenth-century Austrian botanist, Friedrich Welwitsch)

Perennial with annual stems from a woody rootstock. Leaves narrowly elliptical with toothed margins and covered with rough, star-shaped hairs. Flowers in loosely branched clusters with spreading sepals and the petals clustered in the centre, pale yellow, 10 mm diameter. Fruits burr-like and covered with reddish bristles.

Habitat: Grassland and rocky ridges, especially after fire.

Notes: *Triumfetta sonderi* is a shrublet from Gauteng and the Highveld.

Melhania prostrata

HIBISCUS FAMILY

Common melhania (E)

(Latin *prostratus*, prostrate, lying on the ground)

Low-growing shrublet with creeping branches covered with yellowish, star-shaped hairs. Leaves narrow and almost hairless above but greyish velvety beneath. Flowers solitary or in pairs, yellow, 15 mm diameter.

Habitat: Open woodland in rocky grassland.

Hermannia cristata

HIBISCUS FAMILY

Scarlet doll's rose (E)

(Latin *cristatus*, crested)

Low-growing herb with erect stems to 30 cm high from a woody rootstock. Leaves elliptical and covered with rough, star-shaped hairs. Flowers nodding in elongate racemes, bell-shaped, reddish orange, 20 mm long. Fruit erect, five-angled with fringed crests along the angles.

Habitat: Stony grassland.

Radyera urens

HIBISCUS FAMILY

Karoo pumpkin (E), pampoenbossie (A)

(Latin *urens*, stinging, referring to the rough hairs)

Coarse herb with trailing stems from a woody rootstock. Leaves resembling those of a pumpkin, rounded and paler beneath with crinkled margins, on long petioles and covered with rough, star-shaped hairs. Flowers on the ground concealed beneath the leaves, deeply cup-shaped, reddish orange with a dark throat, 15 mm diameter.

Habitat: Dry karroid flats along roadsides and waste places.

Notes: Used traditionally as a remedy for piles.

Hibiscus cannabinus

HIBISCUS FAMILY

Hemp-leaved hibiscus (E), umHlakanye (X), uDekane (Z)

(Latin *cannabinus*, resembling cannabis, *Cannabis sativa*)

Woody annual herb with stiffly erect stems to 2 m high, covered with short prickles. Leaves divided into three to seven, toothed lobes. Flowers solitary in the upper axils, pale yellow with a purple centre, 100 mm diameter, the calyx surrounded at the base by seven or eight narrow bracts.

Habitat: Disturbed ground and roadsides.

Notes: Grown as a source of fibre in India.

Hibiscus diversifolius

HIBISCUS FAMILY

Prickly-leaved hibiscus (E)

(Latin *diversifolius*, with variable leaves)

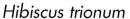

Erect perennial herb with stiffly erect stems to 2,5 m high, covered with short prickles. Leaves on long, prickly petioles, usually divided into three to five, coarsely toothed lobes. Flowers in terminal racemes, yellow with a dark centre, 100 mm diameter, the calyx surrounded by 10 to 12 narrow bracts.

Habitat: Forest margins and bush.

Hibiscus trionum

HIBISCUS FAMILY

Bladder hibiscus (E), terblansbossie (A), iYeza lentshulube (X), uVemvane olukhulu (Z)

(From an old name for the species, *Trionum*, flower of an hour)

Stiffly hairy annual herb to 1 m high. Leaves mostly deeply three- to five-lobed and toothed. Flowers solitary in the upper axils, yellow with a dark eye, 25–40 mm diameter, the calyx bell-shaped with conspicuous purple veins and surrounded at the base by 10 to 12 narrow bracts, swollen like a gooseberry in fruit.

Habitat: Stony slopes and forest margins.

Notes: Introduced from the Old World tropics and now widespread in southern Africa. A decoction is traditionally used as a vermifuge.

Hibiscus aethiopicus

HIBISCUS FAMILY

Cape hibiscus, dwarf hibiscus (E), uVemvane (Z)

(Latin *aethiopicus*, from Africa, usually South Africa)

Roughly hairy subshrub to 30 cm high with stems produced from a woody underground base. Leaves oblong and toothed above with three to five veins from the base, nearly hairless above. Flowers cream to yellow or rarely pink, often with a dark centre, 50 mm diameter, the calyx surrounded by 10 to 12 bracts.

Habitat: Stony grassland and open scrub.

Notes: Used traditionally to treat sprains.

Hibiscus calyphyllus
HIBISCUS FAMILY
Large yellow hibiscus (E), wildestokroos (A)
(Greek *calyphyllus*, leafy calyx)
Shrub to 2 m high. Leaves
rounded or three- to five-lobed and toothed,
velvety. Flowers solitary in the upper axils,
yellow with a dark eye, each lasting less than
a day, 120 mm diameter, the calyx surrounded
at the base by five broad bracts.
Habitat: Thicket and forest margins.

Dissotis canescens
PRIDE-OF-INDIA FAMILY
Marsh dissotis (E), imFeyenkala (Z)
(Latin *canescens*, becoming greyish)
Shrub with erect, reddish stems
to 1,5 m high. Leaves opposite, dark green
and rough above but velvety whitish beneath.
Flowers in branched clusters, brilliant
magenta, 35–45 mm diameter.
Habitat: Marshy grassland.
Notes: Used traditionally as a treatment for
dysentery and hangovers.

Begonia sutherlandii
BEGONIA FAMILY
Orange begonia (E), uQamamawene (Z)
(Named for P.C. Sutherland, Surveyor-
General of Natal and a keen plant collector)
Tuberous perennial with brittle stems to 50 cm
high. Leaves asymmetrical, elliptical and often
lobed with irregularly toothed margins.
Flowers with the sexes separate, orange to
red, to 35 mm diameter.
Habitat: Forest floor in humus or on mossy
rocks.
Notes: Used traditionally to treat heartburn.
Very variable in leaf shape. Other species have
pink flowers: *B. sonderana* from Mpumalanga,
B. homonyma and *B. dregei* from KwaZulu-
Natal and Eastern Cape; *B. geranioides* has
rounded leaves.

Monsonia attenuata

GERANIUM FAMILY

Narrow-leaved monsonia (E)

(Latin *attenuatus,* tapering to a slender point)

Perennial herb with an erect, annual stem from a tuberous rootstock. Leaves crowded, narrow and folded along the midline with toothed margins and often flexed downwards above the petiole. Flowers crowded at the top of the stem, chalky white and finely creased with fine charcoal veining beneath, the petals blunt and toothed at the tips, 30–40 mm diameter.
Habitat: Stony grassland.

Geranium wakkerstroomianum

GERANIUM FAMILY

White geranium (E)

(Latin *wakkerstroomianus,* from the Wakkerstroom district where it was first collected)

Straggling perennial herb to 1 m high from a taproot. Leaves coarsely lobed and toothed, thinly hairy above and variously hairy beneath. Flowers white with pink or red veins and notched petals, 15 mm diameter.
Habitat: Damp sheltered hollows and forest margins.

Geranium pulchrum

GERANIUM FAMILY

Silver geranium (E)

(Latin *pulchrus,* beautiful)

Robust shrublet to 1,2 m high with woody stems. Leaves deeply five- to seven-lobed and toothed, thick-textured and greyish above but silvery-velvety beneath. Flowers pale to deep mauve with rounded or shallowly notched petals, 30 mm diameter.
Habitat: Rocky stream banks and mountain slopes at high altitude.
Notes: Conspicuous on Sani Pass.

Pelargonium luridum

GERANIUM FAMILY

Starburst pelargonium (E), iNyonkulu (Z)

(Latin *luridus*, smoky or drab)

Perennial herb with annual
stems from a tuberous rootstock. Leaves basal,
variably lobed with broad to ribbon- or thread-
like segments. Flowers in a round head on a
slender, hairy stem, pink or pale yellow to
white, 20 mm diameter.

Habitat: Grassland.

Notes: Used traditionally to treat nausea and
vomiting and as a love charm.

Pelargonium schlechteri

GERANIUM FAMILY

Two-tiered pelargonium (E)

(Named for the German botanist and plant
collector, Rudolph Schlechter)

Perennial herb with annual stems from a tuberous rootstock. Leaves basal, coarsely lobed
and toothed. Flowers usually in two-tiered
heads on a slender, hairy stem, greenish yellow
with a more or less well-developed maroon
blotch, 20 mm diameter.

Habitat: Grassland.

Pelargonium schizopetalum

GERANIUM FAMILY

Fringed pelargonium (E),
muishondbossie (A)

(Greek *schizopetalus*, with deeply fringed
petals)

Perennial herb with annual stems from a large,
woody tuber. Leaves basal, deeply lobed and
softly hairy. Flowers in a round head on a slender, hairy stem, pale yellow and variously
tinged with purple with finely fringed petals,
30–40 mm diameter.

Habitat: Grassland.

Cleome gynandra

CABBAGE FAMILY

Spider-wisp cleome, white mouse-whiskers (E), oorpynpeultjie (A), umZonde (Z)

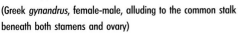

(Greek *gynandrus*, female-male, alluding to the common stalk beneath both stamens and ovary)

Erect annual herb with glandular-hairy stems to 60 cm high. Leaves divided like a hand into several elliptical or paddle-shaped leaflets covered with glandular hairs. Flowers in slender racemes, white fading pink, 10–25 mm diameter.

Habitat: Savannah and open grassland, often in disturbed places.

Notes: A popular spinach in rural areas.

Cleome angustifolia

CABBAGE FAMILY

Yellow cleome, yellow mouse-whiskers (E), peultjiesbos (A)

(Latin *angustifolius*, narrow-leaved)

Erect annual herb with wand-like stems to 1,5 m high covered with conical, whitish protuberances. Leaves divided like a hand into several thread-like leaflets. Flowers in slender racemes, yellow with reddish marks at the base of the two largest petals, closing at midday, 20 mm diameter.

Habitat: Savannah and open scrub.

Cadaba aphylla

CABBAGE FAMILY

Black storm (E), swartstorm (A)

(Latin *aphyllus*, leafless)

Leafless, often tangled shrub with grey or purplish branches to 2 m, often spinescent at the tips. Flowers in clusters on side shoots, greenish to red, 40–50 mm long.

Habitat: Dry bushveld and semi-desert.

Notes: Palatable to game. The red flowers are pollinated by sunbirds.

Chamaecrista comosa

PEA FAMILY

Trailing dwarf cassia (E)

(Latin *comosus*, bearing a tuft of leaves)

Perennial herb with stems to 50 cm high from a woody rhizome. Leaves divided into numerous pairs of narrow leaflets, with the leaf axis grooved above. Flowers clustered at the branch tips, yellow with a reddish calyx, *c*.20 mm diameter.

Habitat: Grassland, often along roadsides.

Notes: The annual *Chamaecrista mimosoides* is somewhat similar in appearance but the leaf axis is crested.

Senna italica

PEA FAMILY

Wild senna (E), elandsertjie (A), imPengu (Z)

(Latin *italicus*, from Italy)

Perennial with glandular-hairy stems to 60 cm high. Leaves divided into several pairs of asymmetrically elliptical leaflets with the margins fringed with orange hairs. Flowers in short racemes, yellow with a dark brown calyx, *c*.20 mm diameter.

Habitat: Bushveld.

Notes: Seeds used as a coffee substitute and to treat pain and roundworm.

Bauhinia galpinii

PEA FAMILY

Pride-of-de Kaap (E), vlam-van-die-vlakte (A)

(Named for the naturalist and plant collector, E.E. Galpin)

Sprawling shrub to 5 m. Leaves broad, folded along the midline and deeply notched. Flowers in clusters on side shoots, carried on brown, velvety pedicels, dull reddish, 40 mm diameter.

Habitat: Scrambling among bushveld and scrub.

Notes: Widely cultivated as an ornamental.

Erythrina zeyheri

PEA FAMILY

Ploughbreaker (E), ploegbreker (A),
umNsinsana (Z)

(Named for the nineteenth-century German
botanist and plant collector, Carl Zeyher)

Dwarf shrublet with short stems to 60 cm high
from a large, underground stem. Leaves divided
into three spade-shaped leaflets covered with
hooked prickles on the veins. Flowers in slender, pointed racemes, drooping, bright red,
45 mm long.
Habitat: Grassland, especially after fires.
Notes: Red and black seeds used as beads.

Lessertia frutescens

PEA FAMILY

(= *Sutherlandia frutescens*)

Scarlet balloon pea (E), kankerbos (A)

(Latin *frutescens*, becoming shrubby)

Erect or sprawling shrublet to 1 m. Leaves
divided into many small oblong leaflets that
are rounded at the tips, greyish green and
mostly thinly hairy above. Flowers in short
racemes, bright red, 20–40 mm long. Pods large
and balloon-like with smooth papery walls.
Habitat: Widespread on a variety of soils but
usually along roads.
Notes: Enjoys a high repute for the treatment
of cancer but there is no evidence in support
of this belief.

Eriosema distinctum

PEA FAMILY

Scarlet eriosema (E), uBangalala
olukhulu (Z)

(Latin *distinctus*, distinct, i.e. not confused
with related species)

Erect herb with annual stems from a woody
rootstock, 10–20 cm high. Leaves divided into
three elliptical leaflets, shortly hairy. Flowers
in short racemes, dull reddish with darker
veins, 15 mm diameter, calyx with silvery hairs.
Habitat: Rocky grassland, especially after fire.
Notes: Unpalatable to cattle and flourishing in
overgrazed grassland.

Eriosema kraussianum

PEA FAMILY

Pale eriosema (E)

(Named for the German naturalist and plant collector, Christian Krauss)

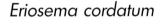

Erect perennial herb, 30–50 cm high, growing in clumps from a woody rootstock. Leaves divided into three narrow leaflets, thinly covered with silky hairs. Flowers in narrow racemes, pale creamy yellow, 10 mm diameter, calyx with golden hairs.

Habitat: Grassland, especially after fire.

Eriosema salignum

PEA FAMILY

Narrow-leaved eriosema (E), lesapho (SS), uQonsi (Z)

(Latin *salignus*, willowy, alluding to the slender stems)

Slender, erect herb, 30–60 cm, from a woody rootstock. Leaves divided into three narrow leaflets, folded and dark green above but velvety-white beneath. Flowers on silvery stalks, yellow to pale orange, 10 mm diameter, calyx shaggy.

Habitat: Grassland.

Notes: Used traditionally as an expectorant and diuretic.

Eriosema cordatum

PEA FAMILY

Heart-leaved eriosema (E), lesapho (SS), uQonsi (Z)

(Latin *cordatus*, heart-shaped)

Straggling perennial herb with creeping stems. Leaves divided into three, broadly elliptical leaflets, shortly hairy on the veins beneath. Flowers in erect racemes, yellow with brownish veins, 10 mm diameter, calyx very shortly hairy.

Habitat: Rocky grassland.

Rhynchosia cooperi
PEA FAMILY

Common creeping rhynchosia (E)
(Named after the English plant collector,
Thomas Cooper)

Trailing perennial herb. Leaves erect, divided
into three, broadly diamond-shaped, shortly
hairy leaflets. Flowers in erect racemes on
slender stalks, bright yellow, 8 mm diameter,
calyx shortly hairy.
Habitat: Grassland.

Lotononis corymbosa
PEA FAMILY

Pincushion lotononis (E), iNcini (Z)
(Latin *corymbosus*, like a corymb, alluding
to the rounded inflorescence)

Perennial herb with annual branches to 30 cm
high from a woody rootstock. Leaves divided
into three elliptical leaflets that are hairless
above and silky on the margins and beneath.
Flowers crowded in dome-like heads nestled in
the upper leaves, yellow, 10 mm long.
Habitat: Grassland, especially after fire.
Notes: Used traditionally as a tonic.

Crotalaria globifera
PEA FAMILY

Round-pod rattle bush (E), jaagsiekte-
bossie (A)
(Latin *globiferus*, globe-carrying, referring
to the ball-like pods)

Shrublet with annual stems to 60 cm high from
a woody rootstock. Leaves divided into three,
narrow leaflets that are folded along the midline. Flowers in racemes, yellow with a sharply
pointed keel, 10 mm long. Pods globular.
Habitat: Drier grassland, especially after fire.

Argyrolobium sandersonii
PEA FAMILY

Common liquorice bean (E)

(Named for John Sanderson, amateur nineteenth-century Natal botanist)

Bushy annual herb, 30–60 cm high. Leaves divided into three, narrowly elliptical leaflets, greyish and hairless. Flowers in elongated racemes, bright yellow, the flag petal narrowly wedge-shaped, scented of wistaria, 10 mm diameter, calyx hairless.

Habitat: Grassland, especially after fire.

Notes: Flowers turn black on drying.

Argyrolobium robustum
PEA FAMILY

Large liquorice bean (E)

(Latin *robustus*, robust)

Bushy annual herb, 30–60 cm high. Leaves divided into three, broadly elliptical leaflets, hairless. Flowers in cylindrical racemes, pale yellowish and orange with darker veins, the flag petal rounded, scented of lemon and wistaria, 10 mm diameter, calyx hairless.

Habitat: Grassland, especially after fire.

Notes: Flowers turn black on drying.

Pseudarthria hookeri
PEA FAMILY

Velvet bean, bug-catcher (E), fluweelboon (A), uPhandosi (Z)

(Named after Sir Joseph Hooker, first director of Kew Gardens)

Shrub with erect, velvety stems to 3 m high. Leaves divided into three, elliptical leaflets that are rough and green above and pale and velvety beneath. Flowers in branched racemes, bright pink, 8 mm diameter, calyx velvety-brown or mauve.

Habitat: Rough grassland in damp places and forest margins.

Notes: The curved, velvety hairs act like Velcro, sticking to other surfaces.

Indigofera hilaris

PEA FAMILY

Red bush indigo (E), iGqokisi (Z)

(Latin *hilaris*, relating to the hilum, where
the funicle attaches to the seed, an obscure
reference)

Perennial with annual stems to 60 mm high
from a woody rootstock. Leaves divided into
five to seven, narrowly elliptical, greyish
leaflets. Flowers in numerous, short racemes,
reddish pink, 10 mm diameter.
Habitat: Grassland, especially after fires.
Notes: Becomes straggly if not burned.

Indigofera oxytropis

PEA FAMILY

Keeled indigo (E)

(Greek *oxytropis*, sharply keeled, referring
to the flag petal)

Shrublet with creeping stems from a woody
rootstock. Leaves divided into 11 to 15 elliptical leaflets that are folded along the midline
and hairless above but covered with appressed
hairs beneath. Flowers in racemes, the flag
petal sharply keeled and folded over the other
petals, silky on the upper surface, reddish
pink, 10 mm long.
Habitat: Grassland.

Tephrosia grandiflora

PEA FAMILY

Pink bush pea (E), iHlozane (Z)

(Latin *grandiflorus*, large flowered)

Shrub to 1,5 m high. Leaves
divided into numerous elliptical leaflets that
are almost hairless and closely parallel-veined
to the margins, subtended by large, many-
veined stipules. Flowers in crowded racemes
on naked stalks, pink or magenta, 15–20 mm
long.
Habitat: Scrub and forest margins.
Notes: Used traditionally to treat chest
ailments and as a fish poison.

Tephrosia macropoda
PEA FAMILY

Creeping tephrosia (E), visboontjie (A),
iHlozane (Z)

(Greek *macropodus*, with large foot or
support, i.e. flower stalk)

Straggling perennial herb with creeping
branches. Leaves divided into numerous elliptical leaflets that are almost hairless above but
silky beneath and closely parallel-veined to the
margins. Flowers in crowded racemes on
naked stalks, pink or magenta, 15–20 mm long.
Habitat: Open and rocky grassland.
Notes: Used traditionally to treat chest complaints, fevers and lice and as a fish poison.

Vigna vexillata
PEA FAMILY

Narrow-leaved sweetpea (E), wilde-ertjie (A),
isiKhwali (Z)

(Latin *vexillatus*, with a (conspicuous)
standard or flag petal)

Slender trailing creeper. Leaves divided into
three leaflets ranging in shape from very
narrow to elliptical, rough. Flowers, one or
two on slender stalks, pale pink to lilac,
sweetly scented, 25 mm diameter.
Habitat: Grassland or open woodland.
Notes: *Vigna unguiculata* is similar but the
central leaflet always bulges at the sides near
the base. Seeds and tubers edible.

Canavalia rosea
PEA FAMILY

Beach-bean canavalia (E),
strandboontjie (A)

(Latin *roseus*, rose-pink)

Robust trailing creeper. Leaves divided into
three broad, rounded leaflets. Flowers, few on
upright stalks, pink to purple, sweetly scented,
25 mm diameter.
Habitat: Coastal dunes and along estuaries.

Polygala virgata

POLYGALA FAMILY

Purple broom (E), bloukappies (A),
iThethe (Z)

(Latin *virgatus*, with slender rod-like stems)

Slender shrub with wand-like stems to 1,5 m
high, branching in the upper parts only. Leaves
soon falling, narrow. Flowers in arching
racemes, pink to magenta, 15 mm diameter.
Habitat: Rough grassland and forest margins.
Notes: Used traditionally as a blood purifier.

Impatiens hochstetteri

BALSAM FAMILY

Wild impatiens (E), iHlula (A)

(Commemorates the German botanist,
Christian Hochstetter)

Soft annual or perennial herb with brittle
stems. Leaves ovate and scalloped along the
margins. Flowers in small groups at the branch
tips, pale pink or mauve, 'butterfly-like' with
the lower part of the petals drawn into a slender 'tail', 20 mm diameter.
Habitat: Shaded and damp forest margins.
Notes: Used traditionally to treat eczema.

Impatiens sylvicola

BALSAM FAMILY

Transvaal impatiens (E)

(Latin *sylvicolus*, forest-dwelling)

Soft annual or perennial herb
with brittle stems. Leaves ovate and scalloped
along the margins. Flowers in small groups at
the branch tips, pale pink or mauve with a distinct dark spot on the deeply two-lobed petals,
20 mm diameter.
Habitat: Shaded and damp forest margins.

Cucumis africanus

PUMPKIN FAMILY

Wild cucumber (E), agurkie (A)

(Latin *africanus*, from Africa)

Perennial herb with trailing annual stems from a tuberous root, covered in white, hooked hairs. Leaves with tendrils at the base, deeply lobed. Flowers unisexual, greenish yellow, 10 mm diameter. Fruits egg-shaped and covered with prickles, dark green with pale bands but turning yellow when ripe, up to 6 cm long.

Habitat: Sandy soils, often along seasonal streams, floodplains or disturbed areas.

Notes: The fruits are poisonous when raw but have been used as pickles after cooking.

Citrullus lanatus

PUMPKIN FAMILY

Tsamma melon (E), t'samma, karkoer (N)

(Latin *lanatus*, woolly)

Robust annual herb with trailing stems to 3 m long, covered in coarse, silky hairs. Leaves with tendrils at the base, deeply lobed. Flowers unisexual, greenish yellow, 15 mm diameter. Fruits globose, hairy at first, mottled yellow and green, up to 15 cm diameter.

Habitat: Seasonal streams, floodplains or disturbed areas.

Notes: The fruits are either bitter and then possibly poisonous, or sweet and then edible and consumed by animals and man for both food and water. The seeds are highly nutritious.

Trichodesma physaloides

BORAGE FAMILY

Chocolate bells (E), sjokaladeklokkies (A)

(Resembling the Cape gooseberry, *Physalis*)

Slender shrublet with annual stems to 50 cm high. Leaves produced after the flowers, lance-shaped and white-spotted on the margins and beneath. Flowers nodding in branched clusters, bell-shaped, bluish white fading brown, 25 mm long.

Habitat: Rough grassland on the edges of marshes and seeps, especially after fires.

Pachypodium saundersii

MILKWEED FAMILY

Kudu lily (E), koedoelelie (A), isiHlele (Z)
(Named after Sir Charles Saunders, brother
of the botanical artist Katherine Saunders)

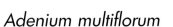

Succulent shrublet with a swollen stem to 1 m
high bearing pairs of long, slender spines on
small cushions. Leaves in tufts on the cushions
above the spines, elliptical and leathery with
the margins sometimes finely toothed. Flowers
trumpet-shaped with a velvety tube 30 mm
long, white, 50 mm diameter.
Habitat: Rock outcrops in savannah.

Adenium multiflorum

MILKWEED FAMILY

Impala lily, Sabi star (E), impalalelie (A),
isiGubengubu (Z)
(Latin *multiflorus*, many-flowered)

Succulent shrublet with a swollen stem to
1,5 m high. Leaves in clusters at the branch
tips, elliptical and leathery, appearing after
the flowers. Flowers trumpet-shaped with a
velvety tube 30 mm long, white with brilliant
pink margins, 50 mm diameter.
Habitat: Dry woodland.
Notes: *Adenium swazicum*, which flowers
in the summer, has uniformly pink to reddish
purple flowers with a tube 50 mm long.

Adenium oleifolium

MILKWEED FAMILY

Tufted impala lily (E), pylgif (A), ouhiep (N)
(Latin *oleifolius*, with leaves like an olive)

Dwarf shrublet with a subter-
ranean swollen stem to 40 cm high. Leaves in
clusters at the branch tips, narrow and leathery, shortly hairy, especially beneath. Flowers
trumpet-shaped with a velvety tube 22–35 mm
long, pink to red with darker margins, 50 mm
diameter.
Habitat: Stony ridges, limestone outcrops and
sandy flats.
Notes: One of the ingredients of arrow poison.
The dried tuber is used to treat insect bites.

Raphionacme hirsuta
MILKWEED FAMILY

False gentian (E), khadiwortel (A), inTsema (X)

(Latin *hirsutus*, hairy, referring to the leaves)

Perennial herb with softly woody annual stems from a large, flattened, tuberous rootstock, exuding milky sap when damaged. Leaves opposite, elliptical and smooth or hairy, often not fully developed at flowering. Flowers in clusters, bright purple with a white or purple central crown, 10–15 mm diameter.

Habitat: Grassland, especially after fire.

Notes: The tuber is used in brewing beer and also to treat ulcers but is possibly poisonous.

Asclepias cucullata
MILKWEED FAMILY

Hooded meadow-star (E), mohlatsisa (SS)

(Latin *cucullatus*, hooded, referring to the corona lobes)

Tuberous perennial herb with annual stems to 30 cm high, exuding milky sap when damaged. Leaves opposite, very narrow with the margins rolled under, roughly hairy. Flowers in flat-topped clusters, whitish flushed with dull purple, 10 mm diameter, the corona lobes pitcher-shaped and yellowish green at the base.

Habitat: Stony grassland, mainly after fire.

Xysmalobium undulatum
MILKWEED FAMILY

Uzura (E), bitterwortel (A), iShongwe (X, Z)

(Latin *undulatus*, undulating, referring to the leaf margins)

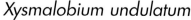

Tuberous perennial herb with annual stems to 1 m high, exuding milky sap when damaged. Leaves opposite, elliptical and roughly hairy with crisped or undulating margins. Flowers in round clusters at the nodes, greenish and covered with long white hairs, 10–15 mm diameter, the corona lobes knob-shaped. Fruits swollen and pear-shaped, covered with soft bristles.

Habitat: Stony open grassland.

Notes: Used traditionally to treat headaches, colic and dysentery but certainly poisonous.

Pachycarpus concolor

MILKWEED FAMILY

Astral-bell (E)

(Latin *concolorus*, uniformly coloured, i.e. not spotted or marked)

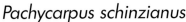

Perennial herb with annual stems to 60 cm high from a tuberous rootstock, exuding milky sap when damaged. Leaves opposite, elliptical and roughly hairy. Flowers in small clusters at the nodes, yellowish to brown, 15–25 mm diameter, the corona lobes slipper-shaped. **Habitat:** Stony open grassland, especially after fire.

Pachycarpus schinzianus

MILKWEED FAMILY

Dark-eyed bell (E), bitterwortel (A)

(Named for the German explorer and plant collector, Hans Schinz)

Perennial herb with annual stems to 60 cm high from a tuberous rootstock, exuding milky sap when damaged. Leaves opposite, elliptical and roughly hairy. Flowers in small clusters at the nodes, white or flushed dull purplish, 15–25 mm diameter, the corona lobes scoop-shaped and marked with a black blotch. **Habitat:** Stony open grassland, especially after fire.

Pachycarpus campanulatus

MILKWEED FAMILY

Fairy bell (E)

(Latin *campanulatus*, bell-shaped)

Perennial herb with slender annual stem to 60 cm high from a tuberous rootstock, exuding milky sap when damaged. Leaves opposite, narrow with the margins rolled under, roughly hairy. Flowers in a cluster at the stem tip, nodding and deeply cup-shaped, pale greenish or pinkish, 20–30 mm diameter.

Habitat: Grassland, especially after fire.

Notes: *Pachycarpus grandiflorus* has similar balloon-shaped flowers, usually speckled with purple, but the corona lobes are long and reach to the rim of the flowers.

Ceropegia ampliata
MILKWEED FAMILY
Bushman's pipe (E), boesmanspyp (A)
(Latin *ampliatus*, enlarged, referring to the
swollen base of the flowers)

Leafless vine with smooth, greyish-green stems
to 1 m long from a tuber, exuding clear sap
when damaged. Leaves short-lived. Flowers
vase-shaped with the petals remaining
attached at the tips, cream coloured to
greenish with fine green veins outside,
50–70 mm long.
Habitat: Scrub and thornveld.

Ipomoea obscura
MORNING-GLORY FAMILY
Yellow ipomoea (E), wildepatat (A),
uSiboniseleni (Z)
(Latin *obscurus*, indistinct, possibly alluding
to the colour, or rather lack thereof)

Slender twiner with shortly hairy stems to 2 m
long. Leaves narrowly heart-shaped and softly
hairy. Flowers pale creamy-yellow, sometimes
with a deep red centre, 12–30 mm diameter,
the sepals narrow.
Habitat: Grassland.
Notes: Leaves cooked as a relish. Used traditionally as a hallucinogenic.

Ipomoea crassipes
MORNING-GLORY FAMILY
Leafy-flowered ipomoea (E), wildewinde (A),
uBoqo (Z)
(Latin *crassipes*, thick foot, i.e. stem)

Trailing perennial with softly hairy stems to
1 m long. Leaves ovate to lanceolate and thinly
hairy. Flowers mauve to cream with a magenta
centre, 35–60 mm diameter, the outer sepals
arrow-shaped and leaf-like.
Habitat: Grassland and roadsides.
Notes: The roots are eaten raw. Traditionally
used to treat dysentery, sores and hiccups.

Ipomoea cairica

MORNING-GLORY FAMILY

Common ipomoea (E), iHlambe (Z)

(Latin *cairica*, from Cairo)

Vigorous climber with slender
stems. Leaves deeply divided into five to seven
lobes, grey beneath. Flowers deep mauve,
40–60 mm diameter, the sepals small.
Habitat: Riverine bush and disturbed places
along the coast.
Notes: Can become weedy. Used traditionally
to treat rashes.

Ipomoea oblongata

MORNING-GLORY FAMILY

(= *Turbina oblongata*)

Turbina (E)

(Latin *oblongatus*, oblong-shaped, alluding
to the leaves)

Perennial creeper with prostrate, hairy stems
to 2 m long. Leaves oblong to elliptical,
covered with yellowish hairs and held erect.
Flowers deep magenta, 40–70 mm diameter,
the sepals lance-shaped and tapering.
Habitat: Open grassland and savannah.
Notes: *Ipomoea pellita* is similar but the
flower clusters are on long stalks and the
sepals are narrow throughout and not tapering.
The tuber is edible.

Wahlenbergia grandiflora

BELLFLOWER FAMILY

Drakensberg bellflower (E)

(Latin *grandiflorus*, large-flowered)

Perennial herb to 50 cm high.
Leaves elliptical and hairy with wavy or
crisped margins. Flowers on loosely branched
stems, cup-shaped, pale blue, 20–30 mm
diameter, the calyx lobes slender and tapering.
Habitat: Damp cliffs or in the shelter of rocks.
Notes: *Wahlenbergia undulata* is similar but
has short calyx lobes.

Erica algida
ERICA FAMILY

Alpine heath (E), sehalahala (SS)

(Latin *algidus*, cold, alluding to the climate)

Dwarf shrub to 30 cm high.
Leaves in whorls of three, needle-like and curved upwards with the margins rolled under, coarsely hairy. Flowers in small clusters of four, urn-shaped, pale pink to white, downy, 3 mm long.

Habitat: Damp grassland.

Notes: Used as fuel.

Erica oatesii
ERICA FAMILY

Oates' heath (E)

(Named for the Victorian naturalist and traveller, Frank Oates)

Shrub to 1,2 m high. Leaves in whorls of three or four, needle-like and spreading or erect with the margins rolled under, coarsely hairy. Flowers in terminal clusters, urn-shaped, pink to red, hairless, 10–13 mm long.

Habitat: Stream banks and damp grassy slopes.

Gnidia compacta
DAPHNE FAMILY

Alpine yellow-head (E)

(Latin *compactus*, compact, alluding to the cushion-like form)

Cushion-forming shrublet to 20 cm high from a woody rootstock. Leaves narrow and bluish green above but softly silky on the margins and beneath, somewhat concave. Flowers in small clusters, bright yellow with a short tube bearing four teeth at the mouth, 5 mm diameter.

Habitat: Rocky montane grassland.

Gnidia capitata

DAPHNE FAMILY

Common yellow-head (E), gifbossie (A),
isiDikili (Z)

(Latin *capitatus*, with a knob-like head,
referring to the flowering stalks)

Many-stemmed shrublet with branches to
70 cm high from a tuberous rootstock. Leaves
narrow and bluish green, the uppermost forming a whorl below the flowers. Flowers in
heads on smooth peduncles, glistening mustard
yellow with a slender tube bearing from none
to five scales at the mouth, 7 mm diameter.
Habitat: Grassland, especially after fires.
Notes: Used traditionally to cure headaches
and as a divining torch to discover thieves.

Gnidia kraussiana

DAPHNE FAMILY

Lesser yellow-head (E), gifbossie (A),
isiDikili (Z)

(Named for the German naturalist and
plant collector, Christian Krauss)

Many-stemmed shrublet with annual stems to
50 cm high from a tuberous rootstock. Leaves
narrow and bluish green, the uppermost forming a whorl below the flowers. Flowers in heads
on hairy peduncles, yellow with a slender tube
bearing five scales at the mouth, 8 mm diameter.
Habitat: Grassland, especially after fire.
Notes: Poisonous to stock. Used traditionally
to treat stomach and chest ailments.

Glumicalyx goseloides

FIGWORT FAMILY

(= *Zaluzianskya goseloides*)

Gooseneck drumstick-flower (E)

(Resembling the genus *Gosela*)

Perennial herb with annual leafy stems from a
woody rootstock. Leaves finely hairy. Flowers
in a dense, nodding raceme that elongates and
becomes erect in fruit, with a slender tube
20–30 mm long, bright orange with a creamy
reverse, 8 mm diameter.
Habitat: Rocky scree, boulder beds and damp
cliffs.

Zaluzianskya microsiphon
FIGWORT FAMILY
Diurnal drumstick-flower (E)
(Greek *microsiphon*, narrow-tubed)

Perennial herb with annual leafy
stems from a woody rootstock. Leaves in a
basal rosette, more or less hairy. Flowers in a
cylindrical raceme, open during the day, with a
slender tube 20–50 mm long and deeply
notched petals, the upper two petals closely
paired, white with deep red reverse, 15 mm
diameter.
Habitat: Montane grassland.
Notes: Most other *Zaluzianskya* species open
only at night and have evenly spreading petals.

Chascanum latifolium
VERBENA FAMILY
Broad-leaved chascanum (E)
(Latin *latifolius*, broad-leaved)

Erect or rounded shrublet to
50 cm high. Leaves opposite and elliptical,
smooth or hairy. Flowers in cylindrical
racemes, two-lipped with a slender tube 15 mm
long, white to pale mauve, 12 mm diameter.
Habitat: Grassland, especially after fire.
Notes: Common in overgrazed grassland.

Plumbago auriculata
PLUMBAGO FAMILY
Plumbago (E), blousyselbos (A),
uMabophe (X), umuThi wamadoda (Z)
(Latin *auriculatus*, eared, alluding to the
little lobes at the base of the leaves)

Shrub or scrambler to 2 m high. Leaves oblong
or paddle-shaped. Flowers in spikes at the
branch tips, pale blue with a slender tube
20–30 mm long, the calyx covered with
glandular hairs.
Habitat: Thicket and scrub.
Notes: Powdered roots or leaves are traditionally used as a snuff for headaches. Charred and
powdered roots also used as an antiseptic.

Pentanisia prunelloides

COFFEE FAMILY

Pentanisia (E), sooibrandbossie (A),
setima-mollo (SS), iCishamlilo (X, Z)
(Resembling self-heal, *Prunella*)

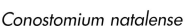

Perennial herb to 40 cm high. Leaves opposite,
variable in shape and hairiness. Flowers in a
round head on a leafless stem, with a slender
tube 15 mm long, pale blue to lilac, 8 mm
diameter.
Habitat: Grassland, especially after fire.
Notes: Used traditionally to treat a variety of
ailments from stomach pains to haemorrhoids.

Conostomium natalense

COFFEE FAMILY

Wild pentas (E), umBophe, uNgcolosi (Z)
(Latin *natalensis*, from Natal)

Erect perennial or shrublet to
1 m high. Leaves opposite and narrow. Flowers
in round heads surrounded by leafy bracts,
with a slender tube 15 mm long, pale blue to
lilac, 8 mm diameter.
Habitat: Forest margins, often in disturbed
sites.

Chironia palustris

GENTIAN FAMILY

Marsh chironia, cerise stars (E),
bitterwortel (A)
(Latin *palustris*, swampy or marshy)

Perennial herb with slender, annual stems to
70 cm high from a woody rootstock. Leaves
opposite, narrow and sometimes leathery.
Flowers in loose clusters, deep pink with a
slender tube 25 mm long, the calyx with short,
sticky, triangular lobes.
Habitat: Damp and marshy grassland.
Notes: *Chironia purpurascens* is similar but
the calyx lobes are long and slender. Used
traditionally to treat colic and diarrhoea.

Sebaea natalensis
GENTIAN FAMILY

Alpine yellowwort (E)

(Latin *natalensis*, from Natal)

Perennial herb with annual
stems to 25 cm high, often branching from the
base. Leaves opposite and rather broad.
Flowers in flat-topped clusters, bright yellow
with a tube 5–7 mm long, the calyx lobes with
a well-developed wing along the keel.

Habitat: Damp montane grassland.

Notes: *Sebaea sedoides*, from lower altitudes,
is very similar but the calyx lobes lack a conspicuous wing on the keel.

Rhigozum obovatum
BIGNONIA FAMILY

Karoo rhigozum (E), wildegranaat (A)

(Latin *obovatus*, obovate, referring to the
leaves)

Stiffly branched, spiny shrub to 4,5 m high.
Leaves in tufts, sometimes divided into
leaflets, elliptical with the margins rolled
under. Flowers one to three on short shoots,
funnel-shaped, yellow, 20–30 mm diameter.
Fruit a flattened pod containing winged,
papery seeds.

Habitat: Dry shale slopes in karroid scrub.

Notes: Common in the Great Karoo.

Rhigozum trichotomum
BIGNONIA FAMILY

Pale rhigozum (E), driedoring (A)

(Latin *trichotomus*, with branches in threes)

Stiffly branched, spiny shrub to
1 m high, with the branches in threes. Leaves
often in tufts, spoon elliptical with wavy
margins. Flowers one to three on short shoots,
funnel-shaped, white to pink, 20–30 mm
diameter. Fruit a flattened pod containing
winged, papery seeds.

Habitat: Dry grassland and karroid scrub,
often along riverbeds and edges of pans.

Notes: Not grazed and very common in the
Great Karoo.

Thunbergia atriplicifolia

ACANTHUS FAMILY

Natal primrose (E), isiPhondo esincane (Z)
(Latin *atriplicifolia*, with leaves resembling
orache, *Atriplex*)

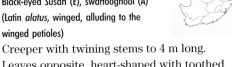

Perennial to 40 cm high from a woody base.
Leaves opposite, ovate and softly hairy, almost
stalkless. Flowers solitary in the leaf axils,
trumpet-shaped, creamy yellow, 50 mm
diameter, the calyx with about 10 slender
teeth and concealed by greenish bracts.
Habitat: Grassland, especially after fire.
Notes: *Thunbergia dregeana* and *T. neglecta*
are creepers in grassland with distinctly
petiolate leaves, the former with heart-shaped
blades and the latter ovate. The green fruits
are used as a hair wash.

Thunbergia alata

ACANTHUS FAMILY

Black-eyed Susan (E), swartoognooi (A)
(Latin *alatus*, winged, alluding to the
winged petioles)

Creeper with twining stems to 4 m long.
Leaves opposite, heart-shaped with toothed
margins. Flowers solitary in the axils, trumpet-
shaped, deep orange or yellow with a blackish
purple throat, 30 mm diameter, the calyx with
about 12 narrow teeth and concealed by green
bracts.
Habitat: Forest margins, often in disturbed
places.

Thunbergia natalensis

ACANTHUS FAMILY

Natal bluebell (E), isiPhondo esikhulu (Z)
(Latin *natalensis*, from Natal)

Shrublet with erect, unbranched
stems to 1,2 m high from a woody base. Leaves
opposite, ovate and toothed. Flowers solitary
in the leaf axils, funnel-shaped, white to pale
mauve with a yellow throat, 80 mm diameter,
the calyx with about five teeth and concealed
by pale bracts that are conspicuously netted
with green.
Habitat: Thick grassland and forest margins.

Crossandra greenstockii

ACANTHUS FAMILY

Bushveld crossandra (E), rooiblom (A)
(Named for William Greenstock, clergyman
and plant collector)

Perennial with annual stems to 20 cm high
from a woody rootstock. Leaves mostly basal,
elliptical and shortly hairy. Flowers in a tight
spike, subtended by ovate bracts with short
teeth on the margins, tubular with a single flaring lip, orange, 20–25 mm diameter.
Habitat: Rocky grassland and open woodland.

Adhatoda densiflora

ACANTHUS FAMILY

Adhatoda (E), valsmoeraskruid (A),
umuSa omncane (Z)
(Latin *densiflorus*, densely-flowered)

Perennial with annual stems to 40 cm high
from a woody rootstock. Leaves opposite,
elliptical to ovate and softly hairy, almost stalkless. Flowers in a dense raceme, two-lipped,
white with pinkish streaks on the lower lip,
15 mm long.
Habitat: Stony grassland, after fire.
Notes: *Adhatoda andromeda*, from higher altitudes, is distinguished by its narrower, almost
hairless leaves. Used traditionally to treat
biliousness.

Tecoma capensis

BIGNONIA FAMILY

(= *Tecomaria capensis*)
Cape honeysuckle (E), trompetters (A),
iCakatha (X), uDodo (Z)
(Latin *capensis*, from the Cape)

Scrambling shrub or small tree to 6 m high.
Leaves opposite and divided into several
toothed leaflets. Flowers in dense racemes at
the branch tips, trumpet-shaped, orange,
50–60 mm long. Fruits a slender pod containing winged papery seeds.
Habitat: Thicket and forest margins.
Notes: Widely grown as an ornamental under
the name *Tecomaria*.

Leonotis ocymifolia

MINT FAMILY

Broad-leaved minaret flower (E), klipdagga
(A), isiHlungu sedobo (X), iMunyane (Z)
(Latin *ocymifolia*, with leaves like sweet
basil, *Ocimum*)

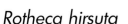

Roughly hairy shrub to 2 m high. Leaves ovate
and toothed. Flowers in well-spaced spherical
clusters, velvety, orange, 40–55 mm long, the
calyx unevenly toothed with the upper tooth
larger.
Habitat: Rocky slopes and forest margins.
Notes: The tubular flowers are visited by sunbirds. Used traditionally to treat colds.

Rotheca hirsuta

MINT FAMILY

(= *Clerodendrum hirsutum, C. triphyllum*)
False violet, bush violet (E), khopa (SS),
uMathanjana, uSikisiki (Z)
(Latin *hirsutus*, hairy, referring to the leaves)

Perennial herb with annual stems to 40 cm
high from a woody rootstock. Leaves opposite
or in whorls of three, elliptical and smooth to
roughly hairy. Flowers solitary or in small
clusters in the axils on slender stalks, pale to
bright purplish blue with two white streaks,
20 mm diameter.
Habitat: Stony grassland and open woodland,
after fire.
Notes: Used traditionally as a vermifuge and
to treat kidney complaints.

Hybanthus enneaspermus

VIOLET FAMILY

Pink lady's slipper (E)
(Greek *enneaspermus*, nine-seeded)

Perennial herb with erect or
trailing annual stems to 20 cm high from a
woody rootstock. Leaves narrow or elliptical,
smooth or thinly hairy with smooth or toothed
margins. Flowers solitary in the axils on slender stalks, with a very large lower lip that is
pouched at the base, pink or lilac, 10–20 mm
diameter.
Habitat: Damp grassland.

Monopsis decipiens
BELLFLOWER FAMILY
Butterfly monopsis (E), isiDala
somkhuhlane (Z)
(Latin *decipiens*, deceptive, alluding to
the resemblance to the genus *Lobelia*)
Perennial rhizomatous herb with slender stems
to 20 cm high. Leaves narrow and roughly
hairy on the margins and midrib beneath.
Flowers solitary, two-lipped, blue and purple
with two yellow blotches on the lower lip,
12–15 mm diameter.
Habitat: Moist grassland in wet places.
Notes: Used traditionally to treat colds, skin
afflictions and rheumatism.

Becium obovatum
MINT FAMILY
Cat's whiskers (E), katsnor (A), iDada (Z)
(Latin *obovatus*, obovate, referring to the
leaves)
Perennial herb with annual stems from a
woody rootstock. Leaves opposite, elliptical
and usually sparsely toothed. Flowers in well-
spaced whorls at the branch tips, white to pale
mauve with darker streaks, two-lipped with
the upper lip four-lobed and fringed, 10–17 mm
long.
Habitat: Grassland, especially after winter
burns.
Notes: Used traditionally as an enema.

Ajuga ophrydis
MINT FAMILY
Blue bugle (E), moonyane (SS)
(Latin *ophrydis*, resembling the bee orchid,
Ophrys)
Perennial herb with annual stems from a
woody rootstock. Leaves mostly in a basal
rosette, usually hairy and tapering to the base
with the margins sparsely toothed. Flowers in
well-spaced whorls subtended by leaves, blue
to mauve, two-lipped with a small upper lip,
12 mm diameter.
Habitat: Moist grassland.
Notes: Traditional cure for female sterility.

Syncolostemon densiflorus

MINT FAMILY

Pink plume (E), isiDleke senqomfi,
iSolelemamba (Z)

(Latin *densiflorus*, densely flowered)

Aromatic shrub to 2 m high, with velvety white
stems. Leaves opposite, elliptical and sometimes sparsely toothed. Flowers scattered in
whorls along the branch tips, pink to crimson,
tubular, 18–23 mm long.
Habitat: Rough grassland and forest margins.

Plectranthus saccatus

MINT FAMILY

Porch jacaranda (E), stoepjakaranda (A)

(Latin *saccatus*, with a sac, alluding to the
flower tube)

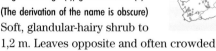

Soft shrublet with purple-tinged stems to 1,2 m
high. Leaves opposite and often leathery,
broadly ovate and coarsely toothed. Flowers
scattered in slender, one-sided racemes, with a
swollen tube that is sac-like at the base, mauve
to pale blue or white, 13–30 mm long.
Habitat: Forest margins and sheltered rocky
places.

Salvia disermas

MINT FAMILY

Large blue sage (E), grootblousalie (A)

(The derivation of the name is obscure)

Soft, glandular-hairy shrub to

1,2 m. Leaves opposite and often crowded
below, elliptical and roughly hairy with toothed
margins. Flowers in whorls along the branch
tips, whitish to mauve, 15–30 mm long.
Habitat: Stream sides, road verges and other
disturbed sites in stony, often lime-rich soil.
Notes: Common around Calvinia and
Kimberley.

Sesamum triphyllum
SESAME FAMILY
Wild sesame (E), brandogie (A)
(Greek *triphyllus*, three-leaved, actually
referring to the lobes of the divided leaves)
Annual herb with erect stems to 1,5 m high,
foetid when bruised. Leaves opposite, the
lowermost divided into three to five narrow
segments. Flowers funnel-shaped, pink with
red markings in the throat, 30–50 mm long.
Fruits narrow with a sharply pointed tip.
Habitat: Grassland and roadsides.
Notes: *Sesamum alatum* has flowers
20–30 mm long, and winged seeds.

Ceratotheca triloba
SESAME FAMILY
Wild foxglove (E), wildevingerhoedjie (A),
uDonqa (Z)
(Latin *trilobus*, three-lobed, alluding to
the leaves)
Annual or short-lived perennial herb with
velvety, purple stems to 1,5 m high, foetid
when bruised. Leaves opposite, elliptical or
three-lobed. Flowers funnel-shaped, pink with
red streaks in the throat, 50–60 mm long.
Fruits with two horns at the tip.
Habitat: Grassland, roadsides and old lands.
Notes: Used traditionally to treat painful men-
struation, stomach cramps, nausea and fever.

Harpagophytum procumbens
SESAME FAMILY
Devil's claw, grapplethorn (E),
bobbejaankloue (A), ghamaghoe (N)
(Latin *procumbens*, procumbent)
Prostrate perennial with a tuberous root.
Leaves deeply lobed or toothed with white
glands on the surface. Flowers funnel-shaped,
deep pink or purple with a yellow throat or
rarely yellowish, 50–60 mm long. Fruits armed
with spiny horns dispersed by antelope.
Habitat: Sandy soils along roadsides and in
waste places.
Notes: Used traditionally to treat rheumatism
and arthritis and as a tonic.

Sopubia cana
BROOMRAPE FAMILY

Silvery sopubia (E), leilane (SS)

(Latin *canus*, greyish white)

Erect shrublet to 45 cm high, entirely covered with silvery grey hairs. Leaves narrow, with leafy short shoots in the axils. Flowers in dense racemes, pink to mauve and short-lived, 20 mm diameter.

Habitat: Grassland. Parasitic on the roots of various grasses.

Notes: Common in overgrazed grassland. Used traditionally to treat fevers, rashes and other sores.

Cycnium tubulosum
BROOMRAPE FAMILY

Small pink mushroom-flower (E)

(Latin *tubulosus*, tubular)

Erect, hairless half-parasitic herb with slender stems to 50 cm high. Leaves narrow and not toothed. Flowers in open racemes, white to pale pink turning black when faded, 30–40 mm diameter, the calyx cup-shaped with slender teeth, exposing the short, transversely oriented fruit at maturity.

Habitat: Moist grassland. Parasitic on the roots of certain grasses and sedges.

Cycnium racemosum
BROOMRAPE FAMILY

Large pink mushroom-flower (E), pienk-inkblom (A), inJanga (X), uHlabahlangane (Z)

(Latin *racemosus*, with the flowers in a raceme)

Erect, rough or shortly hairy half-parasitic herb to 75 cm high. Leaves narrow and toothed. Flowers in open racemes, white to deep pink turning black when faded, 50–60 mm diameter, the calyx tubular and ribbed with very short, hooked teeth, enclosing the longitudinally elongated fruit at maturity.

Habitat: Moist grassland. Parasitic on the roots of certain grasses and sedges.

Notes: The root is used traditionally as an emetic and for general pains.

Cycnium adonense
BROOMRAPE FAMILY

White mushroom-flower, handkerchief flower (E), wit-inkblom (A)

(Latin *adonensis*, coming from Addo, where the type specimen was collected)

Low-growing, roughly hairy half-parasitic herb to 20 cm high. Leaves elliptical and roughly hairy with sharply toothed margins. Flowers in the leaf axils, white turning black when faded, 60–70 mm diameter, the calyx tubular with blunt teeth.

Habitat: Grassland, often in rocky places, especially evident after a fire. Parasitic on the roots of certain grasses and sedges.

Notes: Used traditionally as a remedy for snakebite.

Harveya speciosa
BROOMRAPE FAMILY

Great white inkflower (E), groot-inkblom (A), isiNama (X), umShelezana omhlophe (Z)

(Latin *speciosus*, showy)

Softly hairy parasitic perennial to 1 m high with scale-like leaves, turning black when bruised. Flowers in racemes, narrowly funnel-shaped with a long tube, creamy-white with a yellow throat, fragrant especially at night, 40–60 mm diameter, the calyx shortly toothed.

Habitat: Damp grassland and thicket. Parasitic on the roots of certain grasses and shrubby daisies.

Notes: The roots are pounded with water and used to clean and drain nasal passages.

Streptocarpus grandis
AFRICAN VIOLET FAMILY

Purple fountain (E)

(Latin *grandis*, large or great)

Short-lived herb to 45 cm high. Leaf solitary and velvety. Flowers in elongate or branched racemes, several open at once, trumpet-shaped with a cylindrical tube and relatively short petals, white or mauve to violet, 22–45 mm long.

Habitat: Forest floor in humus or on rocks.

Streptocarpus formosus

AFRICAN VIOLET FAMILY

Natal primrose (E)

(Latin *formosus,* beautiful)

Perennial herb to 20 cm high.
Leaves several in a rosette and velvety.
Flowers, one or two at the tip of a slender
stalk, narrowly funnel-shaped with a straight,
cylindrical tube, pale blue with darker streaks
on the lower lip and yellow in the throat,
70–105 mm long.

Habitat: Forest floor among rocks.

Streptocarpus rexii

AFRICAN VIOLET FAMILY

Cape primrose (E), umFazi onengxolo (X)

(Latin *rexii,* named for George Rex, notary
and pioneer of Knysna)

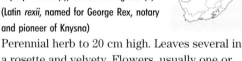

Perennial herb to 20 cm high. Leaves several in
a rosette and velvety. Flowers, usually one or
two, rarely up to six at the tip of a slender
stalk, narrowly funnel-shaped with a straight,
cylindrical tube, pale blue with darker streaks
on the lower lip, 40–75 mm long.

Habitat: Forest floor or shaded banks at the
forest margin.

Notes: Leaves and roots used traditionally as a
love charm.

Streptocarpus dunnii

AFRICAN VIOLET FAMILY

Crimson streptocarpus (E)

(Named for E.G. Dunn who first collected
the species)

Perennial or short-lived herb to 15 cm high.
Leaves one to several and velvety. Flowers in
an elongate raceme with several open at once,
trumpet-shaped with a curved, cylindrical tube
and relatively narrow petals, pink to reddish,
striped on the floor, 40 mm long.

Habitat: In the shelter of rocks in damp
grassland.

Scaevola plumieri
SCAEVOLA FAMILY

Scaevola (E), seeplakkie (A),
umQhapphu (X)

(Commemorates the eighteenth-century
French missionary and explorer, Charles Plumier)

Evergreen perennial with spreading, underground stems that emerge at intervals to form
colonies. Leaves rather fleshy or leathery and
paddle-shaped. Flowers in small stalked clusters in the leaf axils, whitish with crumpled
petals and narrow tube that is slit above and
woolly within, 25 mm diameter.

Habitat: Coastal foredunes.

Notes: The leaf sap is used to treat bluebottle
stings.

Phygelius aequalis
FIGWORT FAMILY

Northern river bell (E), rivierklokkie (A),
mafifi-matso (SS)

(Latin *aequalis*, equal, contrasting with the
oblique tube in *Phygelius capensis*)

Shrub to 2 m high. Leaves opposite, elliptical
and toothed. Flowers nodding in dense
panicles, the floral tube with a horizontal
mouth, reddish with a yellow throat, 40 mm
long.

Habitat: Montane stream sides at high
altitudes.

Notes: Popular garden plant, both yellow and
orange forms.

Phygelius capensis
FIGWORT FAMILY

Southern river bell (E)

(Latin *capensis*, from the Cape)

Shrub to 1 m high. Leaves
opposite, elliptical and toothed. Flowers flexed
backwards in open panicles, the floral tube
with an oblique mouth, orange with a yellow
throat, 30–40 mm long.

Habitat: Montane stream sides at high
altitudes.

Jamesbrittenia breviflora

FIGWORT FAMILY

(= *Sutera breviflora*)

Scarlet sutera (E)

(Latin *breviflorus*, short-flowered, alluding to the short tube)

Straggling, aromatic perennial to 30 cm high. Leaves opposite or alternate, ovate and more or less toothed, covered with glandular hairs. Flowers solitary in the leaf axils, two-lipped with a short tube, reddish with a yellow throat, 15 mm diameter.

Habitat: Rocky slopes, roadsides and stream banks at high altitude.

Nemesia denticulata

FIGWORT FAMILY

Natal nemesia (E), leeubekkie (A)

(Latin *denticulatus*, finely toothed)

Tufted perennial herb with annual stems to 40 cm high from a woody rootstock. Leaves opposite, ovate and toothed. Flowers in rounded racemes elongating in fruit, two-lipped, pink or mauve with paired yellow or orange crests on the lower lip and a pair of raised yellow bumps inside the throat at the mouth of the spur, 10 mm diameter.

Habitat: Stony grassland and open woodland.

Notes: *Nemesia caerulea* from higher altitudes lacks the raised bumps inside the flower.

Diascia anastrepta

FIGWORT FAMILY

Drakensberg twinspur (E)

(Greek *anastreptus*, curved upwards, alluding to the spurs)

Loosely tangled perennial herb to 40 cm high. Leaves ovate and toothed. Flowers in elongate racemes, two-lipped with a pair of spreading spurs, the stamens in two diverging pairs, pink with a yellow and black window in the upper lip and scattered black glands on the lower lip, 20 mm diameter.

Habitat: Damp basalt cliffs and stream sides.

Notes: Most other *Diascia* species have the four stamens clustered together.

Protea dracomontana
PROTEA FAMILY

Drakensberg sugarbush (E)

(Latin *dracomontanus*, growing in the Drakensberg)

Low shrub, 50–150 cm high. Leaves elliptical, leathery with thickened margins. Flower heads cup-shaped, 40–60 mm diameter, the surrounding bracts cream-coloured to carmine, smooth. **Habitat:** Sub-alpine grassland on basalt. **Notes:** *Protea simplex* is very similar but has softer-textured leaves and shorter styles (20–40 mm vs 45–60 mm).

Protea caffra
PROTEA FAMILY

Common sugarbush (E)

(Latin *caffra*, from South Africa)

Shrub or tree, 3–8 m high.

Leaves linear to narrowly elliptical. Flower heads cup-shaped, 45–80 mm diameter, the surrounding bracts usually pink to carmine above but sometimes entirely creamy-green, smooth or silvery-silky.

Habitat: Grassland on sandstone and quartzite.

Protea gaguedi
PROTEA FAMILY

African sugarbush (E)

(*gaguedi*, the vernacular name for this species in Ethiopia)

Shrub or tree, 2–4 m high. Leaves elliptical to oblong, hairy when young but hairless at maturity. Flower heads bowl-shaped, 50–110 mm diameter, the surrounding bracts creamy-green and covered with silvery, silky hairs.

Habitat: Drier rocky grassland, often on quartzite.

Notes: *Protea welwitschii* is very similar but generally smaller with the leaves remaining hairy and the bracts with brownish hairs.

Protea welwitschii

PROTEA FAMILY

Welwitsch's sugarbush (E)

(Named for Friedrich Welwitsch, who collected the species in Angola)

Shrub to 1,5 m high, rarely more. Leaves elliptical to oblong, remaining hairy, at least at the base and on the midrib. Flower heads bowl-shaped, 50–110 mm diameter, the surrounding bracts creamy-green and covered with brownish silky hairs.

Habitat: Drier rocky grassland, often on quartzite.

Notes: *Protea gaguedi* is very similar but is generally a taller tree with the leaves becoming hairless at maturity and the bracts with silvery hairs.

Protea roupelliae

PROTEA FAMILY

Silver sugarbush (E)

(Named after the Victorian flower painter, Arabella Roupell)

Tree, 3–8 m high. Leaves narrowly elliptical, curved upwards. Flower heads conical, 80–100 mm diameter, the surrounding bracts pink to brownish and silky, the inner bracts spoon-shaped.

Habitat: Grassland and protea savannah, mostly on sandstone or quartzite.

Protea subvestita

PROTEA FAMILY

Waterlily sugarbush (E)

(Latin *subvestitus*, somewhat clothed, i.e. with hairs)

Large shrub or tree to 5 m high. Leaves elliptical, densely hairy when young. Flower heads cylindrical, 30–40 mm diameter, the surrounding bracts cream-coloured to pink, hairless or silky and fringed with silky hairs, the inner bracts recurved at the tips.

Habitat: Grassy slopes on sandstone.

Helichrysum glomeratum
DAISY FAMILY

Silver carpet (E)

(Latin *glomeratus*, collected together into a
head, alluding to the flower heads)

Rhizomatous perennial herb with leafy stems
to 45 cm high. Leaves closely overlapping and
not decreasing in size upwards, lance-shaped
and silvery-silky. Flower heads massed in
rounded clusters matted with wool, yellow,
5 mm diameter, surrounded by several series
of brownish bracts.

Habitat: Forming colonies in open grassland.

Helichrysum splendidum
DAISY FAMILY

Cape gold (E)

(Latin *splendidus*, shining)

Sprawling perennial herb with
leafy stems to 1,5 m long. Leaves narrow with
the margins rolled under and whitish woolly
beneath. Flower heads in small, rounded or
flat-topped clusters, yellow, 5 mm diameter,
surrounded by several series of bright yellow
bracts.

Habitat: Sheltered rocky places and forest
margins.

Helichrysum cymosum
DAISY FAMILY

Straggling everlasting (E), imPepho (Z)

(Latin *cymosus*, with the flowers arranged in
the flat-topped inflorescence called a cyme)

Straggling or sprawling shrublet to 1 m high.
Leaves narrow with the margins slightly rolled
under, thinly silky or with skin-like háirs above
but white-felted beneath. Flower heads crowded
in flat-topped clusters, cylindrical, yellow,
3 mm diameter, surrounded by several series
of yellow bracts.

Habitat: Stony or sandy slopes or steep turf in
damp places.

Helichrysum pallidum

DAISY FAMILY

Silver Hottentot's tea (E)

(Latin *pallidus*, pale, referring to the leaf undersides)

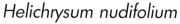

Tufted perennial herb to 65 cm high, the roots producing narrow tubers. Leaves mostly clustered near the base, elliptical and roughly hairy above but white-felted beneath, five to seven net-veined from the base. Flower heads crowded, bell-shaped, pale yellow or brownish, 5–7 mm diameter, surrounded by several series of blunt bracts that are papery at the tips. **Habitat:** Grassland.

Helichrysum nudifolium

DAISY FAMILY

Hottentot's tea (E), Hottentotstee (A), letapiso (SS), iCholocholo (X, Z)

(Latin *nudifolius*, naked-leaved, i.e. without hairs on the leaves)

Tufted perennial herb to 1,5 m high, spreading by stout runners. Leaves mostly clustered near the base, oblong and more or less smooth but roughly hairy on the margins and veins, three to seven net-veined from the base. Flower heads crowded, bell-shaped, pale yellow or brownish, 4–5 mm diameter, surrounded by several series of blunt bracts that are papery at the tips.

Habitat: Grassland.

Notes: Used traditionally as a tea or as a poultice to treat various ailments.

Helichrysum ruderale

DAISY FAMILY

Weedy everlasting (E)

(Latin *ruderalis*, growing among rubbish)

Biennial herb to 1 m high, aromatic when fresh. Leaves decreasing in size upwards, elliptical and clasping the stem, glandular-hairy with the margins often white-woolly as well. Flower heads flattened, yellow, 20–25 mm diameter, surrounded by several series of golden yellow, papery bracts.

Habitat: Weed of roadsides and waste places.

Helichrysum aureum
DAISY FAMILY

Yellow everlasting (E), leabane (SS)

(Latin *aureus*, golden, referring to the bracts)

Tufted perennial herb to 80 cm from a woody rootstock, producing numerous leaf rosettes. Leaves mostly basal, elliptical and roughly hairy above but more or less grey-woolly beneath. Flower heads one to few at the branch tips, flattened, yellow or white, 15–25 mm diameter, surrounded by several series of golden yellow, papery bracts.
Habitat: Grassland.

Helichrysum adenocarpum
DAISY FAMILY

Pink everlasting (E), pienksewejaartjie (A), senko-toana (SS)

(Greek *adenocarpus*, with glandular fruits)

Tufted perennial herb with several leaf rosettes and flowering stems to 45 cm high from a woody rootstock. Leaves elliptical and greyish, usually woolly or cobwebby. Flower heads one to few, bowl-shaped, yellow, 25–30 mm diameter, surrounded by several series of white to red, papery bracts.
Habitat: Moist grassland, often in damp depressions.

Helichrysum ecklonis
DAISY FAMILY

Ecklon's pink everlasting (E), umuThi wechanti (Z)

(Named for the nineteenth-century German apothecary and plant collector, Christian Ecklon)

Tufted perennial herb with several leaf rosettes and flowering stems to 45 cm high from a woody rootstock. Leaves elliptical and greyish, usually woolly or cobwebby, the stem leaves much smaller with papery tips. Flower heads solitary, bowl-shaped, yellow, 30–40 mm diameter, surrounded by several series of white to red, papery bracts.
Habitat: Montane grassland, often on steep slopes.

Vernonia natalenis

DAISY FAMILY

Silver vernonia (E), iLeleva (Z)

(Latin *natalensis,* from Natal)

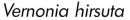

Perennial herb with annual, leafy stems to 1 m high from a woody rootstock. Leaves narrow and silvery-silky on both surfaces. Flower heads in flat-topped clusters, purple, 8–10 mm diameter, surrounded by several series of silvery, bristle-tipped bracts. **Habitat:** Open grassland, especially after fire.

Vernonia hirsuta

DAISY FAMILY

Quilt-leaved vernonia (E), wildeson-soekertjie (A), iKhambi lenyongo (Z)

(Latin *hirsutus,* covered with coarse hairs)

Perennial herb with annual, leafy stems to 1 m high from a woody rootstock. Leaves oblong or elliptical with toothed margins, clasping the stem at the base, roughly hairy above but greyish woolly beneath. Flower heads in flat-topped clusters, purple, 5–8 mm diameter, surrounded by several series of greyish, hairy, bristle-tipped bracts.

Habitat: Rough grassland, often on the edges of forest, especially after fire.

Notes: Used traditionally to treat colic, sore throats, coughs, headaches and rashes.

Vernonia myriantha

DAISY FAMILY

(= *Vernonia stipulacea*)

Wild lilac (E)

(Greek *myrianthus,* with numerous flowers)

Much-branched shrub to 4 m high. Leaves elliptical with a lobed base and toothed margins, thinly woolly beneath, the petioles with a pair of deciduous, ear-like lobes at the base. Flower heads numerous in flat-topped clusters, purple, 3 mm diameter, surrounded by several series of oblong bracts.

Habitat: Forest margins.

Senecio barbatus
DAISY FAMILY

Sticky-plume groundsel (E)

(Latin *barbatus*, bearded, alluding to the conspicuous hairs on the flower heads)

Perennial herb with stems to 30 cm high, covered with soft, shaggy, gland-tipped hairs, often purplish. Leaves in a basal rosette and up the stem, narrowly elliptical with more or less toothed margins. Flower heads in crowded clusters, cylindrical, whitish or yellowish, blue or purple, surrounded by a single series of shaggy bracts.

Habitat: Moist grassland.

Felicia filifolia
DAISY FAMILY

Needle-leaved felicia, fine-leaved felicia (E), draaibos (A)

(Latin *filifolius*, thread-leaved)

Well-branched shrub to 1 m high. Leaves in tufts on short shoots, needle-like and lightly dotted with glands. Flower heads solitary in the leaf tufts, yellow with blue to mauve ray florets, 20 mm diameter, surrounded by three series of narrow bracts.

Habitat: Rocky places in grassland, a weed in overgrazed veld.

Notes: Poisonous to sheep. Used for firewood.

Berkheya umbellata
DAISY FAMILY

Mop-headed berkheya (E), klossiedissel (A), iKhakhasana elincane (Z)

(Latin *umbellatus*, like an umbrella, referring to the clustered flower heads)

Perennial herb to 80 cm high from a creeping woody rootstock, usually in colonies. Leaves mainly in a basal tuft, elliptical with toothed and spiny margins, roughly hairy above and glandular hairy beneath. Flower heads in flat-topped clusters on spiny-winged stems, yellow, 25–30 mm diameter.

Habitat: Rough grassland, especially after fire.

Notes: Used traditionally as a fragrant body lotion by girls.

Berkheya speciosa

DAISY FAMILY

Showy berkheya (E), skraaldisseldoring (A),
uMaphola (Z)

(Latin *speciosus*, showy)

Perennial herb with slender stems to 1 m high
from a woody rootstock. Leaves in a basal tuft,
elliptical and distinctly petiolate with toothed
margins, roughly hairy above but white-
cobwebby beneath. Flower heads yellow with
yellow ray florets, 30–60 mm diameter.
Habitat: Stony, moist grassland, especially
after fire.
Notes: *Berkheya setifera* has bristly leaves.
Used traditionally to treat stomach problems,
bilharzia and to bathe sore eyes.

Berkheya subulata

DAISY FAMILY

Transvaal grass berkheya (E)

(Latin *subulatus*, awl-shaped, referring to
the leaves)

Perennial herb with clumps of annual stems to
50 cm high from a woody rootstock. Leaves
narrow with the margins rolled under and
bearing scattered short bristles, smooth or
roughly hairy above and white-felted beneath.
Flower heads solitary at the stem tips, yellow
with yellow ray florets, 50–70 mm diameter.
Habitat: Rocky grassland, especially after fire.
Notes: *Berkheya insignis*, the Natal grass
berkheya, has long, flexible bristles on the leaf
margins.

Berkheya rosulata

DAISY FAMILY

Drakensberg berkheya (E)

(Latin *rosulatus*, rosetted, referring to the
tufts of leaves)

Bushy shrub to 1 m high. Leaves in clusters at
the branch tips, elliptical with toothed and
spiny margins, glossy dark green above and
white-felted beneath. Flower heads solitary on
white-felted branches, yellow with yellow ray
florets, 25–35 mm diameter.
Habitat: Basalt cliffs at high altitude.

Berkheya cirsiifolia

DAISY FAMILY

Lesser thistle-leaved berkheya (E),
mohata-o-mosoeu (SS)
(Latin *cirsiifolius*, with leaves like the
thistle, *Cirsium*)

Perennial to 1 m high, branching above, often
in colonies. Leaves decreasing in size upwards,
oblong but deeply lobed with the margins
toothed and spiny, shortly hairy above but
white-woolly beneath. Flower heads few on
spiny-winged stems, yellow with white or
yellow ray florets, 50–80 mm diameter, the
outer bracts tipped with a spine 5–8 mm long.
Habitat: Rocky montane grassland.
Notes: *Berkheya onopordifolia* has shorter
spines on the outer bracts, 3–4 mm long.

Berkheya purpurea

DAISY FAMILY

Purple berkheya (E), bloudisseldoring (A),
sehlolo (SS)
(Latin *pupureus*, purple)

Perennial to 1 m high, often in colonies. Leaves
in a basal tuft, lanceolate with the margins
toothed and spiny, roughly hairy above but
white-woolly beneath. Flower heads few on
spiny-winged stems, mauve or white with similar coloured ray florets, 50–80 mm diameter.
Habitat: Montane grassland, often along
streams.

Berkheya multijuga

DAISY FAMILY

Spiny Berg thistle (E), mohatollo (SS)

(Latin *multijugus*, in many pairs, referring to the leaf lobes)

Perennial to 1.8 m high, in small colonies. Leaves mostly in a basal rosette, narrowly oblong and lobed to the midrib with the margins toothed and spiny, shortly hairy above but usually white-woolly beneath. Flower heads yellow with yellow ray florets, 50–80 mm diameter.

Habitat: Montane grassland.

Euryops tysonii

DAISY FAMILY

Tyson's rosinbush (E), sehlakoana (SS)

(Named for William Tyson, teacher and plant collector)

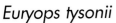

Shrublet to 1,5 m high with the branches leafless below. Leaves overlapping, elliptical and leathery, smooth except for white wool in the axils. Flower heads crowded at the branch tips, yellow with yellow ray florets, fragrant, 10–15 mm diameter, surrounded by a single series of smooth bracts.

Habitat: Rocky slopes, screes and boulder beds.

Senecio microglossus

DAISY FAMILY

Greater two-day cure (E)

(Greek *microglossus*, small-tongued, referring to the short ray florets)

Clump-forming perennial with erect stems, becoming leafless below, to 1,2 m from a creeping, woody rootstock. Leaves scattered along the stems, elliptical with two small lobes at the base, leathery with toothed margins, three-veined from the base. Flower heads orange with bright yellow ray florets, 10 mm diameter, surrounded by a single series of bracts.

Habitat: Rocky grassland, especially after fire.

Notes: *Senecio serratuloides* is similar but the leaves have a single main vein. Re-sprouts rapidly after fire, becoming rather untidy after a few years. Spreads by means of suckers.

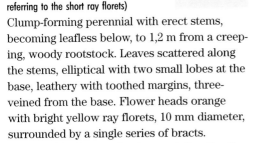

Senecio polyanthemoides

DAISY FAMILY

Weedy ragwort (E)

(Greek *polyanthemoides*, resembling the
polyanthus primulas)

Bushy annual with somewhat woody stems to
1,8 m high. Leaves elliptical with the margins
rolled under and toothed, smooth or rough
above and thinly woolly beneath. Flower heads
yellow with yellow ray florets, 10 mm diameter, surrounded by a single series of bracts.
Habitat: Rough grass on forest margins,
common along roadsides and old fields.
Notes: Reputed to cause death in horses.

Senecio bupleuroides

DAISY FAMILY

Yellow starwort (E), iDwarane (X),
inDabula-luvalo (Z)

(Latin *bupleuroides*, resembling the genus
Bupleurum)

Slender perennial herb with stems to 80 cm
high from a woody rootstock. Leaves few,
lance-shaped and leathery with thickened margins that are often rolled under, greyish and
smooth. Flower heads yellow with yellow ray
florets, 10 mm diameter, surrounded by a
single series of short, smooth bracts.
Habitat: Grassland after fires.
Notes: Used traditionally to treat heart
complaints.

Senecio macrospermus

DAISY FAMILY

Great alpine groundsel (E)

(Greek *macrospermus*, large-seeded)

Robust, clumped perennial herb
to 1 m high from a woody rootstock. Leaves
mainly basal, elliptical with finely toothed
margins, covered with a grey woolly felt.
Flower heads yellow with yellow ray florets,
25–30 mm diameter, surrounded by a single
series of grey-felted bracts.
Habitat: Steep, damp mountain slopes in
grass or scree.

Senecio speciosus

DAISY FAMILY

Magenta groundsel (E), iDambiso (X, Z)

(Latin *speciosus*, showy)

Perennial herb with stems to
70 cm high from a woody rootstock, often
arched at the base then erect. Leaves mostly in
a basal rosette, elliptical and lobed or toothed,
somewhat fleshy and usually glandular-hairy.
Flower heads deep pink to purple with similar
coloured ray florets, 30–40 mm diameter,
surrounded by a single series of hairless or
glandular-hairy bracts.
Habitat: Damp grassland, often in marshy
depressions.

Osteospermum jucundum

DAISY FAMILY

(= *Dimorphotheca jucunda*)

Mauve daisy (E), bergbietou (A),

uMasigcolo-nkonekazi (Z)

(Latin *jucundus*, delightful)

Spreading perennial herb to 30 cm high.
Leaves narrow and tapering below, sometimes
toothed, shortly hairy. Flower heads yellow
and black with pale to deep pink ray florets
that are coppery beneath, 20–30 mm diameter.
Habitat: Rocky grassland and cliffs.
Notes: *Osteospermum caulescens* has white
ray florets. Used traditionally to treat stomach
complaints.

Osteospermum fruticosum

DAISY FAMILY

(= *Dimorphotheca fruticosa*)

Sea boneseed (E), rankmargriet (A)

(Latin *fruticosus*, bushy)

Evergreen perennial with sprawling to prostrate stems that root along their length and
form mats. Leaves leathery, broad but narrowed below and minutely toothed along the
margins. Flower heads purple with white or
mauve ray florets, 30–40 mm diameter.
Habitat: Coastal dunes and rocks.

Aster bakeranus

DAISY FAMILY

Baker's wild aster (E), umThekisana (X), uDlatshana (Z)

(Named after the Victorian botanist, J.G. Baker, who published extensively on African flora)

Perennial herb with roughly hairy, annual stems to 70 cm high from a woody rootstock. Leaves roughly hairy and three- to five-veined from the base. Flower heads yellow with blue or white rays, 20–30 mm diameter.

Habitat: Rocky grassland, especially after fire.
Notes: *Aster harveyanus* is hairless. Used traditionally to treat stomach complaints, internal parasites, various infections and sores and for head ailments.

Callilepis laureola

DAISY FAMILY

Ox-eye daisy (E), wildemagriet (A), iHlamvu (Z)

(Latin *laureolus,* laurel-like)

Perennial herb with erect, annual stems to 60 cm high from a woody rootstock. Leaves three-veined from the base, smooth or softly hairy. Flower heads black with creamy-white ray florets, 20–30 mm diameter.

Habitat: Stony grassland, especially after fire.
Notes: *Callilepis leptophylla* from the Highveld has narrow, one-veined leaves. Used to treat tapeworm and maggots in cattle.

Haplocarpha scaposa

DAISY FAMILY

False gerbera (E), moarubetso (SS), isiKhali (Z)

(Latin *scaposus,* with a well-developed, leafless flowering stalk)

Tufted perennial herb with the flowering stalk to 30 cm high. Leaves in a basal tuft, ovate, hairy above but white-felted beneath with a fringed margin. Flower heads yellow with yellow ray florets, 25–40 mm diameter.

Habitat: Stony grassland or open woodland.
Notes: The white felt from the leaves was used in tinderboxes.

Gerbera piloselloides

DAISY FAMILY

Small gerbera (E), swarttee (A),
moarubetso (SS), ubuLawu (Z)
(Resembling the hawkweed, *Pilosella*)

Tufted perennial herb with the flowering stalk
to 30 cm high. Leaves in a basal tuft, ovate and
tapering below, softly hairy or cobwebby with
a fringed margin. Flower heads yellow or white
with white, pink, red or yellow ray florets,
10–25 mm diameter.
Habitat: Stony grassland or open woodland,
often after fires.
Notes: Recognised by the swollen top of the
flowering stalk. Used traditionally to treat
tapeworm, earache, headache and coughs.

Gerbera ambigua

DAISY FAMILY

Common gerbera (E), griekwatee (A),
moarubetso (SS), uCabazane (Z)
(Latin *ambiguus*, doubtful or uncertain,
suggesting the species was somewhat perplexing)

Tufted perennial with the flowering stalk to
35 cm high. Leaves in a basal tuft, elliptical and
petiolate, silky or almost hairless above but
white- or yellowish-felted beneath. Flower
heads yellow or white to black with white or,
rarely, yellow ray florets that are pink to
coppery beneath, 25–40 mm diameter.
Habitat: Grassland or open woodland, often
near moisture.

Gerbera viridifolia

DAISY FAMILY

Pink gerbera (E)
(Latin *viridifolius*, green-leaved, alluding to
the almost hairless mature leaves)

Tufted perennial with the flowering stalk to
35 cm high. Leaves in a basal tuft, elliptical and
petiolate, silky or almost hairless above and
beneath. Flower heads yellow or white to
violet with white or pink to purple ray florets
that are pink to purple beneath, 25–40 mm
diameter.
Habitat: Grassland or open woodland.

Gerbera aurantiaca

DAISY FAMILY

Hilton daisy (E)

(Latin *aurantiacus*, orange)

Tufted perennial with the flowering stalk to 30 cm high. Leaves in a basal tuft, elliptical and petiolate, velvety above but thinly woolly or smooth beneath. Flower heads reddish with orange to red ray florets that are coppery beneath, 25–35 mm diameter.
Habitat: Rocky grassland.
Notes: Hybridises with *Gerbera ambigua*.

Gerbera jamesonii

DAISY FAMILY

Barberton daisy (E)

(Named for Robert Jameson, businessman and plant enthusiast, who first collected seeds of the species)

Tufted perennial with the flowering stalk to 70 cm high. Leaves in a basal tuft, deeply undulating or lobed and distinctly petiolate, almost hairless except on the margins. Flower heads reddish with slender, red or rarely white or pink ray florets, 40–60 mm diameter.
Habitat: Rocky slopes in woodland, often under trees.

Hirpicium armerioides

DAISY FAMILY

Mountain gerbera (E), skynloodkruid (A)
(Resembling the sea-pink, *Armeria*)

Mat-forming perennial with
flowering stalks to 25 cm high. Leaves in a
basal tuft, narrow with the margins rolled
under, hairy above but white-felted beneath.
Flower heads yellow with white ray florets
that are yellow or black beneath, 25–40 mm
diameter.
Habitat: Poor stony soils and rock sheets.

Gazania krebsiana

DAISY FAMILY

Common gazania (E), bruingousblom (A),
uBendle (X, Z)
(Named for Georg Krebs, who farmed near
Bedford in the Eastern Cape in the nineteenth century)

Tufted perennial herb with flowering stalks to
20 cm high. Leaves in a basal tuft, narrow and
sometimes lobed with the margins rolled
under, roughly hairy above but white-felted
beneath. Flower heads yellow with yellow to
orange rays that are sometimes dark at the
base, 30–70 mm diameter.
Habitat: Roadsides and stony grassland.
Notes: The flowers may be eaten raw, while
the plant is used traditionally to treat sickly
babies, earache and sterility in women.

Arctotis leiocarpa

DAISY FAMILY

Karoo arctotis (E), karoogousblom (A)
(Greek *leiocarpus*, smooth-fruited, referring
to the occasional lack of hairs on the fruits)

Slightly fleshy annual to 45 cm high. Leaves
elliptical or paddle-shaped and toothed or
lobed and often eared at the base, cobwebby
or woolly. Flower heads yellow with white ray
florets tinged purple on the reverse, 50–60 mm
diameter, surrounded by several series of
bracts, the outer with long tails and the inner
with rounded, papery tips.
Habitat: Arid sandy or gravelly flats, often
along washes.

Fynbos

THE TERM FYNBOS has become synonymous with the floral wonderland that characterises the south-western tip of Africa. Derived from the Dutch term for fine-leaved shrubs, it describes the characteristic vegetation of the Cape Floral Region. Covering an area of around 90 000 km², the Cape Floral Region is an L-shaped area centred on Cape Town that stretches northwards about 150 km to the Bokkeveld Escarpment near Nieuwoudtville in the north, and eastwards for 350 km to Port Elizabeth. Nowhere is it more than about 100 km wide. Enclosed within this narrow belt is one of the most remarkable temperate floras in the world. Here almost 9 000 different species of flowering plants are found, accounting for 44% of the total number of species in the country in a region that covers little more than 5% of its land area. Of this extraordinary diversity, a massive 70% of the species do not occur outside the boundaries of the Cape Floral Region.

Rainfall in the Cape region is largely restricted to the winter months, between April and August, especially in the west. Towards the east, however, the rainfall becomes progressively less seasonal. In addition, the seaward slopes of the southern coastal mountain ranges benefit from summer moisture that condenses on their upper slopes, while the West Coast is essentially hot and dry throughout the summer. The seasonality of flowering is closely related to the seasonality of precipitation, and while little can be found in flower along the West Coast in summer there is a relative wealth of plants in flower on the higher slopes in the south-east.

The distinctive fynbos vegetation of the Cape Floral Region is defined by the occurrence of members of the protea, erica and restio families, along with an abundance of bulbous species unmatched elsewhere in the world. True fynbos is an evergreen shrubland confined to acidic, nutrient-poor sandstone soils that predominate in the Western Cape. These soils are derived from the sandstone rocks of the Cape series, which have been dramatically folded into the parallel ranges of the Cape Fold Mountains that dominate the skyline wherever you might find yourself in the region. Some 7 000 species in the region occur in true fynbos, with perhaps an additional 1 500 in the second main vegetation type in the region, renosterveld. Occupying the richer shale soils that lie in the valleys between these fynbos-clad ranges, and forming much of the coastal forelands, renosterveld is an allied but quite distinct vegetation type. It derives its name from the renosterbos or rhinoceros bush, *Elytropappus rhinocerotis*, which gives it a characteristic dull grey cast. Although it receives far less attention than fynbos, renosterveld is much more endangered than its more charismatic cousin and today less than 10% of renosterveld has escaped the plough!

One of the characteristics of the vegetation of the Cape Region is the highly local nature of many of its species. This means that it is easy to see a great number of different wildflower species in a relatively short distance. It also means, of course, that great care must be taken not to overlook superficially similar species. The chances of doing this are greatly increased by another unusual feature of the Cape flora: the diversity is not evenly spread across the different plant families and genera. Out of a total of almost 950 genera of flowering plants that occur in the Cape Region, only 20 of these account for one third of all the species! Among the largest are *Erica* (660 species), *Aspalathus* (272 species),

Pelargonium (148 species) and *Agathosma* (143 species). Distinguishing between many of these is extremely difficult. Many of these species, however, are rare or highly local in occurrence and therefore not often seen. In the Cape, a spring season after a summer fire is almost invariably spectacular, with large numbers of bulbs in particular responding to the removal of choking shrubbery.

The West Coast is a familiar destination for wildflower enthusiasts as its spring displays of annuals are quite spectacular. Despite the encroachment of housing estates, a significant stretch of this coast is preserved in the West Coast National Park. The sands along the West Coast are dominated by large tufts of restios and scattered shrubs of rhus and the rusty-flowered sages, *Salvia lanceolata* and *S. africana-lutea*. The most conspicuous shrub in flower in spring is the broom-like *Nylandtia scoparia*, which forms large purple or lilac mounds thickly covered in small pea-like flowers that perfume the air. Among the numerous annuals it is the daisies that are

The slopes of Kogelberg ablaze with spring bulbs after a summer burn

Gladiolus cardinalis *cascades down a waterfall near Bain's Kloof*

most conspicuous, especially the glistening white *Dimorphotheca pluvialis*, orange *Ursinia anthemoides*, purple *Senecio arenarius* and yellow or white buttons of *Cotula turbinata*. The daisies close their flower heads at night or in inclement weather, making an early start to the day somewhat unrewarding. Another characteristic to take into account is that they face north towards the sun. This means that it is best to be driving south in the afternoon, when you will be able to return the bright gaze of the flowers.

Mixed in with the daisies are pale blue *Heliophila* and several species of nemesia, each with a different charming face. The granite outcrops that fringe the Langebaan lagoon and dot the landscape around the village of Darling are especially rich in lovely plants and repay a prolonged visit. Several

small reserves around Darling are closely studded in brilliantly coloured bulbs in mid- to late September, including the charming winecups, *Geissorhiza*. The comparison between these verdant meadows and the millefiore on medieval paintings is not a difficult one to draw.

The granite domes on the West Coast are home to numerous bulbs that seek shelter from the depredations of baboons and porcupines in the rock crevices. Among these are various species of lachenalia, gladiolus, romulea, spiloxene and ornithogalum. Many striking succulents also cling to the smoothly rounded flanks of these domes. The most spectacular is undoubtedly *Carpobrotus acinaciformis*, which trails its greyish stems over the rocks and shrubs, dazzling in the sun with brilliant purple cups nestling among the fleshy leaves. One of the most characteristic annuals of the West Coast is the Bokbaai vygie. This popular garden plant appears in a bewildering variety of colours, mainly bright pink but more commonly white or lemon yellow around the Langebaan Lagoon. The Cape of Good Hope Nature Reserve is also well worth a visit, particularly for its lovely stands of several Proteaceae, notably *Mimetes hirtus*, *Leucadendron xanthoconus* and the endemic *Serruria villosa*. In early summer it is especially brilliant with glossy white stretches of *Syncarpha vestita* covering the ground in drifts like snow. The Breede River valley between Tulbagh and Bonnievale is another stretch of country that provides flowers over a long period. September is especially good for the many bulbous plants, including the charming orange *Gladiolus alatus*. This little species is easily among the most entrancing of the many gladiolus species that occur in the Western Cape. The glory of the Worcester valley must be its succulents, especially the endemic *Drosanthemum speciosum*. This small shrub bears flowers of almost impossibly brilliant reds and orange in late spring, in October. The best-known river valley in the region, however, is the Olifants River valley, between Citrusdal and Clanwilliam. Nestling on either side of the Cedarberg mountains, the Clanwilliam and Biedouw valleys can justly be described as the Valleys of the Flowers. Unfortunately, like Namaqualand, their glory is short-lived, and they are at their best between August and September.

Unlike Namaqualand, however, it is possible to extend the flower viewing season in the Western Cape by scaling the heights. The grandeur of the Cape mountains is enhanced by their relative accessibility via numerous mountain passes that cut through their jagged slopes. Their flanks are clothed in a rich shrubbery dominated by various proteas, among which the grey-leaved waboom, *Protea nitida*, is probably the most instantly recognisable. Forming a thick understorey

Erica schoemanii *clinging to the summit of the Stettynsberg*

here are numerous needle-leaved shrubs. Although these shrubs may appear to be a uniform and rather uninteresting mass, careful examination will disclose many different species, each with its own distinct flower. It is also one of the characteristics of fynbos that different sites support different suites of species despite appearances to the contrary, and so the secret is to stop frequently and look carefully. It is not unusual to find several different species of proteas, conebushes, ericas or buchus growing together. The record is eight different ericas in a square metre of mountain fynbos! All of the mountain passes are recommended, and they will yield something of interest in any month of the year. It is difficult to pick out particular plants or places but the Hottentots Holland, Outeniqua/Tsitsikamma and Swartberg mountains are all accessible by road. The coastal route along the southern foot of the Outeniqua/Tsitsikamma range, with its breathtaking vistas, is popularly known as the Garden Route, and provides an opportunity to see the largest stretches of forest in the country, between George and Knysna.

The easiest of the Cape mountains to scale is Table Mountain itself and late summer is the time when one of its most glorious wildflowers, *Disa uniflora,* the red disa, comes into flower. This blood red orchid is the flower emblem of the Western Cape and can be seen in bloom along streams and runnels on Table Mountain between mid-February and March. It is little wonder that this lovely flower is an object of annual pilgrimage by many local residents. Another wildflower worthy of a hike in summer is *Gladiolus cardinalis*, the New Year Lily, which cascades from the edges of waterfalls in the Hottentots Holland range. It is easily seen in certain side valleys off the Bain's and Du Toit's Kloof passes.

Zantedeschia aethiopica

ARUM FAMILY

Common calla lily, arum lily, pig lily (E),
varkblom (A)
(Latin *aethiopicus*, from Africa, usually
South Africa)

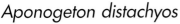

Tuberous perennial, 60–100 cm high. Leaves
arrow-shaped, on long spongy petioles.
Flowers crowded in a narrow yellow spike
8–9 cm long which is partly enclosed by a
flaring, leathery, white bract.
Habitat: Seasonal wetlands or stream sides,
often in quantity.
Notes: The warmed leaves are used as a dress-
ing and the boiled rhizomes mixed with syrup
as a gargle. Uncooked parts must not be eaten
as the needle-like oxalate crystals cause
painful inflammation.

Aponogeton distachyos

APONOGETON FAMILY

Edible pond blossom (E),
waterblommetjie (A)
(Greek *distachyos*, two-spiked)

Rhizomatous aquatic perennial. Leaves on long
petioles with floating, oblong blades. Flowers
in two rows in forked, floating spikes
20–30 mm long, white with one large petal,
gardenia-scented.
Habitat: Pools and ditches.
Notes: Young fruits sold and eaten as a vegetable, particularly in *waterblommetjiebredie*, a
traditional mutton stew.

Asparagus capensis

ASPARAGUS FAMILY

Thorny asparagus (E), katdoring (A)
(Latin *capensis*, from the Cape)

Thorny shrublet to 1 m high
with widely spreading, brush-like branches
bearing whorls or clusters of short branchlets
closely covered with small 'leaves'. Flowers,
one or rarely two at the tips of the branchlets,
white with brown mid-veins, very fragrant of
tuberose, 6 mm diameter.
Habitat: Stony clay flats in scrub.

Chlorophytum triflorum
ANTHERICUM FAMILY

Wire-root grasslily (E)

(Latin *triflorus*, three-flowered, referring to the several flowers per bract)

Tufted perennial to 1 m high, with hard, dark and tapering roots. Leaves strap-shaped with finely hairy margins. Flowers in loose racemes with several flowers in each bract, white with brown keels, each lasting a single day, 15 mm diameter.

Habitat: Sandy soils, often coastal.

Notes: Distinguished from similar species by its characteristic roots.

Ornithoglossum undulatum
GLORIOSA FAMILY

Cockatoo snakelily (E)

(Latin *undulatus*, wavy, a reference to the leaf margins)

Cormous perennial, 5–20 cm high. Leaves lance-shaped and greyish with wavy margins. Flowers nodding on slender stalks with the six petals arranged in a fan, white to pink with purple or maroon tips, fragrant, 20–25 mm diameter.

Habitat: Rocky sandstone or granite slopes.

Onixotis stricta
GLORIOSA FAMILY

Greater waterphlox (E), rysblommetjie (A)

(Latin *strictus*, very straight, referring to the stems)

Cormous perennial with stiffly erect stems, 20–50 cm high. Leaves three, rod-like and triangular in section with the upper two set just below the spike. Flowers in a narrow spike, pink, lightly scented, 15 mm diameter.

Habitat: Marshes and pools.

Wurmbea variabilis

GLORIOSA FAMILY

Stinking spike lily (E)

(Latin *variabilis,* variable, traditionally in colour but here referring to general variability)

Cormous perennial, 5–20 cm high. Leaves three, broadly lance-shaped. Flowers in a cylindrical spike, star-shaped, the petals cream with a brown blotch near the base, 15 mm diameter. **Habitat:** Stony clay or sandstone soils in open scrub.

Bulbinella caudafelis

ALOE FAMILY

Cat's tail bulbinella (E), katstert (A)

(Latin *caudafelis,* cat's tail, alluding to the flower spike)

Rhizomatous perennial to 80 cm high. Leaves narrow and channelled, grass-like and often with finely toothed margins. Flowers in a slender, tapering raceme, white with a pink tinge, 7–8 mm diameter.
Habitat: Often on clay slopes, but also sandstone or granite in scrub.
Notes: Bulbinellas can be distinguished from bulbines by their long-lasting flowers with smooth, thread-like stamen filaments.

Bulbine annua

ALOE FAMILY

Annual bulbine (E)

(Latin *annuus,* annual, referring to the annual habit which is unique in the genus)

Annual herb with wiry roots, 15–40 cm high. Leaves many in a basal cluster, knitting needle-like and slightly fleshy. Flowers in a dense raceme on slender stalks, yellow, 10 mm diameter. Fruits spherical on spreading stalks.
Habitat: Sandy soils, often coastal.
Notes: The flowers, like those of all bulbines, last only a single day. This and the fluffy stamen filaments distinguish them from bulbinellas.

Trachyandra divaricata

ALOE FAMILY

Seaside tumbling starlily (E)

(Latin *divaricatus*, spreading widely, referring to the branching flower stems)

Tufted, rhizomatous perennial to 90 cm high, with many cylindrical, fleshy roots. Leaves many, narrow and oval in section, fleshy and smooth, each individually wrapped at the base in a brown, papery sheath. Flowers nodding in rounded panicles with sharply spreading branches, white, fragrant, 10 mm diameter. **Habitat:** Coastal dunes and sandy flats. **Notes:** The young flower buds can be eaten as a vegetable. The flowering stem dries into a tumbleweed that is blown about by the wind in summer to disperse the seeds.

Trachyandra muricata

ALOE FAMILY

Common tumbling starlily (E)

(Latin *muricatus*, rough, referring to the leaves)

Rhizomatous perennial to 90 cm high, with many cylindrical, fleshy roots. Leaves few to several, lance-shaped, rough or sandpapery, at least along the margins. Flowers nodding in rounded panicles with the stem rough at the base, white, fragrant, 10 mm diameter. **Habitat:** Stony clay slopes in karroid scrub and renosterveld.

Aloe perfoliata

ALOE FAMILY

Cliff aloe, mitre aloe (E), kransaalwyn (A)

(= *Aloe comptonii, A. mitriformis*)

(Latin *perfoliatus*, of leaves that clasp the stem)

Sprawling, often branched succulent shrub with stems 1–2 m high. Leaves succulent and broadly lance-shaped, dark green with few or no white speckles and with coarsely toothed margins. Flowers crowded in branched, head-like racemes, nodding, scarlet, 40 mm long. **Habitat:** Rocky sandstone or granite slopes and cliffs.

Aloe plicatilis

ALOE FAMILY

Fan aloe (E), waaieraalwyn (A)
(Latin *plicatus*, pleated, alluding to the
appearance of the leaf rosettes)

Stout succulent shrub or small tree to 5 m high
with more or less equally forked branches.
Leaves in tight fans, oblong and greyish with
dark margins that are rough but not toothed.
Flowers nodding in short, loose racemes,
scarlet, 40–50 mm long.
Habitat: Cool sandstone slopes.

Aloe microstigma

ALOE FAMILY

Cape speckled aloe (E)
(Greek *microstigma*, little spot, referring to
the white speckling on the leaves)

Rosette-forming succulent to 50 cm high when
not in flower. Leaves tapering and succulent,
often reddish and usually with small white
spots, the margins with sharp, reddish-brown
teeth. Flowers nodding in conical racemes,
usually red in bud but opening yellow,
20–25 mm long.
Habitat: Stony slopes among scrub.
Notes: Exceptionally common in the Little
Karoo, dominating rocky hillsides in places.

Aloe arborescens

ALOE FAMILY

Krans aloe (E), kransaalwyn (A), inHlazi (Z)
(Latin *arborescens*, becoming tree-like)

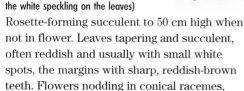

Many-branched shrubs or small
trees to 2 m high with the stems often tilted.
Leaves sickle-shaped with sharp greenish teeth
along the margins. Flowers nodding in conical
racemes, usually pink but also orange to
yellow, 30 mm long.
Habitat: Rocky slopes; exposed ridges in
scrub.
Notes: Common and widespread, often cultivated, especially in the Eastern Cape where it is
used as live fences. The sappy leaves are a
convenient first-aid treatment for burns.

Aloe ferox
ALOE FAMILY

Bitter aloe (E), bitteraalwyn (A), iKhala (X)
(Latin *ferox*, fierce, alluding to the prickly leaves)

Robust single-stemmed succulent to 2 m high, rarely to 5 m, with the old leaves remaining on the trunk. Leaves tapering with sharp brown teeth on the margins and sometimes the leaf surfaces. Flowers nodding in dense, branched candelabras, usually orange to red, about 30 mm long.

Habitat: Widely distributed on stony flats and slopes.

Notes: Probably the most important medicinal plant in the region. For over 200 years the golden-brown leaf sap has been used to make the purgative known as Cape Aloe.

Kniphofia uvaria
ALOE FAMILY

Cape poker (E), vuurpyl (A)
(Latin *uvarius*, clustered like grapes, alluding to the flower spikes)

Rhizomatous perennial, 50–120 cm high, usually growing in small clumps. Leaves strap-shaped, fibrous and keeled. Flowers in oblong to globose racemes, orange in bud turning greenish yellow, 30–40 mm long.

Habitat: Seeps, marshes and streams, usually in peaty soils, flowering well after a burn.

Lachenalia bulbifera
HYACINTH FAMILY

Red lachenalia (E), rooinaeltjie (A)
(Latin *bulbiferus*, bearing bulbils, a reference to the propensity for producing bulblets)

Bulbous perennial, 8–30 cm high. Leaves one or two, lance- to strap-shaped, plain or blotched with dark colour. Flowers nodding, tubular with the anthers enclosed within the flower, orange to red with darker red or brown markings and green tips, 20–35 mm long.

Habitat: Sandy flats and lower slopes, mainly coastal.

Lachenalia aloides

HYACINTH FAMILY

Cape cowslip (E), vierkleurtjie (A)

(Resembling an aloe in its flowers)

Bulbous perennial, 5–31 cm
high. Leaves one or two, lance- to strap-
shaped, sometimes densely spotted with green
or purple. Flowers nodding, tubular with the
anthers enclosed within the tube, combinations of orange, red, yellow or greenish blue
with greenish markings, 20–35 mm long.
Habitat: Granite and sandstone outcrops,
often coastal.

Lachenalia mutabilis

HYACINTH FAMILY

Tasselled lachenalia (E)

(Latin *mutabilis*, changeable, a reference
to the multi-coloured flowers)

Bulbous perennial, 10–45 cm high. Leaf solitary, lance-shaped with wavy margins. Flowers
tubular or urn-shaped with the anthers
enclosed within the tube, pale blue and white
with yellow tips or yellowish green, the upper
flowers often vestigial and sometimes electric
blue, 8–10 mm long.
Habitat: Sandy and stony slopes.

Lachenalia pustulata

HYACINTH FAMILY

Warty lachenalia (E)

(Latin *pustulatus*, warty or blistered)

Bulbous perennial, 15–35 cm
high. Leaves one or two, lance- or strap-shaped
and smooth or densely warty. Flowers on long
pedicels, urn-shaped with the anthers shortly
or well protruding, shades of cream, blue
or pink with green or brownish markings,
7–9 mm long.
Habitat: Clay or granite flats, often in large
colonies.
Notes: Common on granite outcrops near
Langebaan.

Massonia depressa

HYACINTH FAMILY

Common hedgehog lily (E),
bobbejaanboek (A)

(Latin *depressus*, flattened from above,
alluding to the low growth form)

Bulbous perennial to 5 cm high. Leaves broad
and rounded, flat on the ground, plain green or
marked with purple. Flowers clustered
between the leaves, with large bracts, deeply
cupped below, green or yellowish to white or
pink, 10–15 mm diameter.
Habitat: Mainly clay flats.
Notes: Pollinated by rodents that lap the thick
nectar from the flowers at night.

Albuca fragrans

HYACINTH FAMILY

Sandveld slime lily (E)

(Latin *fragrans*, fragrant)

Stout to slender bulbous perennial to 1 m high, the bulb sometimes with
bulbils around the base. Leaves several,
channelled, fleshy and oozing a slimy sap
when torn. Flowers in racemes that droop
in bud, nodding, yellow with green keels,
fragrant, all six stamens with anthers although
three are smaller, 25–30 mm diameter.
Habitat: Sandy slopes and flats, often coastal.

Albuca flaccida

HYACINTH FAMILY

(= *Albuca canadensis*)
Common slime lily (E), tamarak (A)
(Latin *flaccidus*, flaccid, referring to the
rather limp leaves)

Bulbous perennial, 40–100 cm high, the bulb
tunics membranous. Leaves several, channelled and clasping the stem below, fleshy and
oozing a slimy sap when torn. Flowers in loose
racemes, nodding, mostly yellow or with green
keels, lightly fragrant, the inner petals with a
hinged flesh flap at the tips and only three
stamens with anthers, 25–30 mm diameter.
Habitat: Mostly coastal in stony sandstone
and granitic soils.

Albuca maxima
HYACINTH FAMILY

(= *Albuca altissima*)

Greater slimelily (E), wittamarak (A)

(Latin *maximus*, greatest, for its large size)

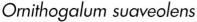

Stout bulbous perennial, usually 1–2 m high, the bulb tunics slightly fibrous at the top. Leaves several, channelled and clasping the stem below. Flowers in racemes that elongate markedly in fruit, nodding, white with green keels, the inner tepals with a hinged flap at the tip and only three stamens with anthers, 25–30 mm diameter.

Habitat: Rocky outcrops.

Notes: Can form dense colonies along road-sides.

Ornithogalum suaveolens
HYACINTH FAMILY

Striped chincherinchee (E), bonttjienk (A)

(Latin *suaveolens*, sweetly fragrant)

Bulbous perennial, 10–50 cm high. Leaves few, sometimes dry at flowering, narrow and channelled. Flowers in loose racemes on slender stalks, greenish yellow with dark green keels, sweetly fragrant, 20–30 mm diameter.

Habitat: Dry stony slopes and flats.

Ornithogalum thyrsoides
HYACINTH FAMILY

Chincherinchee (E), tjienk (A)

(Resembling the inflorescence type known as a thyrse)

Bulbous perennial, 20–80 cm high, the outer layers of the bulb soft and whitish. Leaves sometimes dry at flowering, lance-shaped and usually with minutely hairy margins. Flowers shiny white and often darker in the centre, three of the stamen filaments with broad wings at the base, 20–25 mm diameter.

Habitat: Sandy flats and often in vleis.

Notes: Toxic to stock. *Ornithogalum conicum* lacks the conspicuous wings at the base of the inner filaments. Both species and their hybrids are popular cut flowers.

Ornithogalum dubium
HYACINTH FAMILY

Varicoloured chincherinchee (E), geeltjienk (A)
(Latin *dubius*, doubtful, reflecting the doubts
regarding the true identity of the species)

Bulbous perennial, 10–50 cm high, the outer
layers of the bulb often blackish. Leaves
sometimes dry at flowering, lance-shaped with
minutely hairy margins. Flowers in almost
flat-topped racemes, yellow to orange or rarely
white and often with a green or brown centre
and a very short style, 20–25 mm diameter.
Habitat: Mainly clay or gravelly flats and
lower slopes.

Empodium plicatum
STARGRASS FAMILY

Common autumn star (E), klipsterretjie (A)
(Latin *plicatus*, pleated, referring to the
leaves)

Cormous perennial, 10–30 cm high, with pale
basal sheaths. Leaves several but often only
beginning to emerge at flowering, narrow and
pleated. Flowers solitary on a three-angled
stalk, bright yellow, 20–30 mm diameter.
Habitat: Clay and granite flats and lower
slopes.

Spiloxene capensis
STARGRASS FAMILY

Painted peacockflower (E), poublom (A)
(Latin *capensis*, from the Cape)

Cormous perennial, 10–30 cm
high. Leaves several, grass-like and channelled
with the margins usually minutely toothed.
Flowers one per stalk, the flowering stalk with
a single leaf-like bract, yellow, white or pink
and usually with black or iridescent markings
in the centre, the reverse of the petals boldly
striped, 30–70 mm diameter.
Habitat: Seasonally wet flats.

Spiloxene aquatica

STARGRASS FAMILY

Water star (E), watersterretjie (A)

(Latin *aquaticus*, living in water)

Cormous perennial, 20–45 cm
high. Leaves two to five, knitting needle-like
and somewhat triangular in cross-section.
Flowers two to seven per stalk, the flowering
stalk with two or more bracts, white with
green backs, often scented, 20–30 mm
diameter.

Habitat: Seasonal pools and streams.

Gethyllis afra

AMARYLLIS FAMILY

Kukumakranka (E), koekemakranka (N)

(Latin *afra*, from Africa)

Bulbous perennial to 15 cm
high. Leaves withered at flowering, many,
narrow and spiralled, usually hairless. Flowers
appearing at ground level, cup-shaped, cream
with pink stripes on the reverse, 30–40 mm
diameter.

Habitat: Sandy flats.

Notes: Flowers are followed in the autumn by
a narrow, cylindrical fruit that protrudes from
the ground. This is the famed kukumakranka.
It is highly fragrant, with a fruity scent.
Although edible, the fruit was more often
steeped in brandy or witblits, which was then
taken for colic and indigestion.

Lanaria lanata

KAPOK LILY FAMILY

Kapok lily (E)

(Latin *lanatus*, woolly)

Evergreen tufted perennial,
30–80 cm high. Leaves narrow and channelled,
tough and fibrous with minutely toothed
margins. Flowers in white-woolly flat-topped
panicles, mauve inside but white-woolly on
the outside, 10 mm diameter.

Habitat: Clay and sandstone slopes.

Notes: Flowers mainly after fire.

Dilatris ixioides

BLOODROOT FAMILY

Common bloodroot (E), rooiwortel (A)
(Resembling the genus *Ixia*, not an
accurate simile)

Rhizomatous perennial, 20–40 cm high. Leaves narrow and strap-like, in a narrow fan. Flowers crowded, in flat-topped panicles, mauve with two long stamens twice as long as tepals and one shorter stamen, 15 mm diameter.
Habitat: Rocky sandstone slopes in fynbos.
Notes: Flowers are either left- or right-handed depending on the direction in which the style is flexed.

Wachendorfia paniculata

BLOODROOT FAMILY

Common butterfly lily (E), rooikanol (A)
(Latin *paniculatus*, a branched inflorescence)

Rhizomatous perennial, mostly 20–70 cm high. Leaves narrow and pleated, usually hairy. Flowers in an open or dense panicle, buff to bright yellow, 30–35 mm diameter.
Habitat: Mainly sandy flats or sandstone slopes in fynbos.
Notes: Flowers are either left- or right-handed depending on the direction in which the style is flexed.

Wachendorfia thyrsiflora

BLOODROOT FAMILY

Royal butterfly lily (E), groot rooikanol (A)
(Latin *thyrsiflora*, with flowers arranged in
the inflorescence type known as a thyrse)

Rhizomatous perennial, 1–2 m high. Leaves broad and pleated, hairless. Flowers in a crowded, cylindrical panicle, golden-yellow, 30 mm diameter.
Habitat: Permanent marshes and streams.
Notes: Flowers are either left- or right-handed depending on the direction in which the style is flexed. A wonderful garden plant for pondside plantings.

Cyanella lutea
CYANELLA FAMILY
Yellow lady's hand (E), geelraaptol (A)
(Latin *luteus*, golden-yellow)

Cormous perennial, 12–25 cm
high. Leaves lance-shaped with wavy margins.
Flowers in branched racemes, yellow or rarely
pink, fragrant, with five upper and one larger
lower stamens that are not joined.
Habitat: Mostly clay, or limestone flats.

Cyanella hyacinthoides
CYANELLA FAMILY
Blue lady's hand (E), blouraaptol (A)
(Hyacinth-like, particularly in flower colour)

Cormous perennial, 25–40 cm
high. Leaves slender and often wavy on the
margins, hairless or finely hairy. Flowers in
branched racemes, mauve or rarely white,
fragrant, with five upper and one larger lower
stamens that are joined together at the base.
Habitat: Mostly clay and granite slopes, often
in renosterveld.

Agapanthus africanus
AGAPANTHUS FAMILY
Cape agapanthus (E)
(Latin *africanus*, from Africa)

Evergreen perennial, 25–70 cm
high. Leaves strap-shaped and channelled.
Flowers on pedicels 15–50 mm long, broadly
funnel-shaped and thick-textured with the
stamens shorter than the petals, deep blue,
25–40 mm long.
Habitat: Rocky sandstone slopes.
Notes: Flowers best after fire. Much confused
with *Agapanthus praecox* in the horticultural
trade but not in cultivation at all.

Agapanthus praecox
AGAPANTHUS FAMILY
Agapanthus (E)
(Latin *praecox*, precocious, thus early
flowering, not very appropriate)
Evergreen perennial, 50–100 cm high. Leaves
strap-shaped and channelled. Flowers on
pedicels 40–120 mm long, broadly funnel-
shaped and thin-textured with the stamens
mostly as long as the petals, white to medium
blue, 30–70 mm long.
Habitat: Rocky slopes, often along bush
margins.
Notes: A widely grown ornamental with many
forms.

Tulbaghia violacea
ONION FAMILY
Wild garlic (E)
(Latin *violaceus*, violet-coloured)
Evergreen rhizomatous
perennial smelling of garlic when bruised,
20–35 cm high. Leaves narrow and greyish.
Flowers in rounded clusters, resembling
minute daffodils in shape, mauve, lightly
scented, 10–15 mm long.
Habitat: Forest margins and stream banks.
Notes: Widely cultivated. Traditionally used
for fever and colds. Leaves may be eaten as a
vegetable.

Amaryllis belladonna
AMARYLLIS FAMILY
March lily, belladonna (E)
(Italian *belladonna*, beautiful lady)
Bulbous perennial to 90 cm
high. Leaves dry or absent at flowering,
several, strap-shaped and channelled with a
prominent midrib. Flowers trumpet-shaped,
pink to nearly white and fragrant, 70–80 mm
diameter.
Habitat: Seasonally damp, loamy soils in lowlands.
Notes: One of only two true species of
Amaryllis; plants commonly cultivated under
that name belong to the genus *Hippeastrum*.

Brunsvigia orientalis

AMARYLLIS FAMILY

King's candelabra (E), koningskandelaar (A)

(Latin *orientalis*, eastern, mistakenly thought
to have come from the Far East)

Bulbous perennial, 40–50 cm high. Leaves dry
at flowering, usually six, spreading flat on the
ground, tongue-shaped and leathery with
translucent margins. Flowers in a large,
rounded cluster on long pedicels, red,
trumpet-shaped with the petals rolled back,
50 mm long.

Habitat: Mainly sandy soils, usually coastal
lowlands.

Notes: Pollinated by sunbirds.

Brunsvigia marginata

AMARYLLIS FAMILY

Scarlet candelabra (E)

(Latin *marginatus*, margined, referring
to the leaves)

Bulbous perennial to 20 cm high. Leaves dry at
flowering, four, spreading flat on the ground,
elliptical and leathery with translucent
margins. Flowers crowded in a round cluster,
brilliant scarlet, star-shaped with a short tube
and prominent stamens, 30 mm diameter.

Habitat: Rocky slopes in shale bands.

Notes: Pollinated by the Citrus swallowtail
and Table Mountain beauty butterflies.

Haemanthus coccineus

AMARYLLIS FAMILY

April fool (E)

(Latin *coccineus*, deep red)

Bulbous perennial, 6–20 cm
high. Leaves dry at flowering, two, tongue-
shaped and glossy green above but usually
speckled beneath and often minutely hairy on
the margins. Flowers crowded in a dense,
brush-like cluster on a spotted stalk, red,
40 mm long.

Habitat: Coastal scrub and rocky slopes, often
in the lee of rocks.

Nerine sarniensis

AMARYLLIS FAMILY

Red nerina, Guernsey lily (E)

(Latin *sarniensis*, from Guernsey, from the mistaken belief that the species was native there)

Bulbous perennial, 25–45 cm high. Leaves dry at flowering, several, strap-shaped. Flowers star-shaped with a short tube and prominent stamens clustered together, scarlet or purplish with a golden sheen, 25–30 mm diameter. **Habitat:** Stony slopes, often in the shelter of rocks. **Notes:** Pollinated by the large brown butterfly, *Aeropetes tulbaghia.*

Cybistetes longifolia

AMARYLLIS FAMILY

Malgas lily (E), malgaslelie (A)

(Latin *longifolius*, long-leaved)

Bulbous perennial, 25–35 cm high. Leaves dry or green at flowering, several, sickle-shaped and spreading on the ground, with translucent margins. Flowers widely funnel-shaped, cream to pink turning reddish and very fragrant, 30–40 mm diameter. **Habitat:** Sandy flats.

Cyrtanthus ventricosus

AMARYLLIS FAMILY

Fire lily (E), vuurlelie (A)

(Latin *ventricosus*, swollen, referring to the somewhat inflated flower tube)

Bulbous perennial, 10–25 cm high. Leaves dry at flowering, one to five, narrowly strap-shaped and channelled. Flowers two to ten per stalk, nodding and tubular to narrowly trumpet-shaped, bright shiny red but often with pink petals, 40–50 mm long. **Habitat:** South-facing sandstone slopes in fynbos. **Notes:** Flowering only after fire, appearing within 12 to 14 days after the burn.

Cyrtanthus elatus

AMARYLLIS FAMILY

George lily (E)

(Latin *elatus*, tall)

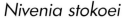

Bulbous geophyte to 60 cm high.
Leaves strap-shaped and slightly channelled.
Flowers two to nine per stalk, widely funnel-shaped, bright red or rarely pink, 70–100 mm.
Habitat: Forest margins and moist mountain slopes.
Notes: Pollinated by the large brown butterfly, *Aeropetes tulbaghia*.

Nivenia stokoei

IRIS FAMILY

Stokoe's bush iris (E)

(Commemorating the Cape Town plant collector, Thomas Stokoe)

Evergreen shrub with woody stems to 60 cm high. Leaves sword-shaped, in flat fans at the branch tips. Flowers aggregated into loose, flat-topped clusters, pale to deep blue or rarely lilac, with a slender tube, 40–50 mm long.
Habitat: Rocky sandstone in fynbos.
Notes: The small Cape genera *Nivenia*, *Klattia* and *Witsenia* are the only members of this family to develop woody stems. They are all rather local and restricted to sandstone soils.

Aristea africana

IRIS FAMILY

Fringed aristea (E)

(Latin *africanus*, from Africa)

Evergreen rhizomatous peren-nial, mostly 10–15 cm high, with flattened, branched stems. Leaves narrow and fibrous. Flowers subtended by greenish bracts with wide membranous margins that are fringed and curled, blue, 15–20 mm diameter. Fruits short and three-winged.
Habitat: Sandy flats and mountain slopes.
Notes: Each flower lasts less than a day.

Aristea bakeri
IRIS FAMILY
(= *Aristea confusa*)
Aristea (E)
(Commemorates the English botanist,
J.G. Baker)

Evergreen rhizomatous perennial to 1 m high, with cylindrical, usually well-branched stems. Leaves strap-like and fibrous. Flowers subtended by rust-brown bracts with transparent margins, blue, 20–25 mm diameter. Fruits three-winged.
Habitat: Stony sandstone slopes in fynbos.
Notes: Flowers mostly after fire and each flower lasts less than a day.

Aristea capitata
IRIS FAMILY
(= *Aristea major*)
Blue sceptre (E), blousuurkanol (A)
(Latin *capitatus*, with a knob-like head,
referring to the crowded flowering stalks)

Evergreen rhizomatous perennial to 1,5 m high, with cylindrical stems that have short, crowded branches above. Leaves strap-like, fibrous. Flowers crowded and subtended by small dark bracts with papery margins, blue, 15–20 mm diameter. Fruits short, three-winged.
Habitat: Sheltered sandstone slopes in fynbos.
Notes: Better known under the name *Aristea major*. Flowers only after fire and each flower lasts less than a day.

Ferraria crispa
IRIS FAMILY
Sea spider iris (E), spinnekopblom (A)
(Latin *crispus*, crisped, referring to the petal
margins)

Cormous perennial, 40–100 cm high, with branched, leafy stems. Leaves sword-shaped and slightly fleshy. Flowers brown or yellowish and speckled, with tightly crisped petal margins, acrid-smelling, 30 mm diameter.
Habitat: Mainly coastal, in sand or among rocks.

Bobartia indica

IRIS FAMILY

Greater rush iris (E), blombiesie (A)

(Latin *indicus*, from India, a mistake arising from the transport of the first specimens on board an East Indiaman returning to Europe from the East)

Evergreen rhizomatous perennial to 1 m or more high. Leaves cylindrical, longer than the stems and trailing. Flowers in a dense head on a slender leafless stalk, yellow, 20 mm diameter. **Habitat:** Sandstone flats and slopes in fynbos. **Notes:** Flowers mainly after fire.

Moraea miniata

IRIS FAMILY

(= *Homeria miniata*)

Common Cape tulip (E), tulp (A)

(Latin *miniatus*, flame-red)

Cormous perennial, 15–60 cm high. Leaves two or three, narrow and channelled, trailing. Flowers star-shaped, salmon-pink or rarely yellow or white, minutely speckled in the centre, the anthers held at the tip of a bulbous filament column, 20–30 mm diameter. **Habitat:** Mainly clay slopes in renosterveld and karroid scrub. **Notes:** Poisonous to stock.

Moraea flaccida

IRIS FAMILY

(= *Homeria flaccida*)

Red Cape tulip (E), rooitulp (A)

(Latin *flaccidus*, flaccid, referring to the rather limp leaf)

Cormous perennial, 35–60 cm high with the stem bent outwards above the leaf sheath. Leaf solitary, narrow and channelled. Flowers cup-shaped, salmon-pink with a yellow centre or entirely yellow, the anthers held beyond the cup on a thick filament column, 30–40 mm diameter. **Habitat:** Seasonally wet sandstone and granitic soils.

Moraea collina

IRIS FAMILY

(= *Homeria collina*)

Yellow Cape tulip (E), geeltulp (A)

(Latin *collinus,* pertaining to hills, alluding to its habitat)

Cormous perennial, 20–50 cm high, stem bent outward above the leaf sheath. Leaf solitary, narrow, channelled. Flowers cup-shaped, yellow or salmon, lightly scented, the anthers held within the cup on a thick filament column.

Habitat: Lower mountain slopes and flats on sand or clay.

Notes: Common after fire.

Moraea fugacissima

IRIS FAMILY

(= *Galaxia fugacissima*)

Needle-leaved clockflower (E), horlosieblom (A)

(Latin *fugacissimus,* very fleeting, referring to the short-lived flowers)

Stemless cormous perennial, 3–6 cm high, often forming little cushions. Leaves narrow and grass-like or needle-like. Flowers yellow, sweetly scented, cup-shaped with a slender tube, 15–20 mm diameter.

Habitat: Wet sand and clay flats.

Notes: Each flower lasts only a single morning.

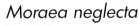

Moraea neglecta

IRIS FAMILY

Rush-leaved moraea (E)

(Latin *neglectus,* neglected, referring to the fact that the species was not recognised as distinct for many years)

Cormous perennial, 20–50 cm high with an unbranched stem that is sticky at the nodes. Leaf solitary, knitting needle-like. Flowers yellow with darkly stippled markings, fragrant, with the three inner petals smaller than the outer and lance-shaped, 50–70 mm diameter.

Habitat: Usually deep sandy soils.

Moraea fugax

IRIS FAMILY

Hottentot nut (E), soetuintjie,
hottentotuintjie (A)

(Latin *fugax*, fleeting, referring to the short-
lived flowers)

Cormous perennial, 12–80 cm high with the
branches crowded together just above the
leaves. Leaves one or two, inserted well above
the ground, narrow or thread-like and channelled, often trailing. Flowers blue, white or
yellow, fragrant, with the three inner petals
lance-shaped, 40–50 mm diameter.

Habitat: Deep sands and rocky sandstone and
granitic slopes.

Notes: Flowers open only in the mid-afternoon
and each lasts less than one day. The corms
were prized as food among early tribes.

Moraea gawleri

IRIS FAMILY

Wire-stemmed moraea (E)
(Commemorates the British botanist,
Ker Gawler)

Loosely branched cormous perennial with wiry
stems, 15–45 cm high. Leaves two or three,
narrow with the margins usually wavy or
crinkly. Flowers yellow, cream or brick-red,
sometimes bicoloured, with the three inner
petals lance-shaped, 15–20 mm diameter.

Habitat: Sandy or clay slopes, usually in
renosterveld.

Moraea tripetala

IRIS FAMILY

Fleur-de-lys moraea (E), blou-uintjie (A)
(Latin *tripetalus*, three-petalled, due to the
reduced or obsolete inner petals)

Slender cormous perennial, 20–45 cm high.
Leaf solitary, narrow and channelled. Flowers
blue to violet or rarely white or pink, the three
inner tepals reduced to a minute thread or
absent, 20–30 mm diameter.

Habitat: Rocky sandstone and clay soils in
fynbos and renosterveld.

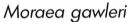

Moraea villosa

IRIS FAMILY

Peacock moraea (E), blouflappie (A)

(Latin *villosus*, shaggy, referring to the hairy leaves)

Cormous perennial, 30–40 cm high. Leaf solitary, narrow and channelled, hairy beneath. Flowers purple, blue, cream or orange with large, dark markings, the inner three petals three-lobed with a long, narrow central lobe, 45–60 mm diameter.

Habitat: Stony granite and clay slopes and flats in renosterveld.

Notes: Increasingly rare.

Moraea ramosissima

IRIS FAMILY

Vleiuintjie (A)

(Latin *ramosissimus*, highly branched)

Highly branched cormous perennial, 50–120 cm high. Leaves several in a fan and shiny green, narrow and channelled. Flowers yellow with darker yellow nectar guides on the outer tepals, the inner three tepals smaller than the others, 30 mm diameter.

Habitat: Damp sandy or stony flats and slopes, often along streams.

Notes: Flowering mostly after fire.

Dietes iridioides

IRIS FAMILY

Wood iris (E)

(*Iris*-like, referring to the flowers and rhizomatous habit)

Evergreen rhizomatous perennial to 60 cm high. Leaves sword-shaped in a tight fan. Flowers in tight clusters on an irrregularly branched stem, white with violet style arms, lasting only one day, 30–40 mm diameter.

Habitat: Evergreen forest and forest margins.

Ixia polystachya

IRIS FAMILY

Dark-eyed ixia (E), kalossie (A)

(Greek *polystachyos*, with many spikes, referring to the branched stems)

Slender cormous perennial, 40–80 cm high, the stem wiry with one to three short side-branches. Leaves narrow to sword-shaped. Flowers in a dense spike, white to pink or mauve or rarely yellow and usually with a darker centre, sometimes lightly fragrant, with a thread-like tube and small, translucent bracts, 10–15 mm diameter.

Habitat: Granite and sandstone slopes.

Ixia maculata

IRIS FAMILY

Black-eyed ixia (E), kalossie (A)

(Latin *maculatus*, blotched)

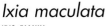

Cormous perennial, 25–60 cm high. Leaves narrowly sword-shaped. Flowers orange with a dark eye, with a thread-like tube and large rusty-spotted bracts, 20–25 mm diameter.

Habitat: Sandy flats and lower slopes.

Ixia dubia

IRIS FAMILY

Orange ixia (E), kalossie (A)

(Latin *dubius*, doubtful, reflecting the doubts regarding the true identity of the species)

Cormous perennial, 25–60 cm high. Leaves narrowly sword-shaped. Flowers orange to yellow and often dark in the centre, with a thread-like tube and small translucent bracts, 15–20 mm diameter.

Habitat: Sandstone and granite flats and slopes.

Ixia scillaris

IRIS FAMILY

Buzz ixia (E), pienk kalossie (A)

(Latin *scillaris*, pertaining to the genus *Scilla*, referring to the open spike of starry pinkish flowers)

Cormous perennial, 25–50 cm high. Leaves sword-shaped with the margins sometimes wavy or crisped. Flowers in an open spike, pale to deep pink, with a thread-like tube and the anthers nodding to one side, 10 mm diameter.
Habitat: Stony sandstone and granite flats and slopes.
Notes: The pollen is buzzed out of the flask-like anthers by visiting bees.

Hesperantha bachmannii

IRIS FAMILY

Ballerina hesperantha (E)

(Named after the nineteenth-century German naturalist, Frans Bachmann)

Cormous perennial, 15–30 cm high, with a rounded corm. Leaves narrowly sword-shaped. Flowers nodding on a slender curved tube, with the petals bent backwards, sweetly scented, opening in the late afternoon, 15–20 mm diameter.
Habitat: Mainly stony clay slopes in renoster-veld.

Geissorhiza aspera

IRIS FAMILY

Blue satinflower (E), satynblom (A)

(Latin *asper*, rough, referring to the stems)

Cormous perennial with velvety stems, 10–35 cm high. Leaves sword-shaped with lightly thickened margins and midrib. Flowers blue-violet or rarely white, 10 mm diameter.
Habitat: Mainly sandy or granite flats and slopes.

Geissorhiza radians

IRIS FAMILY

Wine cup (E), kelkiewyn (A)

(Latin *radians*, radiating, referring to the rings of colour in the flowers)

Cormous perennial, 8–16 cm high. Leaves narrow and conspicuously ribbed. Flowers deep blue with a red centre surrounded by a white ring, with the stamens and style arching downward, 15–20 mm diameter.

Habitat: Seasonally wet sandy or granite soils.

Micranthus junceus

IRIS FAMILY

Marsh combflower (E), vleiblommetjie (A)

(Latin *junceus*, rush-like, referring to the leaves)

Cormous perennial, 25–45 cm high. Leaves slender, cylindrical and hollow. Flowers in a two-ranked spike, subtended by dry bracts with translucent margins, pale or dark blue or rarely white, 6 mm diameter.

Habitat: Seasonal seeps or stream sides on granite or sandstone.

Watsonia meriana

IRIS FAMILY

Wax-flowered watsonia (E), kanolpypie (A)

(Commemorating Maria Sybill Merian, the eighteenth-century painter of plants and animals)

Cormous perennial, 60–200 cm high, sometimes with cormlets at the stem nodes. Leaves sword-shaped. Flowers dull red, pink or mauve with a long tube, 60 mm long. Fruits oblong.

Habitat: Sandy or granitic soils, often in vleis and along streams.

Notes: The tubular flowers are visited by sunbirds.

Watsonia knysnana

IRIS FAMILY

Knysna watsonia (E)

(Latin *knysnana*, of Knysna)

Cormous perennial to 1,6 m high. Leaves sword-shaped. Flowers mostly pale pink to purple but rarely red with a long tube, 60 mm long. Fruits tapering upward.
Habitat: Sandstone slopes and grassy flats.
Notes: Hybridises extensively with both orange-flowered *Watsonia pillansii* and red-flowered *W. fourcadei* around Humansdorp.

Watsonia borbonica

IRIS FAMILY

Purple watsonia (E)

(Latin *borbonicus*, mistakenly thought to originate from Réunion (Île de Bourbon))

Robust cormous perennial to 2 m high, with branched, often purple stems. Leaves sword-shaped, bright green. Flowers purple-pink with a short tube and the stamens and style usually arching downward, 40–50 mm long. Fruits oblong.
Habitat: Mainly rocky sandstone slopes but also granite and clay.
Notes: Flowers best after fire.

Watsonia tabularis

IRIS FAMILY

Table Mountain watsonia (E)

(Latin *tabularis*, pertaining to Table Mountain, where the species is endemic)

Cormous perennial to 1,5 m high. Leaves sword-shaped with those on the stem swollen at the base. Flowers orange and pink with a long tube, 60–70 mm long. Fruits oblong with a blunt tip.
Habitat: Rocky sandstone slopes.
Notes: Endemic to the Cape Peninsula. The tubular flowers are pollinated by sunbirds, especially the Malachite Sunbird.

Watsonia aletroides

IRIS FAMILY

Firecracker watsonia (E)

(Resembling species of *Aletris* in its spike of tubular flowers)

Cormous perennial to 45 cm high. Leaves sword-shaped. Flowers nodding and curved, red or purple to pink, tubular with very short petals, 35–45 mm long. Fruits very narrow and tapering to a pointed tip.
Habitat: Moist clay slopes, mainly in renosterveld.

Watsonia laccata

IRIS FAMILY

Overberg watsonia (E)

(Latin *laccatus*, lake-coloured, crimson)

Cormous perennial to 50 cm high. Leaves sword-shaped. Flowers funnel-shaped, pink to purple or orange with the stamens and style arching downward, 30–40 mm long. Fruits very narrow and tapering to a pointed tip.
Habitat: Moist clay slopes, mainly in renosterveld.

Tritoniopsis triticea

IRIS FAMILY

Summer snakeflower (E), somerpypie (A)

(Latin *triticeus*, of wheat, referring to the dry brown floral bracts)

Cormous perennial, 50–90 cm high. Leaves usually dry at flowering, the basal leaves spear-shaped with three equal veins, abruptly narrowed below into a slender petiole, the stem leaves thread-like and brown. Flowers tubular, scarlet with very small petals marked with black, 25–30 mm long.
Habitat: Rocky granite and sandstone slopes.
Notes: *Tritoniopsis burchellii* is very similar but has larger petals.

Tritoniopsis antholyza
IRIS FAMILY
(= *Anapalina nervosa*)
Common snakeflower (E)
(Greek *anthos-*, *-lyssa*, flower, rage, a poetical allusion to the open-mouthed (= snarling) flowers)
Cormous perennial to 90 cm high. Leaves sword- to strap-shaped with three to six equal veins. Flowers tubular and yellowish pink to red with the upper petals larger than the lower petals, 30–50 mm long.
Habitat: Rocky sandstone slopes.
Notes: Flowers best after a burn.

Tritoniopsis caffra
IRIS FAMILY
(= *Anapalina caffra*)
Outeniqua snakeflower (E)
(Latin *caffra*, from South Africa)
Cormous perennial to 80 cm high. Leaves sword-shaped with two to four equal veins. Flowers tubular with the lower petals smaller, bright red, 40 mm long.
Habitat: Sandstone slopes.
Notes: The odd-shaped flowers are pollinated by sunbirds.

Chasmanthe aethiopica
IRIS FAMILY
Lesser cobra lily (E), klein kapelpypie (A)
(Latin *aethiopicus*, from Africa, usually South Africa)
Cormous perennial with an unbranched stem, 40–65 cm high. Leaves in a tight fan, sword-shaped and thin-textured. Flowers in a single-ranked spike, orange-red and tubular with the tube flared and pouched near the base, 40–50 mm long.
Habitat: Coastal, in bush and forest margins.
Notes: The thinly fleshy, orange seeds are dispersed by fruit-eating birds.

Chasmanthe floribunda

IRIS FAMILY

Greater cobra lily (E), kapelpypie (A)

(Latin *floribundus*, flowering profusely)

Cormous perennial with one or two side branches, 45–100 cm high. Leaves in a tight fan, sword-shaped and thin-textured. Flowers in two ranks, orange-red or rarely yellow, with the tube flaring gradually near the base, 50–60 mm long.

Habitat: Coastal and montane on sandstone and granite in scrub.

Babiana ringens

IRIS FAMILY

(= *Antholyza ringens*)

Rat's tail babiana (E), rotstert (A)

(Latin *ringens*, gaping, a reference to the open mouth of the flowers)

Cormous perennial with the velvety main stem ending in a sterile point and the flowers borne on a short side branch near the ground, 15–40 cm high. Leaves narrow and pleated, smooth. Flowers tubular and strongly two-lipped, bright red with yellowish-green lower petals and spoon-shaped upper petal, 70 mm long.

Habitat: Sandy flats in open fynbos.

Notes: This unusual babiana was originally placed in the genus *Antholyza*. Its curious red flowers are pollinated by sunbirds which perch on the specially modified main stem.

Babiana patersoniae

IRIS FAMILY

Paterson's babiana (E)

(Named after Eastern Cape naturalist, Florence Paterson)

Cormous perennial, 15–25 cm high. Leaves narrowly lance-shaped, pleated and hairy. Flowers narrowly funnel-shaped with a slender tube 20–30 mm long, white to pale blue or mauve with yellow markings, fragrant, the inner floral bracts forked to the base.

Habitat: Clay slopes in renosterveld.

Babiana purpurea

IRIS FAMILY

Purple babiana (E)

(Latin *purpureus*, purple, referring to the flowers)

Slender cormous perennial, 10–15 cm high. Leaves lance-shaped, pleated and hairy. Flowers narrowly funnel-shaped with a slender tube 18–28 mm long, pink to purple with broad blackish anthers, fragrant, the inner bracts forked to the base.

Habitat: Clay flats and slopes in renosterveld.

Notes: Mostly restricted to road verges.

Babiana stricta

IRIS FAMILY

Breede Valley babiana (E)

(Latin *strictus*, very straight, referring to the upright stem)

Slender cormous geophyte, 10–20 cm high. Leaves narrowly lance-shaped, pleated and hairy. Flowers narrowly funnel-shaped with a slender tube 10–16 mm long, purple to blue, white or yellow, unscented or violet scented, the inner bracts forked to the base.

Habitat: Clay soils in renosterveld.

Babiana nana

IRIS FAMILY

Dwarf babiana (E), bobbejaantjie (A)

(Latin *nanus*, dwarf)

Cormous perennial with the stem mostly underground, 3–10 cm high. Leaves ovate to lance-shaped, soft-textured and only weakly pleated, softly hairy. Flowers two-lipped with a funnel-shaped tube 12–17 mm long, blue or purple with white markings, rose-violet scented, the inner bracts forked at the tips.

Habitat: Sandy coastal flats and dunes.

Babiana sambucina

IRIS FAMILY

Fragrant babiana (E)

(Latin *sambucinus*, pertaining to elderberry, *Sambucus*, the fruits of which were used to produce a blue dye, alluding to the flower colour)

Cormous perennial with the stem mostly underground, 5–15 cm high. Leaves strap- or narrowly lance-shaped, pleated and hairy. Flowers funnel-shaped with a long straight tube, 30–50 mm long, mauve to violet with white and sometimes red markings, fragrant, the inner bracts forked at the tips. **Habitat:** Sandstone slopes and flats in fynbos and renosterveld.

Romulea flava

IRIS FAMILY

Yellow romulea (E), geelfroetang (A)

(Latin *flavus*, pale yellow)

Cormous perennial with a short or long stem, 5–30 cm high, the corm with a fringed U-shaped ridge along the base. Leaves one or two, needle-like with four narrow grooves along their length. Flowers cup-shaped, white or yellow, rarely blue or pinkish with a yellow cup, 15–20 mm diameter, the inner floral bract entirely papery. **Habitat:** Seasonally moist sand and clay in fynbos or renosterveld.

Romulea rosea

IRIS FAMILY

Common romulea (E), froetang (A)

(Latin *roseus*, rose-pink)

Cormous perennial, 5–15 cm high, the corm rounded with curved teeth at the base. Leaves several, needle-like with four narrow longitudinal grooves. Flowers cup-shaped, pink to purple or rarely white with a yellow or white cup and the petals darkly striped on the underside, 10–25 mm diameter, the floral bracts with narrow membranous margins. **Habitat:** Sandy and clay slopes and flats.

Romulea hirsuta

IRIS FAMILY

Pink romulea (E)

(Latin *hirsutus*, hairy, referring to the leaves)

Cormous perennial, 5–20 cm
high, the corm bell-shaped with a circular rim
of fibrils. Leaves several, needle-like with four
narrow or wide longitudinal grooves and sometimes minutely hairy along the ridges. Flowers
cup-shaped, pink to salmon or coppery orange
with a yellow cup marked with dark blotches
on the edges, 20–40 mm diameter, the floral
bracts with membranous margins.
Habitat: Seasonally moist sandy flats and
granite hills.

Romulea tabularis

IRIS FAMILY

Blue romulea (E)

(Latin *tabularis*, pertaining to Table
Mountain, where it was first found)

Cormous perennial, 10–35 cm high, the corm
with a fringed U-shaped ridge along the base.
Leaves several, needle-like with four narrow
longitudinal grooves. Flowers cup-shaped,
white or pale blue with a yellow cup, sometimes fragrant, 15–20 mm diameter, the inner
floral bract more or less membranous.
Habitat: Seasonally waterlogged coastal sands
and limestone flats.
Notes: Often forms extensive colonies, especially between Hopefield and Velddrif.

Sparaxis grandiflora

IRIS FAMILY

Cape buttercup (E)

(Latin *grandiflorus*, large-flowered)

Cormous perennial, 10–25 cm
high, unbranched. Leaves sword-shaped.
Flowers cup-shaped with the stamens and
style arched to one side, white or yellow to
purple, 35–45 mm diameter, floral bracts dry
and crinkly.
Habitat: Stony clay in renosterveld.
Notes: The yellow form occurs in the Olifants
River Valley between Citrusdal and Clanwilliam.

Sparaxis bulbifera
IRIS FAMILY

Common Cape buttercup (E)

(Latin *bulbiferus*, bearing bulbils or, in this instance, cormlets)

Cormous perennial with branched stems bearing axillary cormlets after flowering, 15–45 cm high. Leaves sword-shaped. Flowers cup-shaped with the stamens and style arched to one side, white to cream but often purplish on the underside, 35–40 mm diameter, floral bracts dry and crinkly.

Habitat: Seasonally wet sandy or clay flats.

Sparaxis villosa
IRIS FAMILY

(= *Synnotia villosa*)

Purple bonnet (E)

(Latin *villosus*, with long hairs, a somewhat inappropriate allusion to the deep fringing of the floral bracts)

Cormous perennial, 12–35 cm high. Leaves sword-shaped and often rounded at the tips. Flowers two-lipped, purple and yellow, 20 mm long, floral bracts dry and crinkly

Habitat: Stony clay and granite in renosterveld.

Lapeirousia pyramidalis
IRIS FAMILY

Ballerina cabong (E)

(Latin *pyramidalis*, pyramid-shaped, referring to the young spikes in bud)

Cormous perennial, 5–10 cm high. Leaves narrow and ribbed. Flowers with a slender tube 20–40 mm long, cream or pale bluish and fragrant or dark purplish to magenta and scentless, the floral bracts broad and notched at the tips.

Habitat: Mainly stony shale in renosterveld.

Notes: The purple forms are pollinated by magnificent, long-proboscid flies.

Lapeirousia jacquinii
IRIS FAMILY

Harlequin cabong (E)

(Commemorating eighteenth-century
botanist, Nikolaus van Jacquin)

Cormous perennial, 8–12 cm high. Leaves
narrow and ribbed. Flowers with a slender
tube 30–40 mm long, dark purple with cream
and reddish streaks on the lower petals, the
floral bracts two-keeled below and marked
with white.

Habitat: Mainly sandy soils.

Lapeirousia anceps
IRIS FAMILY

Sandveld cabong (E), cabong (N)

(Latin *anceps*, two-edged, referring to the
two-angled stems)

Cormous perennial, 10–30 cm high. Leaves narrow and ribbed. Flowers in short spikes with a
slender tube 30–80 mm long and narrow petals,
cream to pink with red markings on the lower
petals, the floral bracts small.

Habitat: Deep sands or stony sandstone
slopes in fynbos.

Freesia leichtlinii
IRIS FAMILY

Dune freesia (E), duine freesia (A)

(Named after horticulturist Max Leichtlin)

Cormous perennial, 8–20 cm
high. Leaves sword-shaped, often inclined and
sometimes prostrate. Flowers in a horizontal
spike, broadly funnel-shaped, creamy yellow
with broad yellow markings, sweetly scented,
15–25 mm long.

Habitat: Deep sands and limestone in coastal
fynbos.

Gladiolus watsonius

IRIS FAMILY

(= *Homoglossum watsonium*)

Red afrikaner (E), rooi afrikaner (A)

(Latin *watsonius*, watsonia-like, alluding to
the flowers)

Cormous perennial, 30–50 cm high. Leaves
narrow with heavily thickened margins and
midrib. Flowers long-tubed with nearly equal
tepals, red to orange, 50–60 mm long.
Habitat: Clay and granite slopes in renosterveld.
Notes: Pollinated by sunbirds.

Gladiolus liliaceus

IRIS FAMILY

Large brown afrikaner (E),

groot bruinaandblom (A)

(Latin *liliaceus*, lily-like, alluding to the

flowers)

Cormous perennial, 35–70 cm high. Leaves
narrow with heavily thickened margins and
midrib. Flowers narrowly funnel-shaped,
brown to russet or beige but turning mauve in
the evening and then fragrant, 60–70 mm long,
the bracts long and tapering.
Habitat: Clay slopes, mainly in renosterveld.
Notes: The reversible change in colour of the
flowers is most remarkable.

Gladiolus carneus

IRIS FAMILY

Painted lady (E), wit afrikaner (A)

(Latin *carneus*, flesh-coloured, thus pink)

Cormous perennial, 25–60 cm

high. Leaves sword-shaped. Flowers funnel-
shaped, pink or white, often with dark pink
markings on the lower petals, 50–60 mm long.
Habitat: Damp sandstone slopes.
Notes: A well-loved species in the Cape.

Gladiolus alatus

IRIS FAMILY

Turkey-chick (E), kalkoentjie (A)

(Latin *alatus*, winged, referring to the flanged stems)

Cormous perennial with flanged stems, 8–25 cm high. Leaves sickle-shaped and ribbed. Flowers two-lipped with the upper petal straight, orange marked with yellow to greenish on the lower petals, scented, 40 mm diameter.

Habitat: Mainly sandy flats.

Notes: Similar species, *G. pulcherrimus* and *G. speciosus*, can be distinguished by their flat leaves.

Gladiolus venustus

IRIS FAMILY

Bright bonnet (E)

(Latin *venustus*, beautiful)

Cormous perennial, 20–60 cm high. Leaves narrow and grass-like. Flowers two-lipped with the lower petals pinched in and sharply bent near the base, purple to pink with yellow lower petals, fragrant, 30 mm diameter.

Habitat: Clay and sandstone slopes.

Notes: The bright pink form is found only in the Olifants River Valley.

Gladiolus carinatus

IRIS FAMILY

Blue afrikaner (E), sandpypie (A)

(Latin *carinatus*, keeled, referring to the prominent midrib on the leaves)

Cormous perennial, 30–60 cm high, with the base of the stem purple mottled with white. Leaves narrow and grass-like with a prominent midrib. Flowers two-lipped, blue to violet or yellow, rarely pink, strongly violet-scented, 30 mm diameter.

Habitat: Mainly deep coastal sands.

Notes: Favourite cut flower in earlier years, scenting drawing rooms and parlours.

Gladiolus rogersii

IRIS FAMILY

Riversdale bluebell (E)

(Commemorates the Rev. Moyle Rogers, who first collected the species)

Cormous perennial, 30–60 cm high. Leaves rather leathery and almost needle-like with the margins and midrib thickened. Flowers more or less bell-like, blue to purple with yellow or white markings on the lower petals, usually fragrant, 25–35 mm long.

Habitat: Sandstone and limestone slopes in fynbos.

Gladiolus gracilis

IRIS FAMILY

Blue pipe (E), bloupypie (A)

(Latin *gracilis*, slender, referring to the habit)

Cormous perennial, 30–60 cm high. Leaves narrow with the margins raised into wings that arch together over the leaf surface. Flowers two-lipped, blue to grey, rarely pink or yellow, with dark streaks on the lower petals, fragrant, 25 mm diameter.

Habitat: Mostly clay or granite in renoster-veld.

Notes: Easily recognised by its leaves.

Gladiolus cunonius

IRIS FAMILY

(= *Anomalesia cunonia*)

Cockscomb gladiolus (E), lepelblom (A)

(Commemorating eighteenth-century Dutch botanist, J.C. Cuno)

Cormous perennial, 20–45 cm high, producing runners from the base. Leaves sword-shaped, thin-textured. Flowers tubular with the upper tepal long and spoon-shaped, bright red with small, greenish lower petals, 40 mm long.

Habitat: Coastal sands in scrub and fynbos.

Notes: The odd-shaped flowers are pollinated by sunbirds.

Disa ferruginea
ORCHID FAMILY
Cluster disa (E)
(Latin *ferrugineus*, rusty red)

Slender tuberous perennial to
45 cm high. Leaves dry at flowering, narrow
and clustered at the base. Flowers crowded in
a dense raceme, bright red to orange, deeply
hooded with a slender pointed spur, 15 mm
diameter.
Habitat: Rocky sandstone slopes in fynbos.
Notes: Does not secrete nectar but mimics the
flowers of *Tritoniopsis triticea*, which do,
thereby tricking its butterfly pollinator into
visiting it.

Disa uniflora
ORCHID FAMILY
Red disa (E), rooi disa (A)
(Latin *uniflorus*, one-flowered, although
often with more than a single bloom)

Erect or drooping tuberous perennial to 60 cm
high. Leaves clustered towards the base, narrowly lance-shaped. Flowers one to few in a
loose raceme, carmine red to orange, shallowly
hooded with a short spur, 60–80 mm diameter.
Habitat: Wet cliffs, stream sides and seeps.
Notes: One of the most charismatic of the
Cape plants and an icon for many organisa-
tions. Pollinated by the large brown butterfly,
Aeropetes tulbaghia.

Disa racemosa
ORCHID FAMILY
Fire disa (E)
(Latin *racemosus*, in a raceme)

Slender tuberous perennial to
1 m high. Leaves in a basal cluster, narrowly
lance-shaped. Flowers few in an open raceme,
pale pink with darker veins, shallowly hooded
with a short spur, 20–25 mm diameter.
Habitat: Sandstone seeps and marshes.
Notes: Flowers only after fire.

Disa graminifolia

ORCHID FAMILY

(= *Herschelia graminifolia*)

Blue disa (E)

(Latin *graminifolius*, grass-leaved)

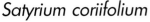

Slender tuberous perennial to 60 cm high.
Leaves dry at flowering, grass-like. Flowers
few in a loose raceme, blue to violet-purple
with the inner petals tipped with green and the
lip dark purple, deeply hooded with a short
club-shaped spur, 20–25 mm diameter.
Habitat: Sandstone slopes in fynbos.

Satyrium coriifolium

ORCHID FAMILY

Orange satyr orchid (E), ewwa trewwa (A)

(Latin *coriifolius*, leathery-leaved)

Stout tuberous perennial to
80 cm high. Leaves two to four, elliptical and
leathery with purple spotting at the base,
spreading. Flowers few to many in a dense
raceme, narrowly hooded with paired spurs,
bright yellow to bright orange, 15 mm
diameter.
Habitat: Moist sandy and clay flats.
Notes: One of the few orchids pollinated by
sunbirds.

Satyrium carneum

ORCHID FAMILY

Waxy satyr orchid (E), rooi trewwa (A)

(Latin *carneus*, flesh-coloured, thus pink)

Stout tuberous perennial to
80 cm high. Leaves two to four with the lowermost more or less spreading on the ground,
thick and fleshy. Flowers in a dense raceme,
broadly hooded with paired spurs, waxy, pale
pink to rose, 20 mm diameter.
Habitat: Coastal flats and low slopes.
Notes: One of the few orchids pollinated by
sunbirds.

Satyrium erectum
ORCHID FAMILY

Pink satyr orchid (E), pienk trewwa (A)

(Latin *erectus*, erect)

Tuberous perennial to 60 cm high. Leaves two, elliptical and spreading on the ground. Flowers in a dense raceme, narrowly hooded with paired spurs, pale to deep pink with darker tinges and spots on the petals, 15 mm diameter.

Habitat: Stony sandstone and clay flats in fynbos and karroid scrub.

Corycium orobanchoides
ORCHID FAMILY

Broomrape orchid (E), bastertrewwa (A)

(Resembling the broomrape, *Orobanche*)

Slender or robust tuberous perennial to 40 cm high. Leaves many, lance-shaped and keeled, banded with purple below. Flowers many in a dense raceme, yellow-green with purple tips, deeply hooded, strongly scented.

Habitat: Sandy coastal flats.

Notes: Pollinated by specialised oil-collecting bees.

Pterygodium catholicum
ORCHID FAMILY

Common bonnet orchid (E), moederkappie (A)

(Latin *catholicus*, alluding to the flowers that recall the wimple of certain Catholic orders)

Slender tuberous perennial to 35 cm high. Leaves two or three, oblong. Flowers few in a loose raceme, yellowish but often flushed with red, shallowly hooded with an upright, triangular lip bearing a small, toothed tip, fragrant, 15–20 mm diameter.

Habitat: Mainly on clay and granite slopes in scrub.

Notes: Pollinated by specialised oil-collecting bees.

Euphorbia caput-medusae

EUPHORBIA FAMILY

Medusa's head (E), vingerpol (A)

(Latin *caput-medusae*, Medusa's head, one of the mythological Gorgons, whose head was covered with snakes and body with scales)

Succulent shrublet, mostly to 40 cm high, with a rosette of sprawling, knobbly branches 10–30 mm in diameter that ooze a milky sap when damaged. Leaves on knobs at the branch tips, narrow and fleshy but withering quickly. Flower heads surrounded by deeply fringed green and white glands resembling petals, 12–20 mm diameter.

Habitat: Sandy flats along the coast and stony slopes.

Euphorbia mauritanica

EUPHORBIA FAMILY

Golden spurge (E), geelmelkbos (A)

(Latin *mauritanicus*, from NW Africa, an incorrect belief)

Much-branched shrub to 2 m with bright green, cylindrical stems that ooze a milky sap when damaged. Leaves opposite, lance-shaped but withering and falling quickly. Flower heads surrounded by glossy yellow lobes resembling petals, 7–15 mm diameter.

Habitat: Sandy coastal flats and stony inland slopes.

Notes: Reputedly poisonous and largely avoided by stock.

Crassula natans

CRASSULA FAMILY

Water crassula (E)

(Latin *natans*, swimming or floating)

Erect or floating annual herb or sometimes a rhizomatous perennial, 2–25 cm high. Leaves opposite, narrow to broadly lance-shaped but the upper floating leaves often broader. Flowers one to three in the upper leaf axils, star-shaped, white or pinkish, 3–5 mm diameter.

Habitat: Moist depressions or pools, often along the margins.

Crassula dichotoma

CRASSULA FAMILY

Orange crassula (E)

(Latin *dichotomous*, branching in pairs, referring to the forked branches)

Annual herb with wiry stems to 20 cm high. Leaves opposite, narrow to lance-shaped. Flowers in a more or less flat-topped cluster, cup-shaped, yellow to orange and often marked with red in the throat, 8–12 mm diameter.

Habitat: Sandy and gravelly flats, often in damp places.

Crassula coccinea

CRASSULA FAMILY

Scarlet crassula (E), rooi crassula (A)

(Latin *coccineus*, deep red)

Succulent perennial with erect branches to 40 cm high. Leaves opposite, broadly lance-shaped to rounded with the margins usually lined with fine, recurved hairs. Flowers in flat-topped clusters, tubular, usually scarlet, 30–45 mm long.

Habitat: Sandstone outcrops.

Notes: Pollinated by the large brown butterfly, *Aeropetes tulbaghia*. Easily seen on Table Mountain.

Crassula rupestris

CRASSULA FAMILY

Concertina plant (E), sosaties (A)

(Latin *rupestris*, rock-dwelling)

Well-branched succulent shrublet to 50 cm high. Leaves opposite, grey-ish and rounded to lance-shaped with horny, red or yellowish margins. Flowers in rounded, stalked clusters, tubular, whitish tinged pink, 5 mm diameter.

Habitat: Dry stony slopes.

Notes: Common around Montagu.

Tylecodon paniculatus

CRASSULA FAMILY

Common butterbush (E), botterboom (A)
(Latin *paniculatus*, bearing the flowers in a
branched raceme or panicle)

Succulent shrublet to 1,5 m high, with stout,
fibrous and fleshy stems covered with yellowish, flaking bark. Leaves deciduous and usually
withered at flowering, broadly rounded and
fleshy, bright green. Flowers in reddish panicles, nodding and shortly tubular, greenish to
orange or red, 20–25 mm long.
Habitat: Dry rocky slopes in scrub.
Notes: Seldom grazed by stock but sometimes
eaten in summer, resulting in cramping and
even death.

Tylecodon cacalioides

CRASSULA FAMILY

Sulphur butterbush, karkay cotyledon (E),
nenta (A)
(Resembling sea rocket, *Cakile*, in its fleshy
leaves)

Succulent shrublet with warty stems to 1 m
high. Leaves dry at flowering and deciduous,
narrowly paddle-shaped, fleshy. Flowers
tubular, sulphur yellow, 17–25 mm long.
Habitat: Rocky sandstone slopes and flats.

Cotyledon orbiculata

CRASSULA FAMILY

Dog's ears (E), plakkie, hondeoor (A)
(Latin *orbiculatus*, circular, referring to the
rounded leaves)

Brittle perennial shrublet to 1 m high, more or
less covered with a powdery white bloom.
Leaves opposite, succulent and very varied in
shape from flat and rounded to almost finger-
like, grey with a red or pale margin. Flowers
pendulous, tubular with recurved lobes, red
or orange, 25–30 mm long.
Habitat: Widespread in coastal and inland
scrub on sandy or stony soils.
Notes: Flower stalks used by early hunters as
a flute to mimic the call of a young klipspringer, luring the adults within arrow range.

Tetragonia namaquensis
MESEMB FAMILY

Namaqua dewbush (E), kinkelbossie (A)

(Latin *namaquensis*, from Namaqualand)

Sprawling perennial with sub-erect branches to 30 cm high. Leaves oblong and fleshy with the margins lightly rolled under. Flowers in clusters on short stalks, yellow, 6–8 mm diameter. Fruit with four soft wings.

Habitat: Stony shale soils.

Tetragonia herbacea
MESEMB FAMILY

Golden dewbush (E)

(Latin *herbaceus*, green and juicy, not woody or dry)

Tuberous perennial with sprawling stems to 50 cm high. Leaves oblong and fleshy. Flowers in clusters on long stalks arising from the same point or solitary in the upper leaf axils, bright yellow, 10 mm diameter. Fruit pear-shaped and smooth but ridged when dry.

Habitat: Mostly clay and granite slopes.

Tetragonia rosea
MESEMB FAMILY

Magenta dewbush (E)

(Latin *roseus*, reddish pink)

Sprawling perennial to 60 cm high. Leaves paddle- or diamond-shaped, fleshy. Flowers in small clusters, magenta, 10–15 mm diameter. Fruits four-winged with knobs between the wings.

Habitat: Sandstone slopes.

Notes: The vivid magenta flowers are a striking sight between Citrusdal and Clanwilliam.

Drosanthemum hispidum
MESEMB FAMILY

Roadside dewflower (E), douvygie (A)

(Latin *hispidus*, bristly, referring to the stems)

Erect or spreading shrublet to 60 cm high with red branches often covered with short, stiff hairs. Leaves sausage-shaped and covered with small bladder cells. Flowers solitary, magenta, 15 mm diameter. Fruits with five segments. **Habitat:** Pioneer of disturbed, dry flats and lower slopes.

Drosanthemum speciosum
MESEMB FAMILY

Scarlet dewflower (E), rooi douvygie (A)

(Latin *speciosus*, showy)

Twiggy shrublets to 60 cm high with short, stiff hairs on the branches. Leaves sausage-shaped and covered with small bladder cells. Flowers in small clusters, orange to red with whitish centre fringed with small black petals, 30–40 mm diameter. Fruits with five segments. **Habitat:** Dry shale hillsides in succulent scrub. **Notes:** Locally common between Robertson and Montagu. Usually in colonies and spectacular when in flower.

Erepsia anceps
MESEMB FAMILY

Breede River erepsia (E)

(Latin *anceps*, two-edged, referring to the angled leaves)

Slender, erect succulent shrublet to 30 cm high. Leaves slender and less than 5 mm diameter. Flowers in open clusters, pink or magenta with the central thread-like petals bright yellow, remaining open in overcast weather, 15 mm diameter. Fruits with five segments, 4–8 mm diameter. **Habitat:** Sandstone slopes and flats. **Notes:** Common in the Breede River Valley near Worcester.

Ruschia tumidula
MESEMB FAMILY
Brilliant ruschia (E)
(Latin *tumidulus*, highly swollen, referring to the succulent leaves)

Rounded succulent shrublet to 40 cm high, with reddish branches. Leaves fleshy and more or less cylindrical and slightly rough. Flowers in large clusters, with a central cone, white or pale to deep pink, 15 mm diameter. Fruits with five segments.
Habitat: Deep, mostly coastal sands.
Notes: Common near Bloubergstrand.

Ruschia tecta
MESEMB FAMILY
Sandveld ruschia (E)
(Latin *tectus*, covered or concealed, referring to the conical tuft of staminodes in the centre of the flower that conceals its inner parts)

Erect succulent shrublet to 1 m high. Leaves fleshy and arching with the leaf pairs united below into a swollen sheath. Flowers in dense, rounded clusters, with a central cone, purplish with a white centre, 15 mm diameter. Fruits with five segments.
Habitat: Sandy coastal flats.

Ruschia caroli
MESEMB FAMILY
Olifants River ruschia (E)
(Named for Dr Charles Juritz of Cape Town, who collected and grew the species)

Rounded succculent shrub to 1 m, with spreading, grey to reddish branches. Leaves succulent and three-angled with green dots. Flowers in clusters, magenta, with a central cone, 15 mm diameter. Fruit five-segmented.
Habitat: Stony slopes.
Notes: Common in dry fynbos in the Olifants River Valley, flowering in late spring.

Gibbaeum pubescens

MESEMB FAMILY

Visbekvygie (A)

(Latin *pubescens*, shortly hairy)

Succulent perennial forming
compact cushions. Leaves in pairs and covered
with white or silvery velvety hairs, unequal in
size with a larger, somewhat cylindrical one
3 cm long and a smaller one about one-third as
long. Flowers solitary, pale to deep purple, to
15 mm diameter. Fruits with six segments.
Habitat: White quartz flats.
Notes: Eaten by ostriches in times of drought.

Lampranthus bicolor

MESEMB FAMILY

Bi-coloured lampranthus (E), bont vygie (A)

(Latin *bicolor*, two-coloured)

Stiffly branched shrublet to
30 cm high. Leaves more or less cylindrical or
weakly three-angled and green with a rough
surface, 12–25 mm long. Flowers solitary or up
to three in loose clusters, yellow with scarlet
or copper on the reverse of the petals, 30 mm
diameter.
Habitat: Sandy flats or slopes.
Notes: Readily seen at Silvermine.

Lampranthus aurantiacus

MESEMB FAMILY

Orange lampranthus (E), rooi vygie (A)

(Latin *aurantiacus*, orange)

Sparsely branched shrublet to
45 cm high. Leaves three-angled with a blunt
tip and greyish bloom, 20–30 mm long. Flowers
solitary on slender stalks, orange, 40–50 mm
diameter.
Habitat: Sandy flats.
Notes: Relatively common near Langebaan.

Lampranthus amoenus
MESEMB FAMILY
Showy lampranthus (E)
(Latin *amoenus,* beautiful)
Succulent shrublet to 40 cm
high. Leaves slightly spreading, cylindrical to
three-angled with a short pointed tip, to 40 mm
long. Flowers in clusters of three, magenta,
30 mm diameter. Fruits with five segments.
Habitat: Sandy flats.
Notes: Common along the West Coast.

Lampranthus watermeyeri
MESEMB FAMILY
Watermeyer's lampranthus
(Named after local resident E.B. Watermeyer
who first collected the species)
Rounded succulent shrublet to 30 cm high.
Leaves incurved and ± cylindrical,
20–35 x 6 mm. Flowers mostly solitary on long
stalks, white or purple, 50–70 mm diameter.
Fruits with five segments.
Habitat: Sandstone slopes in scrub.
Notes: Conspicuous along the road near
Clanwilliam.

Oscularia deltoides
MESEMB FAMILY
Tooth-leaved rock vygie (E)
(Latin *deltoideus,* triangular, referring to
the leaves)
Sprawling or rounded shrublet to 20 cm high,
with shining reddish branches. Leaves with a
greyish bloom, succulent and three-sided with
teeth on the angles. Flowers in dense clusters,
glistening pink, 15 mm diameter.
Habitat: Sandstone rocks.
Notes: Easily seen in Bain's Kloof.

Carpobrotus acinaciformis

MESEMB FAMILY

Dune sourfig (E)

(Latin *acinaciformis*, shaped like an acinacis, a short Persian sabre, referring to the leaves)

Succulent perennial with trailing stems. Leaves sickle-shaped and three-sided. Flowers brilliant purple, the base oblong or rounded and not tapering gradually into the pedicel, 60–70 mm diameter. Fruit fleshy.

Habitat: Coastal sands and granite outcrops.
Notes: Conspicuous on granite outcrops at Langebaan and Saldanha.

Carpobrotus edulis

MESEMB FAMILY

Hottentot sourfig (E), suurvy (A), gaukum (N)

(Latin *edulis*, edible, referring to the fruit)

Succulent perennial with trailing branches. Leaves straight or slightly curved and three-sided. Flowers yellow but fading to pink with age, the base top-shaped and tapering into the pedicel. Fruit fleshy.

Habitat: Coastal and inland slopes, often roadsides.
Notes: Leaf juice used as an antiseptic. Fruits used in jams and curries.

Conicosia pugioniformis

MESEMB FAMILY

Goslings (E), gansies (A)

(Latin *pugioniformis*, dagger-shaped, referring to the leaves)

Tufted succulent perennial to 40 cm high with a thick taproot. Leaves fleshy, slender and three-sided. Flowers solitary, yellow, 50–60 mm diameter. Fruits cone-shaped with 10–25 flaps, opening when dry.

Habitat: Sandy flats, mostly coastal.
Notes: One of very few mesembs with fruits that open when dry rather than when wet.

Jordaaniella dubia

MESEMB FAMILY

Mat vygie (E)

(Latin *dubius,* doubtful)

Mat-forming succulent with long trailing stems. Leaves slender and cylindrical. Flowers usually yellow, 30 mm diameter. Fruit with 10 to 15 segments.

Habitat: Coastal sands.

Notes: Conspicuous along the coast between Cape Town and Langebaan.

Dorotheanthus bellidiformis

MESEMB FAMILY

Common bokbaaivygie (E), bokbaaivygie (A)

(Resembling the daisy, *Bellis,* in its flowers)

Tufted annual herb to 10 cm high. Leaves mostly in a basal tuft, oblong to spatula-shaped and covered with small bladder cells. Flowers on slender stalks, red, yellow, salmon or white, 30–40 mm diameter. Fruit with five segments.

Habitat: Mostly on sandy coastal flats.

Notes: Widely cultivated as an ornamental, available in many colours.

Coleonema album

CITRUS FAMILY

White confetti bush (E)

(Latin *albus,* white)

Shrub to 2 m high, usually compact and densely leafy. Leaves needle-like and sweet-smelling when crushed. Flowers crowded at the branch tips, white, 8 mm diameter.

Habitat: Coastal sandstone or granite outcrops.

Notes: Readily seen in the Cape of Good Hope Nature Reserve.

Agathosma capensis
CITRUS FAMILY
Cape buchu (E)
(Latin *capensis,* from the Cape)
Multi-stemmed shrub to 90 cm
high. Leaves needle-like to narrowly elliptical,
sweetly spice-scented when crushed. Flowers
in loose clusters, white or pink to purple,
8 mm diameter.
Habitat: Slopes and flats on shale, granite or
coastal sands.

Agathosma thymifolia
CITRUS FAMILY
Thyme-leaved buchu (E)
(Latin *thymifolia,* thyme-leaved)
Single-stemmed, rounded shrub
to over 1 m high, branching near ground level.
Leaves narrowly elliptical and mildly aromatic
when crushed. Flowers in loose clusters at the
branch tips, pink or mauve, 8 mm diameter.
Habitat: Coastal sand and dunes on lime-
stone.
Notes: Locally common near Langebaan.

Adenandra uniflora
CITRUS FAMILY
Chinaflower (E), porseleinblom (A)
(Latin *uniflorus,* solitary-flowered)
Sparsely branched shrublet to
50 cm high. Leaves oblong to lance-shaped
with the margins rolled under, aromatic when
crushed. Flowers usually solitary and almost
stalkless, glistening white to pink, 15 mm
diameter.
Habitat: Sandstone slopes in fynbos.

Silene bellidioides

CARNATION FAMILY

Cape campion (E)

(Resembling the daisy *Bellis* in its flowers, an inappropriate comparison)

Erect perennial to 60 cm high, covered with minute glandular hairs. Leaves oblong. Flowers in loose clusters, white or pink to crimson with two-lobed petals, 20 mm diameter.
Habitat: Sandy flats and slopes.
Notes: Similar to *Silene undulata* but calyx *c.*20 mm long vs 25–30 mm long. The flowers open in the evening and are pollinated by moths.

Drosera cistiflora

SUNDEW FAMILY

Rose-flowered sundew (E), snotrosie (A)

(Latin *cistiflora*, resembling the rockrose, *Cistus*, in its flowers)

Slender perennial to 40 cm high, covered with long, sticky hairs. Leaves of two kinds or uniform, the upper scattered along the stem and narrow. Flowers large, few in a more or less flat-topped cluster, mostly mauve to purple or white but sometimes yellow or red and often with a darker centre, 25–35 mm diameter.
Habitat: Seasonally wet sandy flats.
Notes: Carnivorous, trapping and digesting insects with its sticky hairs.

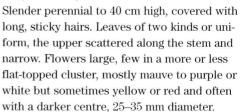

Grielum grandiflorum

DUIKER-ROOT FAMILY

Green-eyed duiker-root (E), platdoring (A)

(Latin *grandiflorus*, large-flowered)

Sprawling white-woolly perennial forming mats. Leaves deeply divided into narrow to thread-like segments, each with a small pointed tip and covered with silvery hairs. Flowers glossy yellow, usually greenish in the centre, 35–50 mm diameter.
Habitat: Sandy and stony coastal flats.

Oxalis pes-caprae

OXALIS FAMILY

Common sorrel (E), suring (A)

(Latin *pes-caprae*, goat's foot, alluding to the leaflet shape)

Stemless or stalked cormous perennial to 25 cm high. Leaves usually all at the base, divided into three wedge- to heart-shaped leaflets that are notched at the tips and hairy beneath. Flowers 3 to 20 per stalk, yellow, 15 mm diameter.

Habitat: Widespread on sandy and clay soils.

Notes: Leaves have a pleasantly sour taste.

Oxalis luteola

OXALIS FAMILY

Golden sorrel (E)

(Latin *luteolus*, yellowish)

Dwarf tufted cormous perennial to 10 cm high. Leaves divided into three broadly wedge-shaped to rounded leaflets that are notched at the tips and usually hairy on the margins, often purple beneath. Flowers solitary on slender stalks that bear a pair of minute scales at a joint near the middle, yellow, 15 mm diameter.

Habitat: Mainly sandy flats and lower slopes.

Notes: An early-flowering species.

Oxalis obtusa

OXALIS FAMILY

Yellow-eyed sorrel (E), geeloogsuring (A)

(Latin *obtusus*, blunt, referring to the leaflets)

Tufted cormous perennial to 10 cm high. Leaves divided into three broad, hairy or hairless leaflets that are deeply notched at the tips. Flowers solitary on slender stalks that bear a pair of minute scales at a joint near the middle, pink, brick-red or pale yellow with a yellow eye and usually with reddish veining on the petals, 20 mm diameter.

Habitat: Common and widespread on sandy, gravelly or clay soils, often in the shelter of rocks.

Oxalis purpurea

OXALIS FAMILY

Grand duchess sorrel (E)

(Latin *purpureus*, purple)

Stemless cormous perennial to 5 cm high. Leaves divided into three heart-shaped leaflets that are hairy on the margins and purple beneath but streaked with black when dry. Flowers solitary, pink, purple, yellow or white with a yellow cup, 20–25 mm diameter.

Habitat: Sandy and gravelly flats and lower slopes.

Notes: A showy species cultivated in Europe and North America.

Oxalis versicolor

OXALIS FAMILY

Sugarstick sorrel (E)

(Latin *versicolor*, variously coloured, referring to the contrasting margins of the petals)

Cormous perennial with a partly leafy stem to 20 cm high, sometimes branched. Leaves mostly crowded at the top of the stem, divided into three narrow leaflets that are folded in the midline. Flowers solitary, white with a yellow cup but the petals with broad reddish margins beneath, 15 mm diameter.

Habitat: Clay flats and lower slopes.

Heliophila africana

CABBAGE FAMILY

Common sunflax (E), sporrie (A)

(Latin *africanus*, from Africa)

Almost hairless or hairy annual to 1 m high. Leaves lance-shaped or sometimes toothed above. Flowers blue or mauve, 10 mm diameter. Fruit slender and not beaded.

Habitat: Sandy flats.

Notes: Distinguished from *Heliophila coronopifolia* by its smaller flowers and smooth fruits.

Heliophila coronopifolia

CABBAGE FAMILY

Showy sunflax (E), sporrie (A)

(Latin *coronopifolia*, with leaves like swine-cress, *Coronopus*)

Annual to 60 cm high, with the stem roughly hairy below. Leaves narrow but sometimes lobed. Flowers blue with a white or greenish centre, 15 mm diameter. Fruit slender and beaded, 30–90 mm long.

Habitat: Gravelly and sandy flats and lower slopes.

Notes: A very showy species.

Brachycarpaea juncea

CABBAGE FAMILY

Wild stock (E), bergviool (A)

(Latin *junceus*, rush-like, alluding to the rod-like stems)

Low shrub to 1 m high, with willowy branches. Leaves narrow to oblong. Flowers crowded along the stem, white to pink to purple, 15 mm diameter. Fruit rounded and slightly rough.

Habitat: Rocky slopes in fynbos.

Notes: Flowers especially well after fire.

Anisodontea scabrosa

HIBISCUS FAMILY

Sandrose (E), sandroos (A)

(Latin *scabrosus*, distinctly rough, alluding to the scurfy leaves and stems)

Shrub to 2 m high, with more or less glandular-hairy stems and leaves. Leaves mostly obscurely three-lobed or oblong and toothed. Flowers solitary or few in the leaf axils on slender stalks, pink, 25 mm diameter.

Habitat: Coastal sands and granite outcrops.

Hibiscus aethiopicus
HIBISCUS FAMILY
Cape hibiscus (E)
(Latin *aethiopicus*, from Africa, especially
South Africa)

Roughly hairy shrublet to 30 cm high, with
stems produced from a woody underground
base. Leaves oblong and toothed above with
three to five prominent veins from the base,
nearly hairless above. Flowers cream to
yellow, often with dark centre, 30–40 mm
diameter.
Habitat: Stony sandstone or clay slopes.

Hermannia pinnata
HIBISCUS FAMILY
Magic carpet (E)
(Latin *pinnatus*, divided into narrow
segments like a feather, referring to the
stipules)

Mat-forming, almost hairless shrublet to 15 cm
high with long creeping stems. Leaves often
appearing as if in rings, narrow and sometimes
three-lobed above, with the stipules divided
into two or three narrow lobes. Flowers on
slender stalks, yellow but orange on the
reverse, fragrant, 10 mm diameter.
Habitat: Sandy coastal flats and dunes.
Notes: Common on the West Coast.

Hermannia althaeifolia
HIBISCUS FAMILY
Furry doll's rose (E), poprosie (A)
(Latin *althaeifolius*, with leaves like mallow,
Althaea)

Softly hairy and mealy, grey-green shrublet to
50 cm high, mostly with sprawling branches.
Leaves on long petioles, oblong and toothed
with crinkly margins, subtended by broad,
leafy stipules. Flowers in loose clusters,
yellow, the calyx balloon-like and reddish but
fading to cream, 7 mm diameter.
Habitat: Clay, granite and limestone slopes.

Hermannia scabra

HIBISCUS FAMILY

Gold cups (E), poprosie (A)

(Latin *scabrus*, rough)

Sprawling, roughly hairy
shrublet to 60 cm high. Leaves shortly stalked,
wedge-shaped to narrow and coarsely toothed
above with the terminal tooth curving back.
Flowers in small clusters along elongate,
raceme-like branches, yellow, 7 mm diameter.
Habitat: Mostly sandstone slopes, rarely
granite or limestone.

Hermannia alnifolia

HIBISCUS FAMILY

Golden bells (E), poprosie (A)

(Latin *alnifolius*, with leaves like alder,
Alnus)

Rounded, grey-mealy shrub with hairy
branches to 1 m high. Leaves wedge-shaped to
oblong and toothed above, pale mealy beneath.
Flowers small, in many-flowered, elongate
terminal clusters, yellow, 5 mm diameter.
Habitat: Shale or rocky slopes.

Phylica plumosa

JUJUBE FAMILY

Plumed phylica (E)

(Latin *plumosus*, feathery)

Sparsely branched shrublet to
60 cm high. Leaves narrowly lance-shaped and
rough with the margins rolled under. Flowers
in dense spikes surrounded by feathery bracts
longer than the leaves.
Habitat: Mainly clay and granite soils in
renosterveld.
Notes: *Phylica pubescens* is a showier species
with the flowers in feathery heads 40–50 mm
in diameter.

Zygophyllum foetidum

(= *Zygophyllum meyeri*)

ZYGOPHYLLUM FAMILY

Scrambling twinleaf (E), spekbos (A)

(Latin *foetidus*, stinking)

Sprawling or climbing shrub to 2 m or more high, foetid-smelling when crushed. Leaves somewhat fleshy and divided into two oblique, broad leaflets. Flowers deep yellow with red markings, 20 mm diameter. Fruit roundish when fresh but five-lobed with prominent bony ribs when dry.

Habitat: Slopes, flats and stream banks.

Zygophyllum flexuosum

ZYGOPHYLLUM FAMILY

Coastal twinleaf (E)

(Latin *flexuosus*, zigzag, referring to the stems)

Sprawling shrublet to 70 cm high. Leaves rather succulent and divided into two oblong leaflets. Flowers with the petals curved back, golden yellow with red markings, 15 mm diameter. Fruit rounded.

Habitat: Coastal sands and limestone.

Monsonia speciosa

GERANIUM FAMILY

Cape parasol-flower (E), sambreeltjie (A)

(Latin *speciosus*, showy)

Sprawling perennial with annual stems from a woody base. Leaves rounded to deeply lobed and nearly hairless. Flowers solitary on long, stout stalks, the petals rather creased and toothed at the tips, white to pink but deep pink beneath, 50–60 mm diameter.

Habitat: Clay and granite slopes and flats, mostly in renosterveld.

Geranium incanum

GERANIUM FAMILY

Cape geranium, carpet geranium (E)
(Latin *incanus*, white with age, referring to
the underside of the leaves)

Sprawling perennial with a thickened taproot.
Leaves on long petioles and finely divided into
narrow segments that are nearly hairless or
sparsely hairy above but densely white-hairy
beneath. Flowers one or two on slender stalks,
white to pink or mauve with dark veins,
15–30 mm diameter.

Habitat: Mainly coastal forelands.

Notes: Wonderful garden plant.

Pelargonium scabrum

GERANIUM FAMILY

Sandpaper-leaved stork's bill (E)
(Latin *scabrus*, rough or gritty, referring to
the leaves)

Shrub to 1,2 m high. Leaves firm, deeply lobed
and roughly hairy, lemon-scented when
crushed. Flowers up to six in short clusters,
white to purplish, 15 mm diameter.

Habitat: Rocky sandstone slopes in fynbos.

Pelargonium capitatum

GERANIUM FAMILY

Seaside stork's bill (E), kusmalva (A)
(Latin *capitatus*, with a knob-like head,
referring to the flower head)

Sprawling shrublet to 50 cm high. Leaves
heart-shaped, with lobed, crinkly margins,
softly velvety and aromatic when crushed.
Flowers many in a rounded cluster on stout
stalks, pink and purple, 15–20 mm diameter.

Habitat: Coastal dunes and sandy flats.

Notes: Leaves a source of Oil of Geranium.

Pelargonium cucullatum
GERANIUM FAMILY
Cape mallow (E), wildemalva (A)
(Latin *cucullatus*, hooded, referring to the rather cupped leaves)

Shrub to 2 m high. Leaves stiff, more or less rounded and cupped with toothed margins. Flowers several in loose clusters, pinkish purple, 25 mm diameter.
Habitat: Sandy and granite slopes along coast.
Notes: One of the parents of the regal pelargonium hybrids. Common on the slopes of Lion's Head and Table Mountain.

Pelargonium magenteum
GERANIUM FAMILY
Magenta stork's bill (E)
(Latin *magenteus*, magenta, referring to the flowers)

Rounded, twiggy shrub to 1 m high. Leaves broadly heart-shaped and shallowly lobed, velvety. Flowers several in clusters, magenta with purple marks, 15 mm diameter.
Habitat: Dry sandstone slopes and rock outcrops in arid fynbos.

Pelargonium fulgidum
GERANIUM FAMILY
Scarlet stork's bill (E), rooimalva (A)
(Latin *fulgens*, shining or brightly coloured, referring to the flowers)

Succulent-stemmed shrublet to 40 cm high. Leaves shallowly to deeply lobed and densely silky hairy, often greyish and soft textured. Flowers few in stalked clusters, red, 15 mm diameter.
Habitat: Rocky slopes, often coastal on granite.
Notes: Pollinated by sunbirds.

Pelargonium elongatum
GERANIUM FAMILY
Lesser stork's bill (E)
(Latin *elongatus*, elongate, referring to the long floral tube)

Soft shrublet to 25 cm high. Leaves heart-shaped and toothed, roughly hairy and often with a reddish circular or zonal marking. Flowers few in stalked clusters, creamy white to pale yellow, 15 mm diameter.
Habitat: Rocky slopes.

Pelargonium triste
GERANIUM FAMILY
Clove-scented stork's bill (E), kaneeltjie (A)
(Latin *tristis*, sad or dull-coloured as in mourning garb)

Perennial with a large, woody tuber. Leaves spreading on the ground, finely divided like those of a carrot into narrow, softly hairy lobes. Flowers in radiating clusters on long stalks, pale yellow with more or less extensive dark maroon to black markings, clove-scented at night, 15 mm diameter.
Habitat: Sandy flats and slopes, often coastal.
Notes: One of several species that are alike in their flowers and distinguished by details of the leaves and habitat preferences.

Cysticapnos vesicaria
FUMITORY FAMILY
Crackerpod (E), klappertjie (A)
(Latin *vesicarius*, swollen and bladder-like, referring to the fruits)

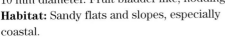

Climbing or trailing annual to 1 m high. Leaves deeply lobed and bearing tendrils, with a greyish bloom. Flowers in short racemes, two-lipped with broadly winged petals, pink, 10 mm diameter. Fruit bladder-like, nodding.
Habitat: Sandy flats and slopes, especially coastal.

Melianthus elongatus

MELIANTHUS FAMILY

(= *Melianthus minor*)

Crested turkeybush (E), kalkoentjiebos (A)

(Latin *elongatus*, elongate, referring to the flower spikes)

Shrub to 2 m high. Leaves divided into toothed leaflets with the margins rolled under, thinly white-felted beneath. Flowers in whorls of two to four in erect racemes among the leaves, with petals that are red in bud but brown at maturity, 20–25 mm long. Fruits with four velvety wings.

Habitat: Sandstone or granite slopes and flats.
Notes: *Melianthus comosus* is very similar but has flat leaflets and solitary flowers arranged in short, pendulous racemes.

Melianthus major

MELIANTHUS FAMILY

Greater turkeybush (E),
kruidjie-roer-my-nie (A)

(Latin *major*, greater)

Foetid-smelling shrub to 2 m high, with sprawling, often dark purplish, branches. Leaves large and with a grey bloom, divided into toothed leaflets. Flowers in whorls of two to four in large racemes on long stems, with petals smaller than the large maroon or greenish sepals, 30–40 mm long. Fruits with four wings.

Habitat: Moist places, often along streams.

Nylandtia spinosa

BUTTERFLY–BUSH FAMILY

Spiny tortoise berry (E), skilpadbessie (A)

(Latin *spinosus*, spiny)

Rounded, thorny shrub to 1 m high, with short lateral branchlets. Leaves oblong, with very short stalks. Flowers solitary in the leaf axils, purplish or pink and white, 6 mm diameter. Fruit reddish and fleshy to yellow and leathery, edible when ripe.

Habitat: Sandy or stony flats and slopes.
Notes: *Nylandtia scoparia* is a much taller shrub with wand-like branches.

Muraltia heisteria

BUTTERFLY-BUSH FAMILY

spiny purple gorse (E), skilpadbos (A)

(Honouring the eighteenth-century German botanist, Lorenz Heister)

Loosely branched shrub with more or less upright stems to 1 m high. Leaves in tufts, stiff and lance-shaped, tapering to a spiny tip, often with finely hairy margins. Flowers crowded in the leaf axils, pinkish purple and white, 5 mm diameter.

Habitat: Rocky slopes, mainly on sandstone.

Polygala ericaefolia

BUTTERFLY-BUSH FAMILY

Heath-leaved butterfly bush (E)

(Latin *ericaefolius*, heath-leaved)

Leafy perennial with slender

stems to 40 cm high. Leaves erect, narrow and channelled, sparsely hairy beneath. Flowers in short, flat-topped racemes, purple, 10 mm diameter.

Habitat: Sandy coastal slopes and flats.

Polygala myrtifolia

BUTTERFLY-BUSH FAMILY

September butterfly bush (E),

septemberbos (A)

(Latin *myrtifolius*, with leaves like myrtle, *Myrtus*)

Sprawling or erect shrub to 2 m high, often velvety on the young parts. Leaves varying from narrow with the margins lightly rolled under to oblong and flat. Flowers in short racemes at the branch tips, purplish, 15 mm diameter.

Habitat: Rocky slopes.

Polygala virgata
BUTTERFLY-BUSH FAMILY
Willowy butterfly bush (E)
(Latin *virgatus*, slender and rod-like)
Slender-stemmed shrub to 2 m
high, with wand-like stems that are only
branched and leafy above. Leaves mostly
narrowly elliptical, sometimes shed before
flowering. Flowers in arching racemes at the
branch tips, purple, 10 mm diameter.
Habitat: Stony slopes, often along forest
margins.

Aspalathus chenopoda
PEA FAMILY
Hiker's horror (E)
(Greek *chenopoda*, goose-foot, alluding
presumably to the three-forked leaves)
Stiff shrub, 1–2 m high. Leaves divided into
three, sharply pointed, needle-like leaflets that
are sparsely and softly hairy. Flowers in head-
like clusters at the branch tips, bright yellow,
the calyx densely woolly and with needle-like
lobes, 8 mm diameter.
Habitat: Stony slopes in mountain fynbos.
Notes: Pioneer colonising recently burned
slopes, sometimes forming impenetrable bush.

Aspalathus cordata
PEA FAMILY
Heart-leaved gorse (E)
(Latin *cordatus*, heart-shaped, of the leaves)
Stiff shrub to 1 m high. Leaves
hard and broadly lance-shaped, more or less
clasping the stem, sharply pointed at the tips
with 11 to 21 veins from the base. Flowers
crowded at the branch tips, bright yellow
fading to bright red, the calyx white-hairy,
10 mm diameter.
Habitat: Stony slopes in mountain fynbos.

Aspalathus capensis

PEA FAMILY

Table Mountain gorse (E)

(Latin *capensis*, from the Cape)

Well-branched shrub, 0,6–2,5 m high. Leaves divided into three sausage-shaped leaflets. Flowers in small clusters at the branch tips or scattered, bright yellow, the calyx fleshy with rounded lobes and mostly hairless, 10 mm diameter.

Habitat: Sandstone slopes in lowland fynbos.

Aspalathus ericifolia

PEA FAMILY

Heather-leaved gorse (E)

(Latin *ericifolius*, with leaves like an *Erica*)

Erect or sprawling shrublet, 20–60 cm high. Leaves divided into three needle-like leaflets that are smooth or hairy. Flowers scattered, pale or bright yellow, the calyx lobes narrow to thread-like, 8 mm diameter.

Habitat: Rocky slopes in fynbos.

Aspalathus cephalotes

PEA FAMILY

Mauve gorse (E)

(Greek *cephalotus*, head-like, referring to the flower spikes)

Greyish shrub, 0,3–2 m high. Leaves divided into cylindrical or slightly flattened leaflets that are thinly hairy. Flowers in a spike or head-like cluster, pale violet or rose to almost white, the calyx silky with needle-like lobes, 8 mm diameter.

Habitat: Stony slope in mountain fynbos.

Indigofera incana
PEA FAMILY

Swartland indigo (E), pienk lewertjie (A)
(Latin *incanus*, frosted, referring to the silvery hairs on the leaves)

Sprawling or prostrate shrublet, 30–60 cm high. Leaves divided into three oblong leaflets that are sparsely hairy above. Flowers in racemes on robust stalks, rose to pink, 10 mm diameter.

Habitat: Renosterveld, often on roadside banks.

Indigofera brachystachya
PEA FAMILY

Powderpuff indigo (E)
(Greek *brachystachyos*, short-spiked, referring to the flower spike)

Dense shrub to 1,5 m high, with thickly greyish hairy stems, mass flowering. Leaves divided into five to seven narrow leaflets that are shortly hairy above and densely grey-hairy beneath with the margins rolled under. Flowers in dense racemes on short or long stalks, mauve to pink, 8 mm diameter. Pods hairy.

Habitat: Coastal sandstone or limestone in fynbos.

Indigofera filifolia
PEA FAMILY

Thread-leaved indigo (E)
(Latin *filifolius*, thread-leaved)

Resprouting, almost leafless shrub with wand-like branches to 3 m high. Leaves mostly on younger plants or new growth, divided into a mix of scale-like and elliptical leaflets that are sparsely hairy beneath. Flowers in racemes on short stalks, white to pink or purple, 10 mm diameter. Pods hairless.

Habitat: Stream sides in fynbos.
Notes: Conspicuous after a burn.

Rafnia angulata

PEA FAMILY

Common widow pea (E)

(Latin *angulatus*, angled, referring to the stems)

Willowy or more or less trailing shrub to 2 m high. Leaves alternate or sometimes opposite on the flowering branches, narrow to more or less diamond-shaped, greyish and leathery. Flowers solitary or up to six in false racemes, yellow but turning black on drying, 10 mm diameter.

Habitat: Stony slopes in fynbos.

Lebeckia plukenetiana

PEA FAMILY

Cat's tail ganna (E)

(Honouring seventeenth-century British botanist, Leonard Plukenet)

Sprawling shrublet with slender stems from a woody base, to 40 cm high. Leaves thread-like and somewhat fleshy. Flowers in cylindrical racemes, yellow, 10 mm diameter.

Habitat: Sandy coastal flats and lower slopes.

Notes: Flowering profusely after a burn.

Lebeckia cytisoides

PEA FAMILY

Bush ganna (E), ganna (A)

(Resembling broom, *Cytisus*)

Silvery shrub or small tree to 2 m high. Leaves divided into three elliptical grey leaflets. Flowers in short racemes, bright yellow, wistaria-scented, 10–15 mm diameter.

Habitat: Stony flats in scrub and fynbos, often along roadsides.

Notes: Distinguished from *Lebeckia sericea* by the smooth, hairless calyx.

Lebeckia sericea

PEA FAMILY

Silver ganna (E), blou fluitjiebos (A), t'aibie (N)

(Latin *sericeus,* covered with silky hairs pressed flat against the surface)

Shrub to 1,5 m high. Leaves divided into three narrow leaflets thinly or more thickly covered with silvery silky hairs. Flowers in dense or open racemes, cream to bright yellow, 10 mm diameter.

Habitat: Gravelly slopes, often along roadsides.

Wiborgia mucronata

PEA FAMILY

Spiny pennypod (E)

(Latin *mucronatus,* abruptly tapered to a point, referring to the leaves)

Erect or spreading, somewhat thorny shrub to 1,5 m high, with smooth, reddish or yellow branches. Leaves greyish and somewhat leathery, divided into three elliptical leaflets. Flowers in slender racemes, pale greenish yellow, 10 mm long. Pods almost circular and flattened with a strongly veined surface and a small wing along the upper edge.

Habitat: Stony soil in fynbos or renosterveld-fynbos scrub.

Xiphotheca fruticosa

PEA FAMILY

(= *Priestleya villosa*)

(Latin *fruticosus,* shrubby)

Silver pea (E), vaalertjie (A)

Slender-stemmed shrub to 2 m high. Leaves elliptical and densely silvery silky. Flowers crowded in head-like clusters nested among the leaves at the branch tips, yellow, 10 mm diameter.

Habitat: Sandstone slopes in fynbos.

Liparia splendens

PEA FAMILY
Mountain dahlia (E)
(Latin *splendens*, brilliant)

Slender-stemmed shrub to 1 m
high, resprouting from a woody base. Leaves
elliptical and leathery, overlapping one
another. Flowers crowded in nodding heads,
orange and red, 40 mm long.
Habitat: Rocky sandstone slopes in fynbos.
Notes: The showy flowers are pollinated by
sunbirds.

Lessertia frutescens

PEA FAMILY
(= *Sutherlandia frutescens*)
Scarlet balloon pea (E), kankerbos,
kalkoentjiebos (A)
(Latin *frutescens*, becoming shrubby)

Erect or sprawling shrublet to 1 m high. Leaves
divided into many small oblong leaflets that
are rounded at the tips, greyish green and
mostly thinly hairy above. Flowers in short
racemes, bright red, 20–40 mm long. Pods large
and balloon-like with smooth papery walls.
Habitat: Widespread on a variety of soils but
usually along roads.
Notes: Very variable in stature and in the size
of its flowers and fruit. Enjoys a high repute
for the treatment of cancer but there is no
evidence in support of this belief.

Dipogon lignosus

PEA FAMILY
Cape sweet pea (E), bosklimop (A)
(Latin *lignosus*, woody, referring to the
stems)

Trailing vine climbing through bush, with
stems that are woody below. Leaves divided
into three diamond-shaped leaflets that are
greyish beneath. Flowers in long-stalked
racemes, magenta or pink, 15 mm diameter.
Habitat: Scrub or coastal forest.

Psoralea pinnata
PEA FAMILY
Fountain bush (E), bloukeurtjie (A)
(Latin *pinnatus*, divided into narrow
segments like a feather, referring to the
leaves)

Willowy tree to 4 m high. Leaves divided into
seven to nine thread-like leaflets that are
dotted with glands. Flowers in dense clusters
at the branch tips, blue, sweetly scented,
10 mm diameter.
Habitat: Mountain fynbos on forest margins
or riverbeds.

Psoralea aphylla
PEA FAMILY
Slender fountain bush (E), fonteinbos (A)
(Latin *aphyllus*, leafless, not actually true
but appearing so)

Willowy or broom-like shrub to 4 m high.
Leaves narrow and very small. Flowers
clustered at the branch tips, blue and white,
10 mm diameter.
Habitat: Stream banks in fynbos.

Psoralea fleta
PEA FAMILY
Blue willow pea (E)
(Latin *fletus*, weeping, alluding to the
willowy habit of the trees)

Willowy tree to 6 m with drooping branches.
Leaves divided into one to three thread-like
leaflets or leafless and with a greyish bloom.
Flowers in slender drooping racemes, blue to
pale mauve, fragrant, 10 mm diameter.
Habitat: Mountain fynbos at 660–1 000 m.
Notes: Perfumes the mountain sides when in
flower. Conspicuous in Bain's Kloof.

Podalyria sericea

PEA FAMILY

Lesser bush sweet pea (E), keurtjie (A)

(Latin *sericeus*, silky, referring to the leaves)

Single-stemmed shrub to 1 m
high. Leaves oblong to rounded and silvery
silky. Flowers in the leaf axils, pink and white
with lance-shaped bracts, 10 mm diameter.
Habitat: Sandstone and granite outcrops near
the coast.

Podalyria calyptrata

PEA FAMILY

Tree sweet pea (E), keurtjie (A)

(Latin *calyptratus*, bearing a cap-like covering, referring to the flower bracts)

Small tree to 5 m high. Leaves elliptical and
silky. Flowers crowded at the branch tips,
bright pink and white with very broad bracts
that are united to form a loose cap over the
bud, 25 mm diameter.
Habitat: Sandstone slopes in damper gullies
in fynbos.
Notes: Very conspicuous when in flower.
Easily seen at Silvermine.

Hypocalyptus sophoroides

PEA FAMILY

Pagoda pea (E)

(Resembling the pagoda tree, *Sophora*)

Shrub or small tree to 6 m high.
Leaves divided into three more or less
triangular leaflets. Flowers crowded into
dense racemes at the branch tips, magenta
with a yellow nectar guide, the calyx smooth
and hairless. Pods narrow and almost
segmented between the seeds.
Habitat: Sandstone slopes along streams in
fynbos.

Cyclopia genistoides
PEA FAMILY

Honeybush tea (E), heuningtee (A)

(Latin *genistoides*, resembling the broom-like genus *Genista*)

Erect, somewhat willowy shrub to 2 m high. Leaves divided into three very narrow leaflets with the margins strongly rolled under. Flowers clustered at the branch tips, yellow, 10 mm diameter.

Habitat: Lowland fynbos, often in moist places.

Notes: The dried leaves are used as a very palatable tea known locally as *heuningtee* or honeybush tea.

Moquiniella rubra
FLOWERING MISTLETOE FAMILY

Matchstickflower (E), vuurhoutjies (A)

(Latin *ruber*, red, referring to the flowers)

Twiggy stem-parasite to 1 m high. Leaves elliptical. Flowers in clusters among the leaves, tubular with five petals and a swelling at the base, mostly orange but red below and with a black tip, 30–35 mm long.

Habitat: A stem-parasite on various trees, including *Acacia* and *Rhus*.

Septulina glauca
FLOWERING MISTLETOE FAMILY

Candles (E), kersies (A)

(Latin *glaucus*, with a greyish bloom)

Twiggy stem-parasite to 50 cm high. Leaves oblong and covered with grey, star-like hairs. Flowers in small clusters among the leaves, tubular with four short petals and a slight swelling at the base, greyish green flushed red, 30–40 mm long.

Habitat: A stem-parasite on various shrubs, often *Lycium*.

Lachnaea grandiflora

DAPHNE FAMILY

Greater mountain carnation (E),
bergangelier (A)

(Latin *grandiflorus*, large-flowered)

Rounded, usually compact shrublet, mostly to
60 cm high. Leaves more or less pressed to the
stems, narrowly oblong to lance-shaped.
Flowers solitary at the branch tips, pink or
white and silky on the outside, 12 mm
diameter.
Habitat: Sandy flats and lower slopes in
fynbos.

Struthiola ciliata

DAPHNE FAMILY

Whip-stemmed featherhead (E),
katstertjie (A)

(Latin *ciliatus*, fringed with hairs, referring
to the leaves)

Wiry shrub to 1,5 m high. Leaves opposite,
lance- or almost needle-shaped with fine hairs
on the margins. Flowers narrowly tubular with
eight small scales in the mouth of the tube,
cream, pink or reddish, scented in the evening,
5 mm diameter.
Habitat: Sandy flats and slopes in fynbos.

Struthiola argentea

DAPHNE FAMILY

Silvery featherhead (E), aandgonna (A)

(Latin *argenteus*, silvery, referring to the
leaves)

Willowy shrub to 2 m high. Leaves opposite
and overlapping, elliptical and leathery with a
silvery sheen and conspicuous white hairs
fringing the margins. Flowers narrowly tubular
with 12 small scales in the mouth of the tube,
yellow or sometimes reddish orange,
5–7 mm diameter.
Habitat: Coastal flats or slopes.

Stilbe ericoides
STILBE FAMILY
Pink stilbe (E)
(Resembling a heath, *Erica*)

Erect or straggling shrublet to
80 cm high. Leaves overlapping, in rings of
four and needle-like with two grooves beneath.
Flowers in cylindrical spikes, pink or mauve,
6 mm diameter.
Habitat: Sandy flats or limestone hills near
the coast.
Notes: The commonest member of this small
endemic Cape family.

Erica cubica
HEATH FAMILY
Lampshade heath (E)
(Latin *cubicus*, cubic, referring to the square
lower half of the flowers)

Erect shrublet to 45 cm high. Leaves needle-
like. Flowers in round clusters at the branch
tips, nodding on slender, hairy stalks, flaring,
pink or reddish, 3–6 mm long.
Habitat: Marshy southern slopes in fynbos.

Erica corifolia
HEATH FAMILY
(Latin *corifolius*, leathery-leaved)
Erect shrublet to 1 m high.
Leaves pressed to the stems,
small and needle-like. Flowers in clusters at
the branch tips, nodding on slender stalks,
flaring, pink but soon turning brown at
the tips.
Habitat: Sandy flats and slopes in fynbos.
Notes: Common in Cape of Good Hope Nature
Reserve.

Erica pulchella

HEATH FAMILY

Pink rattle heath (E)

(Latin *pulchellus,* small and beautiful)

Erect shrublet to 60 cm high.
Leaves needle-like. Flowers in dense, cylin-
drical spikes, urn- to cup-shaped, pink to dark
red, 3–4 mm long.
Habitat: Sandy coastal flats and lower slopes
in fynbos.
Notes: Common in Cape of Good Hope Nature
Reserve.

Erica multumbellifera

HEATH FAMILY

Bead heath (E)

(Latin *multumbelliferus,* bearing many
umbels, referring to the many flower
clusters)

Erect shrublet to 40 cm high. Leaves needle-
like. Flowers in small heads, urn-shaped or
almost bead-like and slightly sticky, purple to
red, musky-scented, 4 mm long.
Habitat: Sandy flats and mountains in fynbos.
Notes: Especially common on the southern
Cape Peninsula.

Erica hirtiflora

HEATH FAMILY

Table Mountain hairy heath (E)

(Latin *hirtiflorus,* hairy-flowered)

Erect, loosely branched
shrublet to 1 m high. Leaves needle-like.
Flowers in loose clusters, egg-shaped and
hairy, mauve-pink, 3–4 mm long.
Habitat: Sandy flats and slopes in fynbos.
Notes: Forms sheets of pink on mountain
sides.

Erica glomiflora
HEATH FAMILY

(Latin *glomiflorus,* with flowers resembling a ball of yarn)

Erect shrublet to 1 m high.
Leaves needle-like. Flowers in dense cylindrical spikes, urn-shaped and slightly sticky, white to deep pink, 6–13 mm long.
Habitat: Sandy flats and slopes in fynbos.

Erica daphniflora
HEATH FAMILY

Daphne-flowered heath (E)

(Latin *daphniflorus,* with flowers resembling those of the genus *Daphne)*

Erect shrublet to 1 m high. Leaves needle-like. Flowers in dense spikes, urn-shaped with flaring petals, white, yellow, pink or red, 6–14 mm long.
Habitat: Sandy flats and slopes in fynbos, often beside water.

Erica sessiliflora
HEATH FAMILY

Bottlebrush heath (E)

(Latin *sessiliflorus,* with sessile or stalkless flowers)

Erect shrub to 2 m high. Leaves needle-like. Flowers in short, dense spikes near the branch tips, tubular, light green, 16–30 mm long, developing into distinctive reddish, nut-like fruits that persist on the older branches.
Habitat: Moist sandstone slopes and seeps in fynbos.
Notes: Unique and highly distinctive in its fruits.

Erica longifolia

HEATH FAMILY

Varicoloured heath (E)

(Latin *longifolius*, long-leaved)

Erect shrublet to 1 m high.
Leaves long and needle-like. Flowers in
spreading clusters at the branch tips, tubular
and usually hairy and slightly sticky, white,
yellow, orange, red, purple, greenish or sometimes bicoloured, 12–22 mm long.
Habitat: Sandy or stony slopes in fynbos.
Notes: Common near Grabouw. Very variable
in flower colour.

Erica abietina

HEATH FAMILY

(= *Erica phylicifolia* and *E. grandiflora*)

Table Mountain red heath (E)

(Resembling a fir tree, *Abies*, in its leaves)

Erect shrublet to 1 m high. Leaves needle-like.
Flowers in spreading clusters at the branch
tips, tubular, bright red to magenta,
10–25 mm long.
Habitat: Rocky sandstone slopes in fynbos.
Notes: This species now includes several
others, such as *Erica grandiflora*.

Erica pinea

HEATH FAMILY

Pine-leaved heath (E)

(Latin *pineus*, pine-like, referring to the
leaves)

Erect shrublet to 1,5 m high. Leaves needle-
like. Flowers in short spikes, tubular and
flaring at the mouth, white or yellow with
white tips, 20–24 mm long.
Habitat: Moist sandstone slopes in fynbos.

Erica curviflora

HEATH FAMILY

Water heath (E), waterbos (A)

(Latin *curviflorus*, with curved flowers)

Erect soft to stout shrub to 1,6 m high. Leaves needle-like, hairy. Flowers in long spikes, tubular and curved, orange, red or yellow, hairy or smooth, 20–30 mm long. **Habitat:** Widespread in damp or wet areas in fynbos.

Erica densifolia

HEATH FAMILY

Harlequin heath (E)

(Latin *densifolius*, densely leafy)

Erect shrub to 1,5 m high. Leaves needle-like, often in tufts. Flowers in short, spreading spikes, curved, tubular and hairy, red with greenish-yellow tips, 24–30 mm long. **Habitat:** Sandstone flats and slopes in fynbos.

Erica discolor

HEATH FAMILY

Bicoloured heath (E)

(Latin *discolorus*, variegated, referring to the two-toned flowers)

Dense resprouting shrublet to 1 m high. Leaves needle-like. Flowers in small clusters at the branch tips, tubular, pink to dark red with pale tips, 18–24 mm long. **Habitat:** Sandy coastal flats and lower slopes in fynbos.

Erica perspicua

HEATH FAMILY

Prince of Wales heath (E), veerheide (A)
(Latin *perspicuus*, transparent, referring to
the translucent flowers)

Erect shrub to 2 m high. Leaves needle-like,
often in clusters. Flowers in elongate spikes,
tubular and hairy, white to pink with white
tips, 10–20 mm long.
Habitat: Marshy lower slopes and coastal flats
in fynbos.
Notes: Common between Hangklip and
Hermanus.

Erica mammosa

HEATH FAMILY

Ninepin heath (E)
(Latin *mammosus*, with breasts, alluding to
the resemblance of the flowers to a cow's
teats)

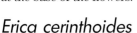

Erect shrub to 1,5 m high. Leaves needle-like.
Flowers in dense clusters, flask-shaped with
four furrows at the base, orange to red or pink,
25 mm long.
Habitat: Sandy flats and rocky slopes in
fynbos.
Notes: Easily recognised by the little furrows
at the base of the flowers.

Erica cerinthoides

HEATH FAMILY

Fire heath (E), rooihaartjie (A)
(Resembling the honeywort, *Cerinthe,* in its
flowers)

Resprouting shrublet, mostly compact but
sometimes with a few slender branches
reaching to 1,2 m high. Leaves needle-like
and glandular-hairy. Flowers in round clusters
at the branch tips, flask-shaped and glandular-
hairy, orange-red, 25–35 mm long.
Habitat: Sandy flats and slopes in fynbos,
especially after fire.

Erica plukenetii

HEATH FAMILY
Coat-hanger heath (E)
(Honouring seventeenth-century British
botanist, Leonard Plukenet)

Erect shrublet to 1,5 m high. Leaves long and
needle-like. Flowers in short spikes, nodding,
flask-shaped with the anthers protruding well
beyond the tube, pink to red or rarely white to
yellowish or green and often with brown or
yellowish tips, 13–18 mm long.
Habitat: Widespread on sandy flats and rocky
slopes in fynbos.

Erica coccinea

HEATH FAMILY
Crimson heath (E)
(Latin *coccineus*, deep red)

Erect, stiffly branched shrub to
1,2 m high. Leaves needle-like, usually in small
clusters. Flowers in short spikes, nodding,
tubular with the anthers protruding well
beyond the tube, yellow, orange or red and
often with brown tips, 6–17 mm long.
Habitat: Common on sandy flats and rocky
slopes in fynbos.
Notes: Distinguished from similar species by
the sepal-like bracts attached to the calyx.

Erica patersonia

HEATH FAMILY
Mealie heath (E), mielieheide (A)
(Honouring the eighteenth-century collector,
Lt William Paterson)

Erect sparsely branched shrublet to 1 m high.
Leaves needle-like. Flowers in dense, cylin-
drical spikes near the branch tips, tubular,
yellow, 14–18 mm long.
Habitat: Marshy coastal flats.
Notes: Common around Betty's Bay.

Saltera sarcocolla

PENAEA FAMILY

Cape fellwort (E), vlieëbos (A)

(Greek *sarco-, colla,* fleshy + glue, referring
to the sticky, leathery bracts)

Sparsely branched shrub to 1,5 m high,
resprouting from a woody base. Leaves more
or less pressed to the stems and overlapping,
rounded and leathery. Flowers crowded in
head-like spikes surrounded by broad, sticky
bracts, glistening pink and waxy in texture,
20 mm diameter.

Habitat: Rocky sandstone slopes.

Notes: Pollinated by sunbirds.

Lycium ferocissimum

POTATO FAMILY

Snake berry (E), slangbessie (A)

(Latin *ferocissimus,* extremely fierce,
referring to the thorns)

Stiffly branched, thorny shrub to 2 m high.
Leaves in tufts on short shoots, leathery and
more or less oblong. Flowers bell-shaped,
white to mauve, 20 mm long. Berries bright
red.

Habitat: Dry stony flats.

Solanum guineense

POTATO FAMILY

Sea nightshade (E)

(Latin *guineense,* from Guinea, a misnomer
due to confusion about the origin of the
species)

Erect or sprawling shrub to 1,5 m high. Leaves
softly leathery and oblong, mostly broader
towards the tips. Flowers one to few among
the leaves, mauve to light blue, 20 mm
diameter. Berries yellow to red.

Habitat: Coastal dunes, slopes and river
banks.

Notes: *Solanum africanum* is similar but has
clusters of flowers and black berries.

Convolvulus capensis
MORNING GLORY FAMILY
Cape bindweed (E)
(Latin *capensis*, from the Cape)
Thinly hairy perennial climber
to 2 m high. Leaves broadly spear-shaped or
lobed and often toothed. Flowers white to
pink, 30 mm diameter.
Habitat: Stony slopes.
Notes: Common along roadsides in the fring-
ing shubbery.

Limonium peregrinum
PLUMBAGO FAMILY
Dune sea pink (E), strandroos,
papierblom (A)
(Latin *peregrinus*, foreign, in relation to the
European species)
Shrub to 1 m high, with the branches leafy at
the tips. Leaves more or less spatula-shaped,
rough and sometimes pitted. Flowers in flat-
topped clusters on long stalks, pink with a
conspicuous papery calyx, 15 mm diameter.
Habitat: Coastal dunes.

Limonium capense
PLUMBAGO FAMILY
Saldanha sea pink (E)
(Latin *capensis*, from the Cape)
Rounded shrublet to 60 cm high.
Leaves elliptical and greyish, rough and
minutely pitted. Flowers in short spikes at the
branch tips, pink with a conspicuous papery
calyx, 10 mm diameter.
Habitat: Coastal limestone flats between
Saldanha and Paternoster.
Notes: Locally common around Saldanha.

Limonium scabrum

PLUMBAGO FAMILY

Creeping sea pink (E)

(Latin *scabrus*, rough, referring to the branches)

Tufted dwarf perennial to 25 cm high. Leaves in a basal tuft, lance-shaped. Flowers in dense, erect or spreading, flat-topped panicles with the lower branchlets often sterile and roughly scurfy, mauve, 5 mm diameter.
Habitat: Coastal dunes and estuaries.

Microloma sagittatum

MILKWEED FAMILY

Firecracker vine (E), melktou (A)

(Latin *sagittatus*, shaped like an arrow-head, referring to the leaves)

Slender climber to 1 m or more high. Leaves opposite, narrow and leathery with a central groove. Flowers in small clusters, cylindrical with the petals twisted together at the tips, pinkish to red with greenish tips, 15 mm long.
Habitat: Stony slopes or sandy flats in scrub.
Notes: Pollinated by sunbirds.

Microloma tenuifolium

MILKWEED FAMILY

Fairy pitcher (E)

(Latin *tenuifolius*, narrow-leaved)

Slender deciduous climber to 1 m high. Leaves opposite, long and narrow, almost thread-like, drooping. Flowers in small clusters, urn-shaped, shiny orange to red, 10 mm long.
Habitat: Stony slopes, usually in renosterveld.
Notes: Pollinated by sunbirds. *Microloma namaquense* from around Springbok is similar but has shorter, erect leaves.

Orbea variegata

MILKWEED FAMILY

Cape carrion flower (E), aasblom (A)
(Latin *variegatus*, variegated, for the
mottled flowers)

Leafless, mat-forming succulent with the stems
bearing conical knobs arranged loosely into
four rows. Flowers leathery and wrinkled,
cream to yellow variously speckled with
purple-brown, with a raised central ring forming a shallow bowl, unpleasantly scented,
50–80 mm diameter.
Habitat: Mainly coastal on north-facing rocks.

Chironia baccifera

GENTIAN FAMILY

Christmas berry (E), aambeibossie (A)
(Latin *bacciferus*, berry-bearing)

Rounded shrublet to 1 m high,
with angular twigs. Leaves opposite, narrow
and spreading. Flowers glossy pink with a
short tube that is pinched above the ovary,
15 mm diameter. Fruit a red, fleshy berry.
Habitat: Sandy or rocky flats and slopes,
often in light bush.
Notes: Traditionally used as a purgative and
blood purifier but potentially toxic.

Chironia linoides

GENTIAN FAMILY

Narrow-leaved centaury (E)
(Resembling flax, *Linum*)

Shrublet to 50 cm high. Leaves
opposite, narrow and erect or spreading.
Flowers pink with a short tube, 15–20 mm
diameter.
Habitat: Sandy or marshy flats and slopes.

Orphium frutescens

GENTIAN FAMILY

Sea rose (E), teringbos (A)

(Latin *frutescens*, becoming shrubby)

Erect shrublet to 80 cm high.
Leaves opposite, oblong and finely hairy with
the margins rolled under. Flowers one or two
at the branch tips and among the upper leaves,
glossy deep pink with twisted anthers that
open through pores, 30 mm diameter.
Habitat: Seasonally waterlogged coastal sands
and pans.
Notes: The flowers are buzzed by carpenter
bees to release the pollen from the tube-like
anthers.

Sebaea exacoides

GENTIAN FAMILY

Painted yellowwort (E), naeltjieblom (A)

(Resembling the Arabian violet, *Exacum*)

Delicate annual herb to 30 cm
high. Leaves opposite, oblong to lance-shaped.
Flowers in a flat-topped cluster, yellow or
cream with orange streaks in the throat,
10–20 mm diameter.
Habitat: Seasonally wet sandy flats and
slopes.
Notes: Easily recognised by the orange
streaks around the throat.

Lobostemon argenteus

FORGET-ME-NOT FAMILY

Blue rocket (E)

(Latin *argenteus*, silvery, referring to the
leaves)

Roughly hairy shrublet to 1 m high. Leaves
lance-shaped with the margins rolled under,
silvery hairy. Flowers in spikes, funnel-shaped
and hairless outside except for the mid-vein
and margins, deep blue, 20 mm long.
Habitat: Shale slopes in renosterveld.
Notes: Easily recognised by the spike-like
inflorescences.

Lobostemon glaucophyllus
FORGET-ME-NOT FAMILY
Smooth-leaved bush bugloss (E)
(Latin *glaucophyllus*, greyish leaved)
Shrublet to 1 m high, with the
young branches hairless. Leaves elliptical and
leathery, smooth apart from some hairs on
the midrib and tip. Flowers in short clusters
at the branch tips, funnel-shaped and hairless
outside, blue or pink, 20 mm long.
Habitat: Sandy flats and slopes.

Lobostemon fruticosus
FORGET-ME-NOT FAMILY
Pyjama bush (E), agtdaegeneesbos (A)
(Latin *fruticosus*, shrubby)
Roughly hairy shrublet to 80 cm
high. Leaves lance-shaped to oblong, roughly
hairy. Flowers in branched clusters, funnel-
shaped and hairy outside, blue or pink,
20 mm long.
Habitat: Sandy or gritty flats.
Notes: Readily seen around Darling.

Wahlenbergia androsacea
BELLFLOWER FAMILY
Lesser bellflower (E), blouklokkie (A)
(Recalling the genus *Androsace* in the
primula family)
Tufted annual herb to 40 cm high. Leaves
mostly in a basal tuft, elliptical and roughly
hairy with wavy margins. Flowers on long
slender stalks, cup-shaped, white to pale blue,
10–15 mm diameter.
Habitat: Sandy flats and lower slopes.
Notes: Similar to *W. annularis*, which has
larger, shallower flowers.

Wahlenbergia capensis
BELLFLOWER FAMILY
Cape bellflower (E)
(Latin *capensis,* from the Cape)

Erect annual herb to 50 cm high
with roughly hairy stems. Leaves sometimes
clustered towards the base, narrowly elliptical
and roughly hairy with wavy or toothed margins. Flowers on long stalks, bowl-shaped,
blue with a darker centre, 10–16 mm diameter.
Habitat: Sandstone slopes and flats.
Notes: The hairy, black centre is distinctive.

Roella incurva
BELLFLOWER FAMILY
White-eyed roella (E)
(Latin *incurvus,* curved inwards, probably
from the leaves)

Shrublet to 40 cm high. Leaves stiff and narrow
and curved inwards with a sharp tip, finely
hairy and often prickly-toothed in the upper
part, often with tufts of smaller leaves in the
axils. Flowers one to three at the branch tips,
white or blue but rarely pink or red and mostly
with dark blotches on the petals, 20–30 mm
diameter, surrounded by long bracts with
prickly margins.
Habitat: Sandy lower slopes.

Monopsis debilis
BELLFLOWER FAMILY
Pansy lobelia (E)
(Latin *debilis,* weak, referring to the
slender stems)

Slender annual herb to 25 cm high. Leaves
small and lance-shaped with lightly toothed
margins. Flowers purple with a darker centre
and rounded petals, 10 mm diameter.
Habitat: Damp, sandy or gravelly places.

Lobelia tomentosa
BELLFLOWER FAMILY

Summer swifts (E)

(Latin *tomentosus*, thickly hairy, referring to the stems)

Shrublet to 40 cm high, with roughly hairy stems branching from a woody base. Leaves narrow with the margins more or less deeply lobed or toothed. Flowers few on long, wiry stalks, dark blue to pinkish, 20 mm long, with the anthers not protruding between the upper petals which are minutely hairy at the tips. **Habitat:** Stony lower slopes.

Lobelia coronopifolia
BELLFLOWER FAMILY

Summer swallows (E)

(Latin *coronopifolia*, with leaves like swine-cress, *Coronopus*)

Tufted shrublet to 30 cm high, with roughly hairy stems branching from a woody base. Leaves narrow with the margins more or less deeply lobed or toothed. Flowers few on long, wiry stalks, dark blue to pinkish, 25–30 mm long, with the anthers protruding between the upper petals which are completely hairless. **Habitat:** Sandstone flats and lower slopes.

Lobelia pinifolia
BELLFLOWER FAMILY

Pine-leaved lobelia (E)

(Latin *pinifolius*, with leaves like the pine, *Pinus*)

Erect shrublet to 50 cm high, with the stems densely leafy in the upper parts. Leaves closely overlapping one another, narrow and stiff. Flowers on short wiry stalks, blue, 10–15 mm long, finely hairy on the outside. **Habitat:** Rocky slopes and flats.

Cyphia volubilis

BELLFLOWER FAMILY

Twining baroe (E), baroe (N)

(Latin *volubilis*, twining)

Twining tuberous perennial to
60 cm high. Leaves narrow to lance-shaped
with the margins toothed or deeply lobed.
Flowers in the axils of the upper leaves, white
to purple, 15–20 mm long, with the stamens
less than half as long as the floral tube.
Habitat: Stony flats and slopes in scrub.
Notes: Tubers eaten by early tribes, with a
sweet but watery taste.

Cyphia bulbosa

BELLFLOWER FAMILY

Larkspur baroe (E), baroe (N)

(Latin *bulbosus*, bulbous, referring to the
root)

Erect tuberous perennial to
30 cm high. Leaves mostly towards the base of
the plant but grading into the floral bracts,
deeply divided with the margins lightly rolled
under, paler beneath. Flowers in racemes,
white to mauve, 20 mm long.
Habitat: Sandy and stony flats and slopes.

Salvia africana-caerulea

MINT FAMILY

Soft blue sage (E), bloublomsalie (A)

(Latin *africanus, caeruleus*, African,
sky-blue)

Grey-hairy shrub to 2 m high. Leaves elliptical
and sometimes toothed. Flowers in whorls in
racemes, mauve to blue or pink with darker
spots, 20 mm long, with a silky calyx.
Habitat: Sandy flats and slopes.
Notes: *Salvia chamelaeagnea*, the rough blue
sage, is similar but the calyx is shortly and
roughly hairy.

Salvia lanceolata
MINT FAMILY

Rusty sage (E)

(Latin *lanceolatus*, lance- or spear-shaped, referring to the leaves)

Aromatic grey shrub to 2 m high. Leaves opposite, elliptical and sometimes obscurely toothed, greyish. Flowers mostly in pairs in short spikes, dull rosy red to greyish blue, 25–35 mm long with the upper lip *c*.17 mm long, the calyx shortly hairy and dotted with glands.
Habitat: Mainly coastal sands and rocky outcrops.

Salvia africana-lutea
MINT FAMILY

Brown sage (E), bruinsalie, strandsalie (A)

(Latin *africanus*, *luteus*, African, golden-yellow)

Aromatic grey shrub to 2 m high. Leaves leathery and broadly elliptical, greyish and sometimes toothed. Flowers mostly in pairs in short spikes, golden brown, 30–35 mm long with the upper lip 25 mm long, with a large greenish or maroon calyx that is shortly hairy.
Habitat: Coastal dunes and lower slopes.
Notes: Leaves can be used to flavour fish dishes.

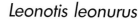

Leonotis leonurus
MINT FAMILY

Wild dagga (E), wildedagga (A)

(Greek *leonurus*, lion-tailed, a fanciful allusion to the inflorescences)

Roughly hairy shrub to 1,5 m high. Leaves narrowly lance-shaped and toothed. Flowers in well-spaced spherical clusters, velvety orange, 40–55 mm long.
Habitat: Forest margins, stony grassland and coastal bush often along roads.
Notes: An important plant in traditional pharmacopoeia. The leaves were smoked as a substitute for tobacco. Decoctions are used externally for skin problems and internally to treat coughs, colds, fever, headaches and high blood pressure.

Plectranthus fruticosus

MINT FAMILY
Common forest sage (E)
(Latin *fruticosus*, shrubby)

Soft shrub to 2 m high, with
purplish branches. Leaves opposite, broadly
elliptical and toothed, more or less hairy and
the underside usually suffused with purple.
Flowers in branched panicles, two-lipped with
a small sac at the base, mauve, blue or pink
with darker speckling, 6–13 mm long.
Habitat: Forests and shaded rocky places.

Ballota africana

MINT FAMILY
Horehound (E), kattekrui (A)
(Latin *africanus*, from Africa)

Aromatic, soft, greyish shrublet
to 1,2 m high. Leaves opposite, softly hairy,
heart-shaped with toothed margins. Flowers in
a dense whorl above each pair of leaves, pink
to purple, two-lipped and 6–8 mm diameter,
calyx densely hairy with 10 to 20 spreading
teeth.
Habitat: Rocky or disturbed places.
Notes: An infusion of the leaves, often mixed
with leaves of salvias, was used by Khoi and
Nama tribes to treat fevers. Brandy tinctures
were used for colds, headaches and other
ailments.

Hyobanche sanguinea

BROOMRAPE FAMILY
Red broomrape (E), katnaels (A)
(Latin *sanguineus*, blood-red)

Fleshy root parasite to 10 cm
high with scale-like leaves. Flowers crimson
red or pink and densely hairy, tubular and
hooded with the stamens hidden in the tube,
30–40 mm long.
Habitat: Sandy slopes and flats, parasitic on
the roots of various shrubs, especially daisies.
Notes: *Hyobanche glabrata* has thinly hairy
flowers with the stamens protruding from
the tube.

215

Diascia capensis

SNAPDRAGON FAMILY

Hook-spur diascia (E), gesiggie (A)

(Latin *capensis*, from the Cape)

Annual herb to 35 cm high.
Leaves mostly basal, narrow, with the margins
lobed or deeply divided. Flowers solitary on
slender pedicels, greyish violet with a dark
magenta and yellow centre, 16 mm diameter,
with a pair of short spurs 2–5,5 mm long and
strongly arching stamens and style.
Habitat: Mainly coastal sandveld.

Diascia longicornis

SNAPDRAGON FAMILY

Long-spurred diascia (E)

(Latin *longicornis*, long-horned, referring to
the two spurs)

Annual herb to 32 cm high, branching from the
base. Leaves mostly basal, narrowly elliptical
and often lobed. Flowers solitary on slender
stalks, reddish or white with a deep magenta
centre and a large and small yellow spot below
each upper lobe, 15 mm diameter, with a pair
of slender spurs 5–18 mm long either turned
upwards or extending downwards.
Habitat: Loamy clay in renosterveld.

Hemimeris racemosa

SNAPDRAGON FAMILY

Common yellowfaces (E),
bobbejaangesiggies (A)

(Latin *racemosus*, with the flowers
in a raceme)

Annual herb, 35–44 cm high, branching from
the base. Leaves opposite, ovate with the
margins toothed or lobed. Flowers on slender
stalks in the upper leaf axils, yellow,
*c.*7,5–13 mm long with two spurs 1,5–3 mm
long.
Habitat: Shaded and moist places, often
among rocks.

Nemesia bicornis

SNAPDRAGON FAMILY

Lilac mist (E)

(Latin *bicornis*, two-horned, referring to the spurs)

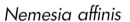

Diffuse annual herb to 80 cm high, branching above. Leaves opposite, narrowly lance-shaped and toothed or lobed. Flowers in branched racemes, pale lilac with grey veins, 10 mm diameter, the upper four petals narrow or oblong and the lower lip with four velvety bumps in the mouth and a swollen spur about 4 mm long.

Habitat: Deep coastal sands.

Nemesia affinis

SNAPDRAGON FAMILY

Sandveld nemesia (E), sandveldleeubekkie (A)

(Latin *affinis*, related to, alluding to its close resemblance to some other species)

Annual herb to 30 cm high. Leaves opposite, lance-shaped and toothed. Flowers in racemes, usually yellow but sometimes white or blue, 15 mm diameter, the upper four petals oblong and the lower lip bulging with two velvety bumps in the mouth and a spur 3–5 mm long.

Habitat: Sandy and granite slopes and flats.

Nemesia strumosa

SNAPDRAGON FAMILY

Nemesia (E), leubekkie (A)

(Latin *strumosus*, with a swelling, referring to the sac-like lower lip)

Annual herb to 40 cm high. Leaves opposite, narrow or lance-shaped and lightly toothed. Flowers clustered in short racemes, white, cream, pink, mauve or red with brown mottling in the throat, 20 mm diameter, the upper four petals rounded and the lower lip sac-like and coarsely hairy in the mouth.

Habitat: Sandy flats, often in sandveld.

Notes: Introduced into cultivation from seed sent to Suttons in 1891 by Hildagonda Duckitt of Darling and now widely grown.

Nemesia cheiranthus

SNAPDRAGON FAMILY

Long-horned nemesia (E),
langoorleeubekkie (A)

(Greek *cheiranthus*, graceful flower)

Slender annual herb to 20 cm high. Leaves opposite, elliptical and lightly toothed. Flowers in loose racemes, two-lipped with the lower lip yellow and the upper lip white with purple at the base, 18–22 mm diameter, the upper four petals narrow and the lower lip bulging and velvety with a short spur 3–5 mm long.
Habitat: Stony sandstone slopes.

Nemesia barbata

SNAPDRAGON FAMILY

Bearded nemesia (E)

(Latin *barbatus*, bearded, alluding to the dark, hairy lower lip of the flowers)

Annual herb to 30 cm high. Leaves opposite, broadly elliptical and toothed. Flowers in short racemes, white to cream with a blue to blackish lower lip, 10–15 mm diameter, the upper four petals small and rounded and the lower lip bulging and velvety with a blunt sac-like spur 2 mm long.
Habitat: Sandy flats and slopes, often after fire.

Polycarena lilacina

SNAPDRAGON FAMILY

Common Cape phlox (E)

(Latin *lilacinus*, lilac)

Well-branched annual herb to 28 cm high. Leaves narrow and often toothed, shortly glandular-hairy. Flowers in flat-topped clusters, white or pale mauve with a yellow patch at the base of the upper lip, 7 mm diameter with a slender tube.
Habitat: Sandy flats near the coast.

Zaluzianskya villosa

SNAPDRAGON FAMILY
Purple drumstick-flower (E)
(Latin *villosus*, shaggy, referring to the
leaves and bracts)

Hairy annual herb to 30 cm high. Leaves more
or less elliptical and hairy. Flowers in crowded
spikes that elongate in fruit, white to mauve
with a yellow or reddish eye and Y-shaped
petals, 10 mm diameter with a slender tube
10–25 mm long.
Habitat: Sandy flats and slopes, often along
the coast.
Notes: Replaced in the north by the less hairy
Z. affinis. In both species the yellow eye in
the flower turns red after pollination.

Manulea corymbosa

SNAPDRAGON FAMILY
Common fingerphlox (E), vingertjies (A)
(Latin *corymbosus*, with flowers in a
rounded cluster)

Glandular-hairy annual herb to 45 cm high.
Leaves crowded at the base, narrow and
toothed. Flowers crowded in round, head-like
racemes on slender stalks with the mouth of
the floral tube circular, creamy white with an
orange centre, 8 mm diameter.
Habitat: Sandy soils near the coast.

Hebenstretia dentata

SNAPDRAGON FAMILY
Common slugwort (E), slakblom (A)
(Latin *dentatus*, toothed, referring to the
leaves)

Erect, sparsely hairy annual herb to 40 cm
high. Leaves narrow and toothed with long
hairs on the margins towards the base.
Flowers in cylindrical spikes, white with
orange marks, 5 mm diameter, with a slit along
the lower side.
Habitat: Rocky sandstone and granite slopes.

Pseudoselago serrata
SNAPDRAGON FAMILY
(= *Selago dentata*)
Purple powderpuff (E)
(Latin *serratus*, saw-edged, referring to the leaves)

Stout, leafy perennial to 40 cm high, with tapering wings down the stems. Leaves overlapping one another, broad and leathery with the tips curved back and the margins sparsely toothed. Flowers crowded in flat-topped panicles, mauve with an orange patch and a narrow tube, 5 mm diameter.
Habitat: Stony sandstone slopes.

Teedia lucida
SNAPDRAGON FAMILY
Blue lazybush (E), bergsukkelbossie (A)
(Latin *lucidus*, shining)

Sprawling shrublet to 1 m high, often dwarfed. Leaves elliptical and finely toothed with winged petioles. Flowers in clusters in the axils of the upper leaves, mauve, 8 mm diameter. Berries glossy black, 6 mm diameter.
Habitat: Montane, in cracks and crevices among rocks.
Notes: *Teedia pubescens* is very similar but has shortly hairy stems.

Oftia africana
SNAPDRAGON FAMILY
Mountain lazybush (E), sukkelbossie (A)
(Latin *africanus*, from Africa)

Sprawling, roughly hairy shrublet with trailing branches to 1 m high. Leaves elliptical and toothed, stiff and roughly hairy. Flowers in the axils of the upper leaves, white, fragrant, 8 mm diameter.
Habitat: Rocky sandstone and granite slopes.
Notes: *Oftia glabra* from the Little Karoo is completely hairless.

Arctopus monacanthus

CARROT FAMILY

Paperfruit sandholly (E), platdoring (A)
(Greek *monacanthus*, one-spined, referring
to the fruit bracts)

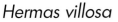

Stemless perennial with a taproot. Leaves
large, broad or almost circular and deeply
lobed or irregularly toothed with bristly
margins. Flowers in tight clusters between
the leaves with the sexes on different plants,
cream to yellow, 5 mm diameter. Fruit
enclosed in large, rounded papery bracts with
a spiny tip.
Habitat: Sandstone and clay slopes and flats.
Notes: *Arctopus echinatus* is very similar but
the fruits are enclosed in small, spiny bracts.

Hermas villosa

CARROT FAMILY

True tinderleaf (E), tontelblaar (A)
(Latin *villosus*, shaggy, referring to the
leaves and bracts)

Single- or few-stemmed shrub to 1 m high.
Leaves stalkless or shortly stalked, oblong to
elliptical with the margins rolled under and
toothed, leathery, hairless above and white-
felted beneath. Flowers crowded in head-like
clusters, cream, 5 mm diameter.
Habitat: Rocky sandstone slopes in fynbos.

Berzelia abrotanoides

BRUNIA FAMILY

Redleg buttonbush (E)
(Resembling wormwood, *Artemisia*
abrotonum, in its small flower heads)

Densely leafy shrub to 1,5 m high, resprouting
from a woody base. Leaves overlapping one
another and needle-like. Flowers crowded in
tight, rounded clusters borne on red, often
swollen and fleshy stalks and aggregated into
flat-topped groups, cream, 5 mm diameter.
Habitat: Rocky sandstone slopes in fynbos.

Berzelia lanuginosa

BRUNIA FAMILY

Common buttonbush (E)

(Latin *lanuginosus*, woolly, referring to the fine hairs often present on the young branchlets)

Finely and densely leafy shrub to 2 m high. Leaves more or less curved upwards and needle-like. Flowers crowded in tight, rounded clusters often grouped together at the branch tips, cream, 5 mm diameter.

Habitat: Damp sandstone slopes, seeps and stream banks in fynbos.

Brunia laevis

BRUNIA FAMILY

Grey snowbush (E)

(Latin *laevis*, smooth, an obscure reference to the leaves, which are actually hairy)

Densely leafy, rounded shrub to 1,5 m high, resprouting from a woody base. Leaves oblong and pressed to the stems, closely overlapping one another and curved inward at the tips, minutely hairy and greyish. Flowers crowded in dense, rounded clusters, cream, 5 mm diameter.

Habitat: Rocky sandstone and limestone slopes in fynbos.

Brunia noduliflora

BRUNIA FAMILY

(= *Brunia nodiflora*)

Common snowbush (E), fonteinbos (A)

(Latin *noduliflorus*, bearing flowers in nodules)

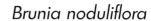

Rounded shrub resembling a cypress, to 1,5 m high, resprouting from a woody base. Leaves almost scale-like, triangular and pressed to the branches. Flowers crowded in dense, rounded clusters loosely grouped together, white, 5 mm diameter.

Habitat: Rocky sandstone slopes in fynbos.

Male

Female

Leucadendron rubrum

PROTEA FAMILY

Spinning top (E), tolletjiesbos (A)

(Latin *ruber*, red, referring to the purplish bracts around the female cones)

Shrub to 2,5 m high, with sexes on separate plants. Leaves elliptical and almost hairless, to 34 mm long on male plants and to 70 mm long on female plants. Male flower heads clustered, ±5 mm diameter, female heads ±20 mm diameter.

Habitat: Sandstone slopes in fynbos.

Male

Female

Leucadendron conicum

PROTEA FAMILY

Garden route conebush (E), vaaltolbos (A)

(Latin *conicus*, conical, referring to the shape of the flower heads)

Shrub or tree to 6 m high, with sexes on separate plants. Leaves narrowly elliptical, 40–50 mm long, those beneath the cones spreading and reddish. Male flower heads ±15 mm diameter, female heads ±12 mm diameter, slightly fruit-scented.

Habitat: Sandstone slopes near streams.

Male

Female

Leucadendron pubescens

PROTEA FAMILY

Grey conebush (E)

(Latin *pubescens*, shortly hairy)

Shrub to 2,5 m high, with sexes on separate plants. Leaves elliptical and hairless or with silvery hairs pressed to the surface, 16–28 mm long on male plants and 25–57 mm long on female plants. Male flower heads 9–18 mm diameter and female heads 10–20 mm diameter, sweetly or yeast-scented.

Habitat: Sandstone slopes in fynbos.

Male

Female

Leucadendron uliginosum

PROTEA FAMILY

Outeniqua conebush (E), silwerbos (A)

(Latin *uliginosus*, growing in marshes)

Single-stemmed shrub to 4 m high but bushy below, with sexes on separate plants. Leaves oblong and almost hairless or covered with silvery silky hairs pressed to the surface, 20–35 mm long but those beneath the cones longer and ivory to pale yellow. Male flower heads ±15 mm diameter and female heads ±12 mm diameter, slightly scented.

Habitat: Sandstone slopes in fynbos.

Notes: Occurs in dense stands.

Male

Female

Leucadendron loranthifolium

PROTEA FAMILY

Green-flowered conebush (E)

(Latin *loranthifolius*, with leaves like a flowering mistletoe, *Loranthus*)

Shrub to 2 m high, with sexes on separate plants. Leaves elliptical and bluish green,

38–70 mm long. Male flower heads 20–40 mm diameter and female heads ±15 mm in diameter, foetid.

Habitat: Sandstone slopes in fynbos.

Male

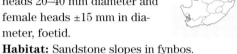

Female

Leucadendron album

PROTEA FAMILY

Silver conebush (E)

(Latin *albus*, white, referring to the silvery appearance)

Shrub to 2 m high, with sexes on separate plants. Leaves narrowly elliptical and covered with silvery hairs pressed to the surface, 28–42 mm long in the male plants and

45–59 mm long in the female plants, but those beneath the cones larger. Male flower heads ±15 mm diameter and female heads ±26 mm diameter, slightly scented.

Habitat: Sandstone slopes in fynbos.

Male

Female

Leucadendron argenteum

PROTEA FAMILY

Silver tree (E), silwerboom (A)

(Latin *argenteus*, silver, referring to the leaves)

Tree to 10 m high, with sexes on separate plants. Leaves lance-shaped, covered with silvery hairs pressed to the surface and with the margins fringed, to 150 mm long. Male flower heads ±50 mm diameter and female heads 40 mm diameter.

Habitat: Granite and clay slopes.

Notes: Almost restricted to the middle slopes of Lion's Head and Devil's Peak.

Male

Female

Leucadendron salignum

PROTEA FAMILY

Sunshine conebush (E)

(Latin *salignus*, willow-like, referring to the slender leaves)

Sprawling or erect shrub to 2 m high resprouting from a woody base, with sexes on separate plants. Leaves narrow, 20–47 mm long on male plants and 48–58 mm long on female plants, the upper leaves on male plants slightly longer and yellow or red and on female plants larger and ivory or red. Male flower heads 10–14 mm diameter and female heads 9–12 mm diameter, sweet or yeast-scented.

Habitat: Sandy and clay slopes and flats.

Male

Female

Leucadendron eucalyptifolium

PROTEA FAMILY

Gum-leaved conebush (E), grootgeelbos (A)

(Latin *eucalyptifolius*, with leaves like a gum tree, *Eucalyptus*)

Shrub or tree to 5 m high, with sexes on separate plants. Leaves narrow and almost hairless, to 105 mm long, with those beneath the cones

longer and yellow. Male flower heads ±16 mm diameter and female heads ±12 mm diameter, fruit-scented, surrounded by conspicuous yellow bracts.

Habitat: Forest margins and open sandstone slopes in fynbos.

Male

Female

Leucadendron xanthoconus

PROTEA FAMILY

Sickle-leaved conebush (E)

(Greek *xanthoconus*, yellow-coned)

Shrub to 2 m high, with sexes on separate plants. Leaves narrowly sickle-shaped and

almost hairless, to 65 mm long with those beneath the cones larger and yellow. Flower heads similar in both sexes, 10–11 mm diameter.

Habitat: Sandstone slopes in fynbos.

Male

Female

Leucadendron meridianum
PROTEA FAMILY
Limestone conebush (E)
(Latin *meridianus*, south, alluding to its distribution near Cape Agulhas)
Densely branched shrub to 2 m high, with sexes on separate plants. Leaves narrowly elliptical and hairless or silky, ±40 mm long but those beneath the cones longer and yellow. Flower heads ±12 m diameter, slightly scented.
Habitat: Limestone flats in fynbos.

Male

Female

Leucadendron microcephalum
PROTEA FAMILY
Oilbract conebush (E)
(Latin *microcephalus*, small-headed, referring to the flower heads or cones)
Shrub to 2 m high, with sexes on separate plants. Leaves oblong, to 90 mm long with those beneath the cones yellow. Male flower heads ±18 mm diameter and female heads ±11 mm diameter, surrounded by conspicuous oily brown bracts.
Habitat: Sandstone slopes in fynbos.

Male

Female

Leucadendron gandogeri

PROTEA FAMILY

Gandoger's conebush (E), berggeelbos (A)

(Honouring French botanist, Michel Gandoger)

Rounded shrub to 1,6 m high, with sexes on separate plants. Leaves elliptical and almost hairless, 42–85 mm long in male plants and 60–105 mm long in female plants but those beneath the cones larger and yellow tinged with red. Male flower heads ±24 mm diameter and female heads ±18 mm diameter, fruit-scented.

Habitat: Rocky sandstone slopes in fynbos.

Male

Female

Leucadendron laureolum

PROTEA FAMILY

Golden conebush (E)

(Latin *laureolus*, laurel-like, referring to the leaves)

Rounded shrub to 2 m high, with sexes on separate plants. Leaves oblong and almost hairless, to 75 mm long on male plants and to 95 mm long on female plants, the upper leaves larger and yellow and hiding the young heads. Male flower heads ±20 mm diameter and female heads ±14 mm diameter, lightly fruit-scented.

Habitat: Sandstone slopes in fynbos.

Male

Female

Leucadendron sessile

PROTEA FAMILY

Western sunbush (E)

(Latin *sessilis*, stalkless, referring to the leaves)

Shrub to 1,5 m high, with sexes on separate plants. Leaves narrowly elliptical, to 64 mm long on male plants and to 80 mm long on female plants with those beneath the cones yellow turning red. Male flower heads ±35 mm diameter and female heads 14–18 mm diameter, lemon-scented. **Habitat:** Granite slopes and flats. **Notes:** Common on Sir Lowry's Pass.

Male

Female

Leucadendron tinctum

PROTEA FAMILY

Toffee-apple (E)

(Latin *tinctus*, dyed, referring to the coloured leaves around the cones)

Rounded shrub to 1,3 m high, with sexes on separate plants. Leaves elliptical with the lower ones curved upwards, to 90 mm long on male plants and to 115 mm long on female plants, with those beneath the cones larger and yellow turning red. Male flower heads ± 35 mm diameter, female heads ±27 mm diameter, spicy scented, surrounded by oily bracts that are bent down at the tips. **Habitat:** Sandstone slopes in fynbos.

Serruria decipiens

PROTEA FAMILY

Sandveld spiderhead (E)

(Latin *decipiens*, deceiving, referring to its
similarity to other species)

Rounded shrub to 1 m high. Leaves finely
divided into thread-like segments, almost hairless. Flower heads in clusters 20–25 mm
across, without surrounding bracts, creamy-
white and fragrant with styles 8–9 mm long.
Habitat: Sandy flats and slopes, mainly
coastal.

Serruria fasciflora

PROTEA FAMILY

Pinleaf spiderhead (E)

(Latin *fasciflorus*, with flowers in clusters)

Sprawling to erect shrublet to
1 m high. Leaves finely divided into thread-like
segments, sparsely hairy. Flower heads in
clusters 15–50 mm across, surrounded by
lance-shaped bracts, silvery pink and sweetly
scented with styles 5–7 mm long.
Habitat: Sandy flats and lower slopes.

Serruria elongata

PROTEA FAMILY

Long-stalked spiderhead (E)

(Latin *elongatus*, elongated, referring to
the flower stalk)

Erect shrub to 1,5 m high. Leaves in whorls,
finely divided into thread-like segments.
Flower heads several on a long stalk, silvery
pink and fragrant with styles 7–11 mm long.
Habitat: Sandy flats and slopes.

Serruria villosa

PROTEA FAMILY

Golden spiderhead (E)

(Latin *villosus*, shaggy, referring to the silky leaves)

Compact rounded shrublet to 80 cm high. Leaves finely divided into silky, thread-like segments. Flower heads solitary and nested among the upper leaves, 20–25 mm diameter, yellow, fragrant, with styles ±10 mm long. **Habitat:** Sandy flats and slopes. **Notes:** Common in the Cape of Good Hope Nature Reserve.

Leucospermum rodolentum

PROTEA FAMILY

Sandveld pincushion (E), beesbos (A)

(Latin *rodolentum*, compound of nibbled and tough, alluding to the leathery leaves that look as though they have been gnawed at the ends)

Erect or spreading shrub to 3 m high. Leaves elliptical to triangular and blunt with three to six teeth at the tips, densely grey-velvety. Flowers in rounded heads 30–35 mm diameter, bright yellow, with the styles 15–25 mm long. **Habitat:** Sandy flats, mainly coastal.

Leucospermum hypophyllocarpodendron

PROTEA FAMILY

Creeping pincushion (E)

(Greek *hypophyllocarpodendron*, fruit-bearing tree growing beneath its leaves)

Sprawling to prostrate shrublet with trailing stems. Leaves all pointing upwards, narrowly elliptical with two to four teeth at the tips, smooth or grey-felted. Flowers in rounded heads 30–40 mm diameter, yellow, with styles 20–26 mm long. **Habitat:** Sandy flats, often coastal.

Leucospermum calligerum
PROTEA FAMILY
Strawberry pincushion (E), pienk
luisiesbos (A)
(Greek *calligerus*, beauty-bearing)

Shrub to 2 m high. Leaves elliptical with one or
rarely two or three teeth at the tips, grey-hairy.
Flowers in round heads 20–35 mm diameter,
cream-coloured fading dull red, with styles
21–25 mm long.
Habitat: Dry sandy or stony slopes.

Leucospermum oleifolium
PROTEA FAMILY
Overberg pincushion (E)
(Latin *oleifolius*, with leaves like an olive
tree, *Olea*)

Rounded shrub to 1 m high. Leaves elliptical
with one to five teeth at the tips, smooth or
hairy. Flowers in flat-topped heads 25–40 mm
diameter, yellow-green fading red, with styles
25–30 mm long.
Habitat: Sandstone slopes in fynbos.

Leucospermum cuneiforme
PROTEA FAMILY
Warty-stemmed pincushion (E),
gewoneluisiesbos (A)
(Latin *cuneiformis*, wedge-shaped,
referring to the leaves)

Many-stemmed shrub to 2 m high, resprouting
from a woody base with the stems warty
below. Leaves more or less wedge-shaped
with three to ten teeth at the tips. Flowers in
rounded heads 50–90 mm diameter, yellow
fading to red, with styles 38–55 mm long.
Habitat: Sandstone slopes and flats in fynbos.

233

Leucospermum conocarpodendron

PROTEA FAMILY

Cripplewood (E), kreupelhout (A)

(Greek *conocarpodendron*, cone-fruited tree)

Rounded shrub or tree to 5 m high, with thickly hairy branches. Leaves wedge-shaped with three to ten teeth at the tips, leathery and sometimes felted. Flowers in rounded heads 70–90 mm diameter, yellow, with styles 45–55 mm long.

Habitat: Dry rocky sandstone slopes in fynbos.

Leucospermum tottum

PROTEA FAMILY

Ribbon pincushion (E)

(Derived from the word Hottentot, alluding to its provenance)

Rounded shrub to 1,3 m high, with spreading branches. Leaves elliptical with one to three teeth at the tips. Flowers in rounded heads 90–150 mm diameter, pink, with styles ±50 mm long.

Habitat: Rocky sandstone slopes in fynbos.

Leucospermum vestitum

PROTEA FAMILY

Cedarberg pincushion (E)

(Latin *vestitus*, clothed, referring to the silky hairs on the flowers)

Rounded shrub to 2,5 m high. Leaves elliptical with two to four teeth at the tips. Flowers in round heads 70–90 mm diameter, orange to scarlet, with curved styles 50–60 mm long.

Habitat: Rocky sandstone slopes in fynbos.

Notes: *Leucospermum cordifolium* from further south has flower heads 100–120 mm diameter.

Male

Female

Aulax pallasia
PROTEA FAMILY

Coppicing featherbush (E)

(Possibly from *palla*, an overmantle held by brooches and worn by Roman women, alluding to the brooch-like female flower heads)

Sparsely branched shrub to 2 m high, coppic-ing from a woody rootstock, with the sexes on different plants. Leaves needle-like. Flowers in racemes crowded into flat-topped clusters, yellow, the female flowers surrounded by feathery branchlets.

Habitat: Sandstone slopes in fynbos.

Male

Female

Aulax umbellata
PROTEA FAMILY

Featherbush (E), kanariebos (A)

(Latin *umbellatus*, like an umbrella, referring to the clustered flower heads)

Single-stemmed shrub to 2,5 m high, with the sexes on different plants. Leaves narrow.

Flowers in racemes crowded into flat-topped clusters, yellow, the female flowers surrounded by feathery branchlets.

Habitat: Sandstone slopes and flats.

Notes: *Aulax cancellata* is similar but has needle-like leaves.

Paranomus sceptrum-gustavianus
PROTEA FAMILY
King Gustave's sceptre (E),
septerpluimbos (A)
(Latin *sceptrum-gustavianum*, an allusion by the Swedish
naturalist Sparrmann to the sceptre of the King of Sweden)
Shrub to 1,8 m high. Leaves of two types, the
lower ones finely divided and the upper ones
spoon- or diamond-shaped. Flowers in small
heads 16–22 mm long, clustered in cylindrical
spikes, cream-coloured and strongly scented.
Habitat: Damp, sandstone mountain slopes
in fynbos.

Mimetes pauciflorus
PROTEA FAMILY
Outeniqua flame (E), vlambos (A)
(Latin *pauciflorus*, few-flowered, referring
to the individual flower heads)
Single-stemmed shrub, 2–4 m high. Leaves
elliptical and held upright, hairy when young.
Flower heads in narrow spikes surrounded by
orange-yellow bracts, cream-coloured with
orange styles tipped with red.
Habitat: Moist sandstone slopes in fynbos.

Mimetes hirtus
PROTEA FAMILY
Marsh pagoda (E), vleistompie (A)
(Latin *hirtus*, hairy, referring to the flowers)
Slender, single-stemmed shrub
to 2 m high. Leaves elliptical and more or less
hairless. Flower heads in spikes among yellow
bracts with red tips, white with red styles.
Habitat: Peaty marshes.
Notes: Good stands can be seen in the Cape of
Good Hope Nature Reserve.

Mimetes cucullatus
PROTEA FAMILY
Red-crested pagoda (E), rooistompie (A)
(Latin *cucullatus*, hooded, referring to the
spoon-shaped inflorescence leaves)

Many-stemmed shrub to 1,4 m high. Leaves
oblong to elliptical with those among the
flowers spoon-shaped and red. Flower heads
in spikes, white with red styles.
Habitat: Sandstone slopes and flats.
Notes: Resprouts rapidly after fire.

Mimetes fimbriifolius
PROTEA FAMILY
Tree pagoda (E), maanhaarstompie (A)
(Latin *fimbriifolius*, fringe-leaved, referring
to the hairy leaf margins)

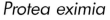

Single-stemmed tree to 4 m high. Leaves
oblong to elliptical with hairy margins, those
among the flowers spoon-shaped and dull red.
Flower heads in spikes, white with yellow
styles tipped with red.
Habitat: Rocky slopes.
Notes: Endemic to the Cape Peninsula. Easily
distinguished by its tree-like growth.

Protea eximia
PROTEA FAMILY
Broad-leaved sugarbush (E)
(Latin *eximius*, distinguished)

Large shrub to 4 m high.
Leaves egg-shaped and lobed at the base.
Flowers in conical heads, 90–120 x 50–80 mm,
surrounded by cream-coloured to red bracts,
the inner ones spoon-shaped, the individual
flowers tipped with black and with styles
±65 mm long.
Habitat: Sandstone slopes in fynbos.

Protea compacta
PROTEA FAMILY

Bot River protea (E)

(Latin *compactus*, pressed together, referring to the dense leaves)

Large shrub to 4 m high. Leaves oblong and lobed at the base. Flowers in conical heads, 90–120 x 50–80 mm, surrounded by cream-coloured to red bracts, the inner ones spoon-shaped, with styles ±65 mm long. **Habitat:** Coastal slopes and flats.

Protea aurea
PROTEA FAMILY

Shuttlecock sugarbush (E)

(Latin *aureus*, golden, an inappropriate reference to the bracts which appear yellowish when dry)

Shrub or tree to 5 m high. Leaves oblong. Flowers in shuttlecock-shaped heads 90–120 mm long, surrounded by silky pink to creamy green bracts, with styles 85–105 mm long.

Habitat: Cool sandstone slopes in fynbos.

Protea nitida
PROTEA FAMILY

Waboom (A)

(Latin *nitidus*, shining, referring to the leaves)

Tree 5–10 m high. Leaves elliptical with a greyish bloom. Flowers in cup-shaped heads 80–160 mm diameter, surrounded by short, silver-grey and sometimes silky bracts, with styles 60–80 mm long.

Habitat: Drier sandstone slopes in fynbos.
Notes: The wood was used for wagon wheels.

Protea glabra

PROTEA FAMILY

Chestnut sugarbush (E)

(Latin *glabrus*, smooth or hairless, referring
to the stems and leaves)

Shrub or tree to 5 m high, coppicing from a
woody rootstock. Leaves elliptical. Flowers
in rounded heads 70–120 mm diameter,
surrounded by short, dull brownish bracts
that are smooth or velvety, with styles
40–50 mm long.

Habitat: Dry sandstone slopes and plateaus in
arid fynbos.

Protea punctata

PROTEA FAMILY

(Latin *punctatus*, marked with dots,
referring to the stomata on the leaves)

Shrub to 4 m high. Leaves
broadly elliptical and almost hairless with a
grey bloom. Flowers in bowl-shaped heads
20–25 mm diameter, surrounded by silky pink
or white bracts with fringed margins, with
styles ±50 mm long.

Habitat: Rocky sandstone slopes in fynbos.

Protea scabra

PROTEA FAMILY

Sandpaper-leaved sugarbush (E)

(Latin *scabrus*, rough)

Mat-forming shrublet with
sprawling stems coppicing from a woody rootstock. Leaves tufted and needle-like to narrow
and channelled with a sandpapery surface.
Flowers in cup-shaped heads
50–80 mm diameter, surrounded by silky
brown and cream-coloured bracts, with styles
30–35 mm long.

Habitat: Sandstone slopes in fynbos.

Protea repens

PROTEA FAMILY

Sugarbush (E), suikerbos (A)

(Latin *repens*, creeping, a misnomer based on an illustration)

Shrub or tree to 4,5 m high. Leaves narrow. Flowers in narrowly conical heads, 100–160 x 70–90 mm, surrounded by sticky cream-coloured to red bracts, with styles 70–90 mm long.

Habitat: Sandstone and clay flats and slopes.

Notes: The copious nectar was commonly collected in the nineteenth century and boiled down to make a syrup known as *bossiestroop*.

Protea cynaroides

PROTEA FAMILY

King protea (E)

(Resembling the globe artichoke, *Cynara*, in its flower heads)

Shrub to 3 m high, coppicing from a woody base. Leaves with long petioles and an elliptical to rounded blade. Flowers in large conical to cup-shaped heads 120–300 mm diameter, surrounded by pale or deep pink and often silky bracts, with styles 80–95 mm long.

Habitat: Moist sandstone slopes in fynbos.

Protea laurifolia

PROTEA FAMILY

Grey-leaved bearded protea (E)

(Latin *laurifolius*, with leaves like a laurel)

Small tree to 8 m high. Leaves narrow and with a greyish bloom. Flowers in oblong heads, 100–130 x 40–60 mm, surrounded by silky, cream-coloured to pink bracts, the inner ones with a dense blackish beard and the outer with brown horny margins, with styles 65–70 mm long.

Habitat: Sandstone slopes in fynbos.

Notes: *Protea neriifolia* is similar but has distinctly green leaves.

Protea speciosa

PROTEA FAMILY
Brown-bearded sugarbush (E)
(Latin *speciosus*, showy)
Shrub to 1,2 m high, coppicing
from a woody base. Leaves elliptical. Flowers
in oblong heads on short, hairy stems,
90–140 x ±70 mm, surrounded by silky,
greenish to pink bracts with a heavy brown or
sometimes white beard, with styles 65–75 mm
long.
Habitat: Sandstone flats and slopes in fynbos.

Scabiosa africana

SCABIOUS FAMILY
Cape scabious (E)
(Latin *africanus*, from Africa)
Straggling shrublet to 1 m high.
Leaves elliptical and toothed or deeply divided,
softly velvety. Flowers in button-shaped heads
on slender stalks, mauve, 5 mm diameter.
Habitat: Sheltered sandstone slopes.
Notes: *Scabiosa columbaria* is a tufted
perennial with hairless leaves and white or
mauve flower heads.

Stoebe alopecuroides

DAISY FAMILY
Cattail snakebush (E), katstertslangbos (A)
(Resembling the fox-tail grass, *Alopecurus*,
in its flower spikes)
Grey shrub to 1 m high. Leaves stiffly needle-
like with the margins rolled in, spreading and
twisted. Flower heads massed in elongate
spikes, without ray florets, white, surrounded
by several series of brown papery bracts.
Habitat: Forest margins and fynbos.

241

Metalasia densa
DAISY FAMILY
Common flowerbush (E), blombos (A)
(Latin *densus*, dense)

Rounded shrub with white-
woolly branches, mostly to 2,5 m high. Leaves
often arching downward, lance-shaped and
stiff with a sharp point, twisted and with the
margins rolled over. Flower heads in flat-
topped clusters at the branch tips, without ray
florets, 5 mm diameter, surrounded by several
series of bracts with the inner petal-like at the
tips and white or sometimes brown.
Habitat: Sandy or stony flats and slopes.

Eriocephalus africanus
DAISY FAMILY
Wild rosemary (E)
(Latin *africanus*, from Africa)

Twiggy shrub to 1 m high.
Leaves in tufts, thread-like or three-forked.
Flower heads in flat-topped clusters at the
branch tips, purple with a few white ray
florets, 8 mm diameter, surrounded by several
series of pointed bracts.
Habitat: Mostly clay or granite slopes.
Notes: Used medicinally for dropsy and
stomach ache.

Eriocephalus racemosus
DAISY FAMILY
Sandveld rosemary (E), kapkoppie (A)
(Latin *racemosus*, bearing flower heads
in a raceme)

Erect, silky shrublet to 1,5 m high. Leaves
cylindrical and often somewhat fleshy. Flower
heads solitary in the leaf axils and forming
long racemes, apparently without ray florets,
3 mm diameter, surrounded by several series
of bracts.
Habitat: Coastal dunes and sandy flats.
Notes: Conspicuous in fruit. The fluffy seeds
are used by many birds to line their nests.

Helichrysum pandurifolium

DAISY FAMILY

Fiddle-leaved strawflower (E)

(Latin *pandurifolius,* with leaves shaped
like a fiddle)

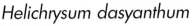

Straggling, grey-woolly shrublet or shrub.
Leaves paddle-shaped and narrowed below
with ear-like expansions at the base and
crinkly margins. Flower heads few to many in
flat-topped clusters at the end of leafless
branches, bell-shaped, cream-coloured without
ray florets, 5 mm diameter, surrounded by
several series of pointed papery bracts.
Habitat: Sandy flats and slopes.

Helichrysum dasyanthum

DAISY FAMILY

Brown-tipped strawflower (E)

(Greek *dasyanthus,* with shaggy flowers,
referring to the woolly bases of the flower
heads)

Straggling shrub to 1,5 m high. Leaves spreading, narrow with the margins often wavy and
lightly rolled under, grey-woolly. Flower heads
crowded in flat-topped clusters, without ray
florets and straw-yellow, 6 mm diameter,
surrounded by several series of papery bracts
with brown tips.
Habitat: Sandy flats and slopes.

Helichrysum retortum

DAISY FAMILY

Sea strawflower (E)

(Latin *retortus,* bent back, referring to the
leaves)

Straggling, closely leafy, silvery shrublet to
50 cm high. Leaves overlapping, spreading or
the upper ones curved back, oblong and folded
with hooked tips, silvery-silky with tissue-
paper-like hairs. Flower heads solitary and
nested in the leaves at the branch tips,
top-shaped and without ray florets, 15 mm
diameter, surrounded by several series of
glossy white papery bracts that are often
flushed with pink and brown.
Habitat: Coastal sands and cliffs.

Edmondia sesamoides
DAISY FAMILY
Common paperflower (E), sewejaartjie (A)
(Resembling sesame, *Sesamum*, an
obscure allusion)

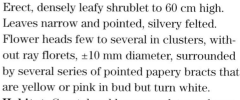

Sparsely branched shrublet to 30 cm high.
Leaves of two kinds, the stem leaves spreading
and narrow with the margins rolled upward
but those on the flower stalks short and
pressed against the stem. Flower heads
solitary on long stalks, yellow and without
ray florets, 20 mm diameter, surrounded by
several series of papery bracts, mostly glistening white to yellow.
Habitat: Sandstone slopes in fynbos.

Syncarpha paniculata
DAISY FAMILY
(= *Helichrysum paniculatum*)
Narrow-leaved everlasting (E),
sewejaartjie (A)
(Latin *paniculatus*, a branched inflorescence)

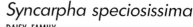

Erect, densely leafy shrublet to 60 cm high.
Leaves narrow and pointed, silvery felted.
Flower heads few to several in clusters, without ray florets, ±10 mm diameter, surrounded
by several series of pointed papery bracts that
are yellow or pink in bud but turn white.
Habitat: Coastal and lower sandstone slopes
in fynbos.

Syncarpha speciosissima
DAISY FAMILY
(= *Helipterum speciosissimus*)
Cape everlasting (E)
(Latin *speciosissimus*, most showy)
Sprawling shrublet with erect annual stems,
20–60 cm high. Leaves narrow or oblong and
clasping the stem at the base, white-woolly.
Flower heads large, solitary on long stalks,
cream without ray florets, 30–40 mm diameter,
surrounded by several series of white to
cream, sharply pointed papery bracts.
Habitat: Sandstone slopes in fynbos.

Syncarpha vestita

DAISY FAMILY

(= *Helichrysum vestitum*)

Cape snow (E)

(Latin *vestitus*, clothed, referring to the woolly hairs on the leaves)

Densely leafy shrublet to 1 m high. Leaves slightly broader at the tips and grey-woolly. Flower heads large, few to several in loose clusters nested in the leaves, white without ray florets, 35–40 mm diameter, surrounded by several series of pointed, white papery bracts. **Habitat:** Sandstone slopes and flats in fynbos. **Notes:** Common in the Cape of Good Hope Nature Reserve.

Syncarpha eximia

DAISY FAMILY

(= *Helipterum eximium*)

Strawberry everlasting (E)

(Latin *eximius*, distinguished)

Mostly single-stemmed, robust, closely leafy shrub to 40 cm high. Leaves elliptical and overlapping one another, silvery felted. Flower heads large and crowded in dense, flat-topped clusters nested in the leaves, without ray florets, 20–25 mm diameter, surrounded by several series of blunt, bright red papery bracts. **Habitat:** Cool sandstone slopes in fynbos.

Syncarpha canescens

DAISY FAMILY

(= *Helipterum canescens*)

Pink everlasting (E), pienksewejaartjie (A)

(Latin *canescens*, greyish)

Sparsely branched, closely leafy shrublet to 50 cm high. Leaves small and overlapping, elliptical and grey-felted. Flower heads mostly solitary at the branch tips, without ray florets, conical and 25–35 mm diameter, surrounded by several series of pointed papery bracts that are pink to red. **Habitat:** Rocky sandstone slopes in fynbos.

Phaenocoma prolifera

DAISY FAMILY

Red everlasting (E)

(Latin *prolifer*, producing offsets, referring
to the many short branchlets)

Stiffly branched, white-stemmed shrublet to
60 cm high with short branchlets. Leaves
minute and overlapping. Flower heads large
and solitary without ray florets, 30–40 mm
diameter, surrounded by several series of
sharp papery bracts that are pink shading
to red.

Habitat: Sandstone slopes in fynbos.

Leysera gnaphalodes

DAISY FAMILY

Shrubby wireweed (E), skilpadteebossie (A)

(Resembling the genus *Gnaphalium*)

Slender shrublet to 40 cm high,
branching from the base. Leaves grey and
hairy, narrow and thread-like. Flower heads
loosely clustered at the ends of the branches
on wiry stalks, yellow with yellow rays,
15–18 mm diameter, surrounded by several
series of stiff bracts that are papery at the tips.

Habitat: Sandy flats.

Notes: *Leysera tenella* (page 326) is similar
but is an annual herb to 20 cm high and the
bristles on the seeds are feathery only in the
upper part.

Pteronia divaricata

DAISY FAMILY

Round-leaved gumbush (E), geelgombos (A)

(Latin *divaricatus*, spreading widely,
referring to the branches)

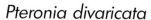

Rounded leafy shrub to 2 m high. Leaves
broadly elliptical, shortly and often roughly
hairy. Flower heads in dense, flat-topped clusters, without ray florets, yellow or whitish,
5 mm diameter, surrounded by several series
of narrow green bracts.

Habitat: Sandy and stony slopes and flats.

Athanasia trifurcata

DAISY FAMILY
common klaaslouw bush (E), kouterbos (A)
(Latin *trifurcatus*, three-forked, referring to
the leaves)

Hairless or grey-velvety shrub to 1,5 m high.
Leaves triangular with three to five teeth at the
tips. Flower heads in flat-topped clusters,
without ray florets, yellow, 6 mm diameter,
surrounded by several series of blunt bracts.
Habitat: Flats and rocky slopes.
Notes: Common along roads and in fallow
lands.

Cotula turbinata

DAISY FAMILY
Common button daisy (E), ganskos (A)
(Latin *turbinatus*, top-shaped, referring to
the swollen tips of the fruiting stalks)

Softly hairy annual herb 5–30 cm high. Leaves
twice- or thrice-divided into narrow or thread-
like segments. Flower heads solitary on slender,
naked peduncles which are swollen and hollow
above in fruit, yellow or white with short white
ray florets, 5–10 mm diameter, surrounded by
two series of small scale-like bracts.
Habitat: Sandy or disturbed areas.
Notes: *Cotula duckittiae* has larger yellow to
orange flower heads.

Chrysocoma ciliata

DAISY FAMILY
(= *Chrysocoma tenuifolia*)
Bitter cowcud (E), bitterbos (A)
(Latin *ciliatus*, fringed with fine hairs,
referring to the leaves)

Slender-stemmed, closely leafy shrublet to
60 cm high. Leaves narrow or needle-like with
minute stiff hairs on the margins, sub-erect.
Flower heads solitary at the branch tips,
without ray florets, yellow, 6–8 mm diameter,
surrounded by several series of narrow
bracts.
Habitat: Rocky slopes and stony flats.

Chrysocoma coma-aurea
DAISY FAMILY

Golden cowcud (E), beesbos (A)
(Latin *coma*, tuft or crown, *aureus*, golden yellow, referring to the flower heads)

Densely leafy shrublet to 50 cm high. Leaves narrow with minute stiff hairs on the margins, spreading or curved back. Flower heads solitary, without ray florets, yellow, 8–10 mm diameter, surrounded by several series of narrow bracts.

Habitat: Sandstone and granite slopes.

Cullumia squarrosa
DAISY FAMILY

Coastal bush thistle (E), steekhaarbos (A)
(Latin *squarrosus*, rough with scales or bracts spreading sharply outwards)

Sprawling shrublet to 50 cm high, cobwebby on the young parts. Leaves bent down, narrowly lance-shaped and spine-tipped with the margins strongly rolled under and bristly. Flower heads yellow with yellow ray florets, 20 mm diameter, surrounded by several series of sharp bracts but the inner bracts unlike the outer and without spines or bristles.

Habitat: Coastal bush on sandstone.

Oncosiphon suffruticosum
DAISY FAMILY

(= *Pentzia suffruticosa*)
Cluster stinkweed (E), stinkkruid, wurmbossie (A)

(Latin *suffruticosus*, somewhat woody only at the base)

Much-branched annual herb to 50 cm high, highly aromatic when bruised. Leaves twice- or thrice-divided into narrow segments. Flower heads many in dense, flat-topped clusters, without ray florets, yellow, 6 mm diameter, surrounded by several series of narrow bracts with papery margins.

Habitat: Sandy flats and slopes, often coastal.
Notes: Common in disturbed sites, often forming dense stands.

Foveolina tenella

DAISY FAMILY
lazy daisy (E)
(Latin *tenellus,* delicate)

Sprawling, thinly hairy annual
herb to 25 cm high, aromatic when bruised.
Leaves twice-divided into thread-like segments. Flower heads solitary on long naked
stalks, yellow with a few white ray florets that
bend down at night, 15–20 mm diameter,
surrounded by several series of blunt bracts
with papery margins.
Habitat: Sandy flats, mostly coastal.

Cineraria geifolia

DAISY FAMILY
Coastal cineraria (E)
(Latin *geifolius,* with leaves like avens,
Geum)

Roughly hairy perennial to 60 cm high. Leaves
kidney-shaped and lobed and toothed, the
slender petioles with large ear-like lobes at
the base. Flower heads in flat-topped
clusters, yellow with yellow ray florets,
10 mm diameter, surrounded by a single
series of narrow bracts.
Habitat: Mainly coastal bush.

Senecio burchellii

DAISY FAMILY
Poison ragwort (E)
(Honouring the nineteenth-century
naturalist, William Burchell)

Softly woody shrublet to 40 cm high, sometimes roughly hairy below. Leaves narrow with
the margins rolled under and sometimes
toothed, usually with additional tufts of leaves
in the axils. Flower heads in loose, flat-topped
clusters, yellow with yellow ray florets, 10 mm
diameter, surrounded by a single series of
narrow bracts.
Habitat: Sandy and stony slopes.
Notes: One of many *Senecio* species that are
poisonous to stock, especially horses. The dan-
ger is highest in spring when the young plants
are cropped along with grass.

Senecio littoreus
DAISY FAMILY

Coastal ragwort (E), geelhongerblom (A)

(Latin *littoreus*, of the seashore)

Hairless or shortly hairy annual
herb to 40 cm high. Leaves elliptical and
toothed or lobed, sometimes eared at the base.
Flower heads in loose, flat-topped clusters,
yellow with yellow ray florets, 10 mm
diameter, surrounded by a single series of
narrow bracts.

Habitat: Mainly coastal sands, often along
roadsides.

Senecio arenarius
DAISY FAMILY

Lesser purple ragwort (E),
pershongerblom (A)

(Latin *arenarius*, growing in sand)

Glandular-hairy annual herb to 40 cm high.
Leaves toothed to lobed with the margins
sometimes rolled under. Flower heads several
in branching, flat-topped clusters, yellow with
mauve or rarely white ray florets, 20 mm
diameter, surrounded by a single series of
narrow, sticky bracts forming a cylinder.

Habitat: Sandy flats, often coastal.

Senecio elegans
DAISY FAMILY

Greater purple ragwort (E)

(Latin *elegans*, elegant)

Densely glandular-hairy annual
to 1 m high. Leaves fleshy and cut or deeply
lobed with the margins rolled under. Flower
heads numerous in dense, flat-topped clusters,
yellow with mauve ray florets, 20 mm
diameter, surrounded by a single series of
narrow bracts with black tips that form a
globular involucre.

Habitat: Coastal sands.

Senecio umbellatus

DAISY FAMILY

Purple mountain groundsel (E)

(Latin *umbellatus*, like an umbrella, refer-
ing to the clustered flower heads)

Finely leafy perennial to 80 cm high, with the
stems sometimes sparsely hairy near the base.
Leaves thread-like or deeply divided into narrow to thread-like segments with the margins
rolled under and minutely toothed. Flower
heads in loosely branched, flat-topped clusters,
yellow with magenta to pink or rarely white
ray florets, 15 mm diameter, surrounded by a
single series of narrow bracts.
Habitat: Sandstone flats and slopes.

Amellus tenuifolius

DAISY FAMILY

Grey-leaved wild aster (E), astertjie (A)

(Latin *tenuifolius*, narrow-leaved)

Grey-silky, much-branched
perennial or shrublet to 50 cm high. Leaves
narrow to lance-shaped. Flower heads solitary
at the branch tips, yellow with mauve ray
florets, 15–20 mm diameter, surrounded by
several series of narrow, pointed bracts.
Habitat: Sandy flats, often near the coast.

Felicia fruticosa

DAISY FAMILY

Bush felicia (E)

(Latin *fruticosus*, shrubby)

Well-branched shrub to 1 m
high. Leaves in tufts, small and fleshy, elliptical
and lightly gland-dotted. Flower heads solitary
at the branch tips, yellow with blue to mauve
ray florets, 15 mm diameter, surrounded by
three series of narrow, pointed bracts.
Habitat: Rocky lower slopes.
Notes: *Felicia filifolia* (page 323) has
needle-like leaves.

Felicia aethiopica

DAISY FAMILY

Garden felicia (E)

(Latin *aethiopicus*, from Africa, usually South
Africa)

Shrublet to 1 m high. Leaves lance-shaped or
broader and often bent down, usually roughly
hairy. Flower heads solitary on slender stalks,
yellow with blue ray florets, 15–20 mm
diameter, surrounded by two series of narrow
pointed bracts, the outer series each with
three veins.

Habitat: Rocky sandstone flats and slopes.
Notes: *Felicia amelloides* is very similar but
the bracts have only a single vein each.

Felicia tenella

DAISY FAMILY

Dainty felicia (E)

(Latin *tenellus*, delicate)

Thinly hairy annual herb
5–25 cm high. Leaves narrow with rough hairs
on the margins. Flower heads solitary on wiry
stalks, yellow with blue, violet or white ray
florets, 15–20 mm diameter, surrounded by
three series of narrow, pointed bracts.
Habitat: Seasonally moist sandy soils and
coastal dunes.

Euryops abrotanifolius

DAISY FAMILY

Common rosinbush (E)

(Latin *abrotanifolius*, with leaves like
Artemisia abrotonum)

Densely leafy shrub to 1 m high. Leaves usually
divided into narrow or thread-like segments,
60–90 mm long. Flower heads solitary on
naked stalks which are woolly at the base, yellow with yellow ray florets, 30 mm diameter,
surrounded by two series of bracts joined at
the base into a cup.
Habitat: Sandstone slopes in fynbos.
Notes: Readily seen on the slopes of
Lion's Head.

Euryops speciosissimus

DAISY FAMILY

Giant rosinbush (E), grootharpuisbos (A)

(Latin *speciosissimus*, extremely showy)

Slender or willowy shrub to
over 2 m high. Leaves rather fleshy and divided
into drooping needle-like or thread-like
segments, 60–200 mm long. Flower heads
solitary on thick naked stalks, yellow with
straggling yellow ray florets, 50–60 mm
diameter, surrounded by two series of bracts
that are joined below into a cup.
Habitat: Drier, rocky sandstone slopes in
fynbos.

Euryops tenuissimus

DAISY FAMILY

Rosinbush (E), harpuisbos (A)

(Latin *tenuissimus*, extremely narrow,
referring to the leaves)

Shrub to 2,5 m high, often mealy on the young
parts. Leaves needle-like and sometimes
three-lobed, 15–150 mm long. Flower heads
clustered among the leaves on short, wiry
stalks, yellow or orange with yellow ray
florets, 10–12 mm diameter, surrounded by two
series of bracts joined at the base into a cup.
Habitat: Stony karroid slopes.
Notes: *Euryops thunbergii* has shorter leaves
10–50 mm long.

Euryops virgineus

DAISY FAMILY

Outeniqua rosinbush (E), rivierharpuisbos (A)

(Latin *virgineus*, pure white, an inexplicable
choice for the name)

Densely leafy shrub to 3 m high, with stiffly
erect stems. Leaves ascending, elliptical and
narrowly lobed to toothed above, 5–12 mm
long. Flower heads solitary on short wiry
stalks among the upper leaves, yellow with yellow ray florets, 10 mm diameter, surrounded
by two series of bracts joined at the base into
a cup.
Habitat: Sandstone slopes in fynbos.

Gymnodiscus capillaris
DAISY FAMILY
Yellowweed (E), geelkruid (A)
(Latin *capillaris*, thread-like, referring to the
flower stalks)

Tufted annual herb to 20 cm high. Leaves in a
basal rosette and somewhat succulent, lance-
shaped to lyre-shaped and usually lobed below.
Flower heads in small clusters on slender
branched stalks, yellow with yellow ray florets,
6–8 mm diameter, surrounded by a single
series of broad bracts.
Habitat: Sandy flats and lower slopes.

Othonna cylindrica
DAISY FAMILY
Common babooncress (E),
bobbejaankool (A)
(Latin *cylindricus*, cylindrical, referring to
the leaves)

Brittle-stemmed succulent shrub to 1 m high.
Leaves clustered at the branch tips, more or
less cylindrical and fleshy. Flower heads few in
loose, flat-topped clusters on slender stalks,
yellow with yellow ray florets, 20 mm diameter, surrounded by a single series of bracts.
Habitat: Sandy and stony flats and rocks,
often coastal.

Othonna quinquedentata
DAISY FAMILY
(= *Othonna parviflora*)
Mountain babooncress (E)
(Latin *quinquedentatus*, five-toothed,
referring to the leaves)

Shrub with several slender, erect stems to 1 m
high. Leaves crowded toward the bottom of
the stems, leathery and lance-shaped or broad
and often toothed above. Flower heads many
in loose, flat-topped clusters on wand-like
stalks, yellow with yellow ray florets, 5 mm
diameter, surrounded by a single series of
bracts.
Habitat: Rocky sandstone slopes in fynbos,
often in damp places.

ripteris clandestina

AISY FAMILY

(Osteospermum clandestinum)

icky windowseed (E), trekkertjie (A)

atin clandestinus, hidden, possibly a
ference to the relatively inconspicuous ray florets)

landular-hairy, aromatic annual herb to 40 cm
igh, often with purplish stems. Leaves
lliptical and toothed to lobed. Flower heads
urplish with pale yellow ray florets that are
rown at the base, 20 mm diameter, surrounded
y two series of narrow bracts, nodding in
eed. Seeds large and three-winged, papery.
abitat: Sandy and gravelly flats, often in
isturbed places along roadsides or in lands.

ripteris oppositifolia

AISY FAMILY

(Osteospermum oppositifolium)

inter windowseed (E), stinkskaapbos (A)

atin oppositifolius, opposite-leaved)

ounded, brittle-stemmed shrub to 1 m high,
etid-smelling. Leaves opposite, narrow and
bscurely toothed, leathery with a grey bloom.
lower heads black with pale to golden yellow
ay florets, 30–40 mm diameter, drooping in
eed, surrounded by two series of narrow
racts. Seeds conspicuously three-winged and
apery.
abitat: Dry sandstone or granite outcrops
mong rocks.

hrysanthemoides monilifera

AISY FAMILY

mmon tickberry (E), bietou, bosluisbessie (A)

atin moniliferus, bead-carrying, referring
 the round seeds)

ounded shrub to over 1,5 m high, thinly
oolly on the young parts. Leaves leathery,
blong to elliptical with coarsely toothed
argins. Flower heads in clusters, yellow
ith yellow ray florets, 20 mm diameter,
urrounded by several rows of pointed bracts.
eeds round and glossy black.
abitat: Sandstone and limestone slopes and
ats.

Dimorphotheca pluvialis

DAISY FAMILY

Rain daisy (E), reënblommetjie (A)
(Latin *pluvialis*, relating to rain, referring to
the growth of the plants in the wet season)

Erect to sprawling, glandular-hairy annual herb
to 30 cm high. Leaves lance-shaped and lobed
or toothed. Flower heads solitary and nodding
in fruit, purple with white ray florets which
have a purple band at the base and a darker
underside, and which close at night, 30–45 mm
diameter, surrounded by a single row of
narrow pointed bracts forming a shallow cup.
Seeds disc-like.
Habitat: Sandy and clay flats and slopes.

Ursinia cakilefolia

DAISY FAMILY

Glossy-eyed parachute-daisy (E)
(Latin *cakilefolius*, with leaves like the
sea rocket, *Cakile maritima*)

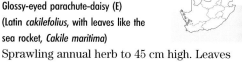

Sprawling annual herb to 45 cm high. Leaves
mostly twice-divided into narrow segments.
Flower heads solitary on long stalks, glossy
blackish with yellow or orange ray florets, the
inner florets covered with shiny scales in bud
to form the glossy eye, 30–35 mm diameter,
surrounded by many series of overlapping
bracts, the innermost with large, papery tips.
Seeds with five white, papery scale-like wings.
Habitat: Sandy flats and slopes.

Ursinia anthemoides

DAISY FAMILY

Common parachute-daisy (E)
(Resembling chamomile, *Anthemis*)

Annual herb to 50 cm high.
Leaves divided or twice-divided into narrow
segments. Flower heads solitary at the branch
tips, dull blackish with yellow or orange ray
florets with a dark underside and sometimes
a dark band at the base, 30–35 mm diameter,
surrounded by many series of overlapping
bracts, the innermost with large, papery tips.
Seeds with five white, papery scale-like wings.
Habitat: Sandy and gravel slopes and flats.

Ursinea paleacea

DAISY FAMILY

Shrubby parachute-daisy (E), geelmagriet (A)
(Latin *paleaceus*, chaffy, referring to the
papery scales among the florets)

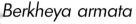

Short-lived shrublet to 90 cm high, single-stemmed at the base. Leaves divided into narrow segments. Flower heads solitary on long stalks, yellow with yellow ray florets, 20–50 mm diameter, surrounded by many series of overlapping bracts, the innermost with large, papery tips. Seeds with five white, papery scale-like wings.
Habitat: Sandstone slopes after fire.

Berkheya armata

DAISY FAMILY

Greater berkheya (E), grootdissel (A)
(Latin *armatus*, armed, referring to the
spines)

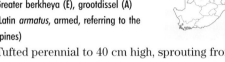

Tufted perennial to 40 cm high, sprouting from a woody rootstock. Leaves crowded at the base of the stem, broad, with the margins lightly rolled under and toothed and spiny, hairless above and white-felted beneath. Flower heads loosely clustered, yellow with yellow ray florets, 40–50 mm diameter, surrounded by several series of spiny bracts, the innermost smooth on the margins.
Habitat: Clay and granite slopes after fire.

Berkheya barbata

DAISY FAMILY

Holly-leaved berkheya (E)
(Latin *barbatus*, bearded, alluding to the
copious prickles on the bracts)

Shrublet with grey-felted branches to 60 cm high, sprouting from a woody rootstock. Leaves opposite, elliptical, with the margins rolled under and lightly toothed and spiny, leathery, hairless above and white-felted beneath. Flower heads solitary, yellow with yellow ray florets, 40–50 mm diameter, surrounded by several series of bracts with long spines on the margins.
Habitat: Rocky sandstone slopes after fire.

Didelta spinosa

DAISY FAMILY

Namaqua salad thistle (E), slaaibos (A)
(Latin *spinosus*, spiny, referring to the leaves)

Shrub to 2 m high. Leaves opposite, glossy, elliptical and spine-tipped, lobed at the base with the margins lightly rolled under and sometimes prickly. Flower heads yellow with yellow ray florets, 40–50 mm diameter, surrounded by two rows of bracts, the outer four bracts large and leafy and the inner narrow with prickly teeth.

Habitat: Dry granite and sandstone slopes.
Notes: Highly palatable, especially the dry leaves in summer.

Didelta carnosa

DAISY FAMILY

Dune salad thistle (E), kusslaaibos (A)
(Latin *carnosus*, fleshy, referring to the leaves)

Rounded shrublet to 1 m high. Leaves fleshy and lance-shaped with the margins usually rolled under, thinly or densely cobwebby. Flower heads yellow with yellow ray florets, 40–50 mm diameter, surrounded by two rows of bracts, the outer four bracts large and leafy and the inner narrow with prickly teeth.

Habitat: Coastal dunes and sandy flats.

Gazania rigens

DAISY FAMILY

Strand gazania (E), strandgazania (A)

(Latin *rigens*, stiff, referring to the leaves)

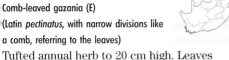

Sprawling, mat-forming peren-
nial to 20 cm high. Leaves usually narrowly
elliptical with the margins rolled under but
sometimes divided into narrow lobes, smooth
above but white-felted below with smooth
petioles. Flower heads yellow with yellow ray
florets, 30–40 mm diameter, surrounded by
several series of partially white-woolly bracts
that are joined into a cup, the inner bracts
pointed.
Habitat: Coastal dunes, rocks and sandy flats.

Gazania pectinata

DAISY FAMILY

Comb-leaved gazania (E)

(Latin *pectinatus*, with narrow divisions like
a comb, referring to the leaves)

Tufted annual herb to 20 cm high. Leaves
mostly divided into narrow segments with the
margins rolled under, sometimes rough above
but white-felted beneath. Flower heads
blackish with yellow or orange ray florets
marked with a dark band at the base,
40–50 mm diameter, surrounded by several
series of bracts that are joined into a cup, the
inner bracts gradually tapering.
Habitat: Coastal flats and sandy lower slopes.

Osmitopsis asteriscoides

DAISY FAMILY

Marsh daisy (E), belskruie (A)

(Resembling the genus *Asteriscus*)

Sparsely branched shrub to 2 m
high with erect stems which are densely leafy
at the ends. Leaves lance-shaped and smooth
or felted, aromatic when bruised. Flower
heads in flat-topped clusters at the branch tips,
yellow with white ray florets, 20 mm diameter,
surrounded by several series of bracts.
Habitat: Marshes and seeps on sandstone.
Notes: Brandy tinctures (*belsbrandewyn*) traditionally used for chest and stomach ailments.

Arctotheca calendula

DAISY FAMILY
Cape weed (E)
(Referring to the marigold, *Calendula*)

Tufted to sprawling annual herb
to 20 cm high. Leaves mostly in a basal tuft,
lyre-shaped or divided into oblong, toothed
segments, rough above and woolly beneath.
Flower heads blackish with pale yellow ray
florets usually with darker yellow or blackish
bands at the base, 30–35 mm diameter,
surrounded by several series of bracts with
papery margins. Fruits woolly.
Habitat: Coastal areas or disturbed soil.

Arctotheca populifolia

DAISY FAMILY
Sea pumpkin (E)
(Latin *populifolius*, with leaves resembling
those of a poplar, *Populus*)

Creeping, mat-forming perennial to 10 cm high.
Leaves stalked and heart-shaped or rarely
lobed with the margins sparsely toothed,
white-felted. Flower heads yellow with yellow
ray florets, 30 mm diameter, surrounded by
several series of woolly bracts with papery
margins. Fruits woolly.
Habitat: Seashore.

Arctotis hirsuta

DAISY FAMILY
Common arctotis (E), gousblom (A)
(Latin *hirsutus*, covered with coarse hairs)

Slightly fleshy, often robust
annual herb to 45 cm high. Leaves lyre-shaped
and divided, often with ear-like lobes at the
base, sparsely hairy. Flower heads blackish
with yellow, cream or orange ray florets
marked with a dark band at the base,
40–50 mm diameter, surrounded by several
series of bracts with papery margins, the inner
with large papery tips.
Habitat: Sandy slopes and coastal flats.

Arctotis acaulis

DAISY FAMILY

Tufted arctotis (E), renostergousblom (A)

(Latin *acaulis*, stemless)

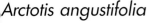

Stemless perennial to 20 cm
high. Leaves lyre-shaped and divided or broad
and toothed, rough above and grey-felted
beneath. Flower heads blackish with orange,
yellow or cream ray florets marked with a
dark band at the base, 40–50 mm diameter,
surrounded by several series of bracts
with papery margins, the inner with large
papery tips.
Habitat: Clay, granite and limestone flats.

Arctotis angustifolia

DAISY FAMILY

Sandveld arctotis (E)

(Latin *angustifolius*, narrow-leaved)

Creeping perennial to 40 cm
high, with stems arising from a diffuse underground system. Leaves broadly to narrowly
elliptical and toothed or divided with the
margins weakly rolled under, thinly white-
woolly and usually paler beneath. Flower
heads blackish with white or yellow ray florets
that are reddish reverse beneath, 35–45 mm
diameter, surrounded by several series of
thinly woolly bracts with papery margins, the
inner with large papery tips.
Habitat: Sandy slopes and flats.

Arctotis stoechadifolia

DAISY FAMILY

Silver arctotis (E)

(With leaves resembling those of French
lavender, *Lavandula stoechas*)

Sprawling perennial with erect shoots to 35 cm
high. Leaves lance-shaped or divided and
silvery-felted. Flower heads blackish with
cream ray florets that are reddish beneath,
40–50 mm diameter, surrounded by several
series of thinly woolly bracts with papery
margins, the inner with large papery tips.
Habitat: Dunes and sandy flats, mostly
coastal.

Namaqualand

THE AREA KNOWN AS NAMAQUALAND is a narrow stretch of country along the south-west coast, extending for 200 km in a band little more than 80 km wide, from the mouth of the Olifants River in the south to the mouth of the Orange River in the north. This arid strip is home to a unique assemblage of plants that is without equal elsewhere in the world. Packed into an area of around 50 000 km² are about 3 000 different species of wildflowers in a concentration that is at least four times richer than that found in comparable winter-rainfall desert areas. Furthermore, about 50% of these do not occur outside of the area, a staggering proportion in the context of its desert climate. Around one third of all the plants in the region are succulents, a number that encompasses one tenth of all the succulents in the world! They come in a great variety of sizes, around a quarter of them minuscule plants little more than 1 cm high. At the other extreme are the towering quiver trees that reach 9 m in height. The majority, however, are small, succulent-leaved shrublets less than 50 cm high that fall between these extremes. The most common succulents by far are members of the Mesemb family. Like the Cape Region to the south, Namaqualand also has a wonderfully rich bulb flora. With almost 500 different species, representing about 16% of the flora, it has five to ten times the number of bulbs typically found in other winter-rainfall deserts. Namaqualand has been well described as a succulent desert, enriched by a large and beautiful bulb flora.

Rainfall in the region is strictly confined to the winter months, between April and August, but sea fogs are an invaluable source of moisture for many plants. The cold Benguela current, which is responsible for the condensation of these fogs, also ensures that temperatures near the coast never soar to blistering levels in the summer. The dominant vegetation in Namaqualand is a low shrubland dominated by dwarf shrubs with succulent leaves, known as Succulent Karoo. Along the coastal plain and on the highest peaks of the Kamiesberg and Richtersveld mountains are patches of depauperate fynbos, but these are relatively unimportant. Although it may scarcely cover the ground and appear threadbare in comparison with the lush grasslands and thickets to the east, Succulent Karoo deserves our highest admiration. Not only does it support between four and six times as many species as are found in other winter-rainfall deserts around the world but the large numbers of leaf succulents and bulbs that occur in it are completely lacking in these areas. Finally, the reliable rains mean that prolonged droughts are not a feature of Namaqualand, allowing this unique assemblage of plants to thrive.

Namaqualand is famous for its brilliant displays of spring annuals. A really fine flower season, however, occurs only once every eight to ten years. In these years the landscape is transformed into a kaleidoscope of dazzling colours by great swathes of annuals that cover the fallow fields and line the roadsides. Less disturbed veld is often covered in a haze of yellow cotula with pools of pale blue *Felicia merxmuelleri*. Unfortunately these massed displays, remarkable though they may be, are artefacts of cultivation, often obscuring the true glory that the countryside has to offer to the more discerning visitor.

Namaqualand's flower season is the shortest of the three floral areas, with the main spring displays lasting for little more than a month and peaking for a few brief weeks in August. Flowering usually starts earlier in the north and on the coast, which are often best in late July or early August. The flats near Port Nolloth can be carpeted with annuals in July, including the pale yellow *Grielum humifusum*, although this is considered to be early in the season. The coastal strip can be golden with *Didelta carnosa*. At this time, too, the lovely apricot *Jordaaniella cuprea* and the brilliant white *Osteospermum scullyi* are also conspicuous. By August, however, these same coastal flats are often already dry and brown, although the succulent *Cephalophyllum spongiosum*, with its lusciously coloured purple and orange flowers, is a spectacular exception. The higher country between Steinkopf and Garies is best a little later, during the second half of August, when several types of glorious flowering shrubs dot the rocky slopes. Among the most spectacular are the golden mounds of *Tripteris oppositifolia*, and several gorgeous

Spring annuals, like Cleretum papulosum, *blanket fallow lands near Kamieskroon*

magenta pelargoniums, among which the rather rare *P. sericifolium* stands out for the brilliance of its colouring. At this time it is well worth wandering among the granite domes around Springbok or Kamieskroon. Tucked between the coppery boulders and contorted quiver trees are numerous flowering shrubs, annuals and bulbs. Among the shrubs, the most conspicuous are the silvery-leaved bushes of *Lebeckia sericea*, bearing trusses of pale creamy yellow flowers. A variety of orange annual daisies occur in these outcrops and careful examination is necessary to distinguish between *Tripteris hyoseroides*, *T. amplectens*, *Dimorphotheca sinuata*, *Ursinia calenduliflora*, *Arctotis fastuosa* and *Gorteria diffusa*, among others. Later than elsewhere, the top of the Kamiesberg only comes into full bloom in early or mid September, when it becomes a wonderland of brightly coloured bulbs. The mountain passes that wend onto the coastal plains are often very rewarding. They include the Spektakel Pass east of Steinkopf and the Anenous Pass east of Springbok. The two main wildflower reserves, Skilpad in the south near Kamieskroon and Goegap further north outside Springbok, are almost always rewarding for the easy access that they provide to visitors walking among the flowers themselves. Because the rains are often local and the flowers go over so rapidly it is always advisable to check with local sources for the best sites before visiting.

In the southern part of Namaqualand, there is a similar relationship between altitude and flowering time, with the Knersvlakte at its best early in the season and the Hantam, 600 m higher up on the Bokkeveld Escarpment, only coming into full bloom in early September. The Knersvlakte is famous among succulent enthusiasts for its unique

The sculptural Aloe dichotoma

flora of dwarf succulents. This arid basin is characterised by glittering stretches of quartz fields that sparkle over its gently undulating plains. These quartz fields are home to a bewildering array of minute succulents, each beautifully adapted to these highly unusual habitats. They cannot be seen from a vehicle and a hands-and-knees approach is the only way to appreciate these miniature jewels. Among the larger, cushion-forming species, *Argyroderma fissum*, with magenta flowers, and *Cephalophyllum spissum*, with delicate salmon-pink flowers, are common but the real gems must be searched for. Here, concealed among pebbles, and often stepped on in ignorance, are thousands of cryptic little silver bodies belonging to various species of *Argyroderma*, *Conophytum* and *Oophytum*. The first two genera flower in early winter and only their strange leaf pairs are discernible in spring.

Overlooking these flats in the east are the ramparts of the Bokkeveld Mountains, on which lies the settlement of Nieuwoudtville. It is no idle boast that this village has dubbed itself the Bulb Capital of the World. Incredibly, researchers have excavated well over 20 000 bulbs, corms and other forms of underground roots in a square metre of soil near the village! It comes as no surprise, then, that Nieuwoudtville can produce swathes of colourful bulbs that rival the daisies of Namaqualand in their sheer abundance. Among the jewels of the region are the large red romuleas or satinflowers, with their enormous poppy-like blooms, several species of *Bulbinella* with their poker-like spikes of flowers and the three species of *Sparaxis* that are the parents of cultivated sparaxis hybrids that brighten gardens the world over. The staggering profligacy of individual plants is not, however, the whole tale of the Hantam's glory. The secret to its botanical riches lies in the confluence, around Nieuwoudtville itself, of several very different types of soils, each supporting its own distinctive suite of species. Here it is common for pairs of closely related species to occur, one on the sticky red soils derived from the dolerite intrusions and another on the lighter soils from either the shales of the Karoo or the tillites deposited by ancient glaciers.

One of the features of the flowers of many Namaqualand annuals is that they close at night and in cool or wet weather. This means that an early start in winter or spring is not recommended, as the flowers will not be open until the day warms up. The display is characterised by a distinctive combination of magenta and orange colours that is not found elsewhere. The orange is due to an almost bewildering array of daisies, mainly annuals but also shrubs. The cerise, magenta

or purple is provided by a range of bulbs, particularly the Springbok painted petals, *Lapeirousia silenoides*, and the T'neitjie, *Pelargonium incrassatum*. Altogether, an impressive total of 20 different species of iris and pelargonium produce similar magenta or purple, long-tubed flowers. This extraordinary floral convergence is due to the occurrence in Namaqualand of two highly specialised flower-visiting flies that survive by sucking nectar from flowers. These flies have developed long, straw-like mouth parts that are ideal for reaching the nectar held at the base of long floral tubes. They are the main or only pollinators of these plants and the existence of some of Namaqualand's most characteristic flowers is thus due to the activities of these marvellous insects.

Although Namaqualand is known for its spring wildflower displays, there are other times of the year during which the countryside bursts into bloom. For a brief few weeks in autumn the dry, barren ground is transformed by a flowering that is even more remarkable than the spring season. Responding to the cooling temperatures of autumn and the first rains of the season, the dramatic flower spikes of numerous species of amaryllid burst through the soil. Pink brunsvigias and scarlet haemanthus appear almost overnight, to be followed by a range of smaller species in the early winter. The flowering of stone plants also enlivens the quartz patches of the Knersvlakte, while the flats around Nieuwoudtville become a shifting tapestry of colour as several species of oxalis carpet the ground. Unfortunately the exact timing of this floral spectacle is highly dependent on rains and is impossible to predict far in advance. This is one show for which tickets must be bought on the night but it is one that is well worth seeing.

Aloe dichotoma

ALOE FAMILY

Quiver tree (E), kokerboom (A), choje (N)
(Latin *dichotomous*, branching in pairs, a
reference to the repeatedly forked branches)

Sturdy tree to 9 m high. Leaves bluish green,
tapering with inconspicuous teeth along the
margins. Flowers in short, branched racemes
among the leaves, yellow, urn-shaped with conspicuous reddish stamens protruding from the
mouth, 30 mm long.

Habitat: Dry rocky slopes.

Notes: The hollow branches were used as
quivers by the San people. In a few localities
the plants grow in dense stands of thousands,
the famous Quiver Tree forests.

Aloe pearsonii

ALOE FAMILY

Pearson's aloe (E)
(Named after Prof. Harold Pearson, the first
director of the National Botanical Gardens)

Large shrub with erect stems to 2 m high bearing leaves along their length. Leaves dull bluish
but turning red in times of drought, curved
downwards and neatly arranged in vertical
rows, triangular with toothed margins. Flowers
in head-shaped racemes, red to yellow with the
stamens shortly protruding from the mouth,
30 mm long.

Habitat: Arid stony slopes.

Aloe microstigma

ALOE FAMILY

(= *Aloe framesii, A. khamisensis*)
Cape speckled aloe (E)
(Greek *microstigma*, little spot, referring to
the white speckling on the leaves)

Single-stemmed or clump-forming succulent to
3 m high. Leaves tapering, often reddish and
usually with small white spots, the margins
with sharp, reddish-brown teeth. Flowers
nodding in conical racemes, usually red in bud
but opening yellow, 20–30 mm long.

Habitat: Stony slopes and granite outcrops
among scrub.

Aloe falcata
ALOE FAMILY
Sickle-leaved aloe (E)
(Latin *falcatus*, sickle-shaped, a reference
to the curved leaves)

Stemless or short-stemmed succulent, usually growing in clumps with the rosettes pointing outwards. Leaves greyish green, lance-shaped and curved inwards with a rough, sandpapery surface and coarsely toothed margins. Flowers in conical, branched racemes, nodding, red or yellow with green tips, tubular with the stamens protruding from the mouth, 40 mm long.
Habitat: Dry sandy flats.

Aloe variegata
ALOE FAMILY
Partridge aloe (E), kanniedood (A)
(Latin *variegatus*, variegated, for the
conspicuously mottled leaves)

Stemless succulent to 50 cm high. Leaves in compact, three-ranked rosettes, keeled, green to brown and boldly mottled with white, the margins horny and white with minute teeth. Flowers in conical racemes, nodding, pink to red, tubular with the stamens not protruding from the mouth, 40 mm long.
Habitat: In the shelter of bushes on stony flats.
Notes: This beautiful species is widely grown and in some parts of the Karoo is planted on graves.

Kniphofia sarmentosa
ALOE FAMILY
Karoo poker (E), vuurpyl (A)
(Latin *sarmentosus*, producing long runners,
although this species actually produces
numerous short rhizomes)

Rhizomatous perennial to 60 cm high. Leaves greyish, strap-shaped, channelled and V-shaped in cross section. Flowers in dense, ovoid to cylindrical racemes, nodding, tubular, pinkish red in bud but tipped with buff when open, 20–25 mm long.
Habitat: Along mountain streams and in moist hollows, often in dense colonies.

Bulbinella latifolia

ALOE FAMILY

Broad-leaved bulbinella (E), rooikatstert,
rooidirk (A)

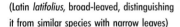

(Latin *latifolius*, broad-leaved, distinguishing
it from similar species with narrow leaves)

Sturdy tufted perennial to 1 m high. Leaves
broadly strap-shaped and tapering. Flowers in
dense, cylindrical racemes, yellow, cream or
orange, 6–8 mm diameter.
Habitat: Seasonally damp soils.
Notes: Varies in flower colour and soil prefer-
ence. The striking orange-flowered subspecies
occurs only around Nieuwoudtville.

Bulbinella eburniflora

ALOE FAMILY

Scented bulbinella (E), bleekkatstert (A)
(Latin *eburniflora*, with ivory-coloured
flowers)

Tufted perennial to 75 cm high. Leaves slender
and channelled with finely toothed margins.
Flowers in dense, conical racemes, creamy
white with a musty odour, 6–8 mm diameter.
Habitat: Gravelly clay soils in renosterveld.
Notes: The strong, musty odour of the flowers
is distinctive.

Bulbinella nutans

ALOE FAMILY

Marsh bulbinella (E), waterkatstert (A)
(Latin *nutans*, nodding, an exaggerated
reference to the slight curvature evident in
young flower spikes)

Sturdy tufted perennial to 80 cm high. Leaves
narrowly strap-shaped and channelled.
Flowers in dense, conical racemes, yellow or
cream, 6–8 mm diameter.
Habitat: Damp clay or peaty soils in open
scrub, often forming colonies.

Bulbine praemorsa

ALOE FAMILY

Common bulbine (E)
(Latin *praemorsus,* as if bitten off, for the
abruptly truncated base of the tuberous
root)

Deciduous perennial with a tuberous root,
40–60 cm high. Leaves narrow and channelled,
thick and fleshy with slimy sap, surrounded at
the base by a short fibrous collar. Flowers in
a loose raceme, yellow to salmon, 10 mm
diameter, lasting a day.
Habitat: Stony slopes in open scrub.
Notes: The soothing, gel-like sap of *Bulbine*
species is widely used as an emollient to treat
skin abrasions.

Trachyandra falcata

ALOE FAMILY

Namaqua starlily (E), Namakwakool (A)
(Latin *falcatus*, sickle-shaped, a reference to
the curved leaves)

Robust tufted perennial to 60 cm high. Leaves
leathery, flat and curving with a grey bloom.
Flowers in a dense, few-branched raceme with
the lowest bract forming a collar around the
flower stalk, white or pinkish, only a few open
each afternoon, 10 mm diameter, lasting a day.
Habitat: Common on sandy soils, often near
the coast.
Notes: The young flower shoots can be
cooked and eaten as a vegetable, much like
asparagus.

Chlorophytum undulatum
ANTHERICUM FAMILY
Namaqua grasslily (E), namakwagifkool (A)
(Latin *undulatus*, wavy, a reference to the
unnaturally limp leaves in the cultivated
specimen from which the species was originally described)

Tufted perennial to 50 cm high, with numerous
slender, wiry roots and sometimes additional
small tubers. Leaves strap-shaped, narrow or
broader with finely hairy margins. Flowers in
loose racemes with several flowers in each
bract, white with brown keels, each lasting a
single day, 15 mm diameter.
Habitat: Stony clay or loamy flats.
Notes: Species of grasslily, *Chlorophytum*,
like *Trachyandra*, have short-lived flowers and
the two are often confused. Grasslilies can be
recognised by their fibrous, not succulent
leaves, by having more than one flower in each
bract and by their distinctly three-winged fruits.

Ornithogalum pruinosum
HYACINTH FAMILY
Grey-leaved chincherinchee (E)
(Latin *pruinosus*, covered with a whitish
bloom, a reference to the leaves)

Bulbous perennial, 10–50 cm high. Leaves
three to six, oblong and firm-textured with a
greyish bloom and the margins sometimes
wavy. Flowers in a short, dense raceme,
white and fragrant with rather shiny petals,
20–25 mm diameter.
Habitat: Stony slopes in open scrub.

Ornithogalum polyphyllum
HYACINTH FAMILY
Large striped chincherinchee (E)
(Greek *polyphyllus*, many-leaved)

Bulbous perennial, 25–35 cm
high. Leaves many, grass-like and channelled
with the tips sometimes dry and coiled.
Flowers in a cylindrical raceme on long stalks,
white or pale yellow with green keels, fragrant,
20–30 mm diameter.
Habitat: Gravelly clay flats in open scrub.

Ornithogalum xanthochlorum

HYACINTH FAMILY

Slangkop (A)

(Greek *xantho-*, *chloro-*, yellow-green, for the greenish flowers)

Stout bulbous perennial to 60 cm. Leaves 9 to 14 in a spreading tuft, strap-shaped. Flowers in a dense, cylindrical raceme, waxy, green with white stamens, scented, 25 mm diameter.

Habitat: Open sandy or gravelly flats and low hills in open scrub.

Notes: Plants are poisonous.

Albuca maxima

HYACINTH FAMILY

(= *Albuca altissima*)

Greater slime lily (E), wittamarak (A)

(Latin *maximus*, greatest, for its large size)

Stout bulbous perennial, usually 1–2 m high, the bulb tunics slightly fibrous at the top. Leaves several, channelled and clasping the stem below, fleshy and oozing a slimy sap when torn. Flowers in racemes that elongate markedly in fruit, nodding, white with green keels, the inner tepals with a hinged flap at the tip, 25–30 mm diameter.

Habitat: Rocky outcrops.

Notes: Can form dense colonies along roadsides.

Albuca cooperi

HYACINTH FAMILY

Warty slime lily (E), geldbeursie (A)

(Named after Thomas Cooper, a Victorian plant collector)

Bulbous perennial to 40 cm high, the bulb tunics becoming fibrous at the top. Leaves two or three, slender and grooved above, distinctly warty at the base just above the bulb, oozing a slimy sap when torn. Flowers in loose racemes, nodding, yellow with green keels, the inner three petals with a hinged flap at the tip, lightly scented, 20–25 mm diameter.

Habitat: Sandy and rocky soils in open scrub.

Notes: Distinguished from other slime lilies by the conspicuous warts at the base of the stem.

Lachenalia framesii

HYACINTH FAMILY
Frames' lachenalia (E)
(Named after Percy Ross Frames, a keen
grower of succulents, who first collected the
species)

Bulbous perennial to 15 cm high. Leaves one
or two, narrow and plain green with wavy
margins. Flowers in narrow spikes, without
pedicels, urn-shaped with the anthers enclosed
within the flower, the outer petals yellowish
green but the inner whitish with spreading
bright purple or magenta tips, 8–10 mm long.
Habitat: Sandy flats, often in large colonies.
Notes: A dainty species especially common on
the Knersvlakte just north of Vanrhynsdorp.

Lachenalia elegans

HYACINTH FAMILY
Elegant lachenalia (E), fraaiviooltjie (A)
(Latin *elegans*, elegant)

Bulbous perennial to 20 cm
high. Leaves one or two, ovate, often with
green or maroon spots. Flowers in narrow
spikes, without pedicels, urn-shaped with the
anthers enclosed within the flower, in shades
or combinations of yellow, blue, mauve or
purple, with white tips, 8–10 mm long.
Habitat: Sandstone outcrops and gravelly clay,
often in large colonies.

Lachenalia carnosa

HYACINTH FAMILY
Fleshy-leaved lachenalia (E)
(Latin *carnosus*, fleshy or succulent, for the
leaves)

Bulbous perennial to 25 cm high. Leaves two,
ovate and fleshy with parallel grooves on the
upper surface and sometimes also green or
brownish warts. Flowers in dense spikes,
without pedicels, urn-shaped with the anthers
enclosed within the flower, whitish with the
inner petals broadly tipped with purple or
magenta, 8–10 mm long.
Habitat: Rocky outcrops in gravelly soil.

273

Lachenalia violacea
HYACINTH FAMILY

Karoo lachenalia (E), karooviooltjie (A)

(Latin *violaceus*, violet, for the flowers)

Bulbous perennial to 20 cm high. Leaves one or two, lanceolate, plain green or variously spotted or banded, with smooth or wavy margins. Flowers in a cylindrical raceme on distinct pedicels, goblet-shaped with the anthers conspicuously protruding, green or brownish with purple tips and violet stamens, scented of coconut, 10–12 mm long.

Habitat: Gravelly soils in open scrub.

Veltheimia capensis
HYACINTH FAMILY

Winter veltheimia (E), sandlelie (A)

(Latin *capensis*, from the Cape)

Robust bulbous perennial to 40 cm high. Leaves several in a spreading tuft, bluish green with a grey bloom, tapering with the margins more or less wavy or crisped. Flowers in a dense conical raceme, drooping, pink with darker speckling and green tips, tubular, 25–30 mm long.

Habitat: Sandy or gravelly flats and rocky outcrops, often in the shelter of shrubs.

Notes: The flowers, which resemble those of an aloe or red hot poker, give way to attractive papery, three-winged fruits.

Whiteheadia bifolia
HYACINTH FAMILY

Pagoda lily (E)

(Latin *bifolius*, two-leaved)

Bulbous perennial, 8–12 cm high. Leaves two, spreading on the ground, fleshy and fragile in texture. Flowers in a dense, cylindrical spike topped with a tuft of leaf-like bracts, creamy, 20 mm diameter.

Habitat: Mostly in the lee of rocks.

Notes: Pollinated by rodents.

Daubenya aurea

HYACINTH FAMILY

Jewel of the desert (E)

(Latin *aureus*, golden yellow, after the yellow form which was discovered first)

Bulbous perennial, 5–8 cm high. Leaves two, spreading on the ground, ovate and leathery with longitudinal grooves. Flowers crowded between the leaves, the outer flowers with much larger petals than the inner, usually red but some populations yellow, the flower head 30–50 mm diameter.

Habitat: Red doleritic clays.

Notes: Restricted to a few populations near the village of Middelpos. Bulbs of both colour forms are available commercially.

Spiloxene serrata

STARGRASS FAMILY

Common Cape star (E), sterretjie (A)

(Latin *serratus*, saw-edged, referring to the toothed leaf margins)

Cormous perennial, 6–20 cm high. Leaves several, grass-like and channelled with the margins minutely toothed. Flowers one per flowering stalk, subtended by two narrow bracts, yellow, orange or white with the petals green on the reverse, 15–25 mm diameter.

Habitat: Seasonally moist stony clay flats and lower slopes in open scrub.

Empodium flexile

STARGRASS FAMILY

Fragrant autumn star (E), klipsterretjie (A)

(Latin *flexilis*, flexible, referring to the slender appendages at the tips of the anthers)

Cormous perennial to 10 cm high. Leaves three and usually not developed at flowering, lance-shaped and pleated. Flowers solitary on a three-angled stalk, pale to bright yellow and lemon-scented, 30 mm diameter, the stamens tipped with slender orange appendages.

Habitat: Stony or sandy flats.

Ornithoglossum vulgare
COLCHICUM FAMILY
Common snakelily (E), slangkop (A)
(Latin *vulgaris,* common or ordinary)

Cormous perennial, 6–30 cm high. Leaves narrow and tapering with the margins usually wavy, greyish. Flowers nodding on long, spreading pedicels, the petals green with maroon margins or red to brown, 10–15 mm diameter.

Habitat: Stony flats or gentle slopes in open scrub.

Notes: Like all members of this family these plants are poisonous.

Cyanella alba
CYANELLA FAMILY
Hooded lady's hand (E)
(Latin *albus,* white)

Cormous perennial, 12–25 cm high. Leaves several in a tuft, thread-like, round in cross section. Flowers one or two on long stalks, white to pink or yellow, fragrant, with five smaller stamens clustered together above one larger stamen.

Habitat: Stony clay and sandstone flats.

Cyanella orchidiformis
CYANELLA FAMILY
Orchid-flowered lady's hand (E)
(Latin *orchidiformis,* orchid-shaped, a reference to the exotic flowers)

Cormous perennial, 30–40 cm high. Leaves lance-shaped and tapering, soft-textured and often with wavy margins. Flowers in branched racemes, mauve with a darker purplish centre, fragrant, with three smaller stamens clustered above three larger ones.

Habitat: Seasonally moist rocky flats and lower slopes.

Androcymbium capense

COLCHICUM FAMILY

White cup-and-saucer (E)

(Latin *capensis*, from the Cape)

Cormous perennial, 5–8 cm
high. Leaves two, spreading on the ground and
lance-shaped with finely hairy margins.
Flowers clustered between the leaves and
enclosed in large, white bracts sometimes
striped with green, the flower head 30–50 mm
diameter.

Habitat: Clay or loamy flats.

Androcymbium latifolium

COLCHICUM FAMILY

(= *Androcymbium pulchrum*)

Red cup-and-saucer (E)

(Latin *latifolius*, broad-leaved)

Cormous perennial, 5–8 cm high. Leaves two,
spreading on the ground and lance-shaped
with finely hairy margins. Flowers clustered
between the leaves and enclosed in large, red
to purple bracts, the flower head 30–50 mm
diameter.

Habitat: Clay flats, usually in red doleritic clay.

Strumaria truncata

AMARYLLIS FAMILY

Namaqua snowdrop (E)

(Latin *truncatus*, abruptly cut off, a reference
to the blunt sheath that encircles the bases
of the leaves)

Slender bulbous perennial to 40 cm high.
Leaves just emerging at flowering, two to four
in a basal fan, strap-shaped and twisted,
enclosed at the base in a swollen purple
sheath. Flowers nodding on a slender
peduncle, funnel-shaped, white to pink,
8–10 mm long.

Habitat: Seasonally moist stony and gravelly
flats.

Haemanthus barkerae
AMARYLLIS FAMILY
Bokkeveld paintbrush lily (E)
(Commemorating Cape Town botanist,
Miss W.F. Barker)

Bulbous geophyte, 10–15 cm high, often
growing in clumps. Leaves withered at
flowering, two, narrow and smooth or shortly
hairy, barred with maroon at the base on the
underside. Flowers in a loose head surrounded
by four to six pointed bracts, usually pink but
rarely reddish, the flower head 30–40 mm
diameter.
Habitat: Dolerite and shale flats.
Notes: Common around Nieuwoudtville.

Haemanthus crispus
AMARYLLIS FAMILY
Crispy-leaved paintbrush lily (E)
(Latin *crispus,* crisped or wavy, a reference
to the leaf margins)
Bulbous geophyte, 4–10 cm high, often
growing in clumps. Leaves withered at flowering, two, narrow and channelled with wavy or
crisped margins and speckled with purple at
the base on the underside. Flowers in a small,
compact head surrounded by four or five
blunt, waxy bracts, usually red but rarely pink,
the flower head 20–30 mm diameter.
Habitat: Gravelly flats and lower slopes.
Notes: Common on the granite flats around
Springbok and Garies.

Crossyne flava
AMARYLLIS FAMILY
(= *Boophone flava*)
Yellow parasol lily (E), geelsambreel-
blom (A)
(Latin *flavus,* pale yellow)
Bulbous perennial to 30 cm high. Leaves withered at flowering, four to six, spreading flat on
the ground, oblong and leathery with coarsely
bristly margins. Flowers in large round heads
on long pedicels, pale yellow, lightly scented,
12–15 mm diameter.
Habitat: Gravelly flats and lower slopes.

Crinum variabile

AMARYLLIS FAMILY

roen River lily (E), turflelie (A)

(Latin *variabilis,* varying in colour)

Robust bulbous perennial to
m high. Leaves withered or just emerging
at flowering, several, strap-shaped and
channelled with minutely toothed margins.
Flowers large and trumpet-shaped, nodding,
pale to deep pink, 60–80 mm diameter.
Habitat: Stream sides and riverbeds among
rocks.
Notes: Pollinated by hawk moths at dusk.

Brunsvigia bosmaniae

AMARYLLIS FAMILY

scented candelabra (E), soet kandelaar (A)

(Named after a Mrs Bosman who collected
the first plant on her farm near Kuils River
between Cape Town and Stellenbosch)

Bulbous perennial to 20 cm high. Leaves dry at
flowering, five or six, spreading flat on the
ground, tongue-shaped with firm translucent
margins. Flowers crowded in a large round
head, the tepals broadly oblong and pink with
darker veins, scented of narcissus, 30–40 mm
diameter.
Habitat: Clay or gravelly flats.
Notes: In good seasons can flower in the
thousands, covering the autumn veld with its
pink balloons. There are especially large
colonies between Klawer and Nieuwoudtville.

Cybistetes longifolia

AMARYLLIS FAMILY

Malgas lily (E)

(Latin *longifolia,* long-leaved)

Bulbous perennial, 25–35 cm
high. Leaves dry or green at flowering, sickle-
shaped and spreading on the ground with
translucent margins. Flowers in a large round
head, widely funnel-shaped, cream to pink and
wonderfully fragrant, 40–60 mm diameter.
Habitat: Open sandy flats.
Notes: Flowering occurs within one or two
weeks after a summer shower.

Ferraria divaricata

IRIS FAMILY

Yellow spider iris (E), geelspinnekopblom (A)
(Latin *divaricatus,* spreading widely, referring
to the branching stems)

Cormous perennial, 6–20 cm high, the stem
often much-branched. Leaves sword-shaped
with thickened margins. Flowers yellowish to
brown with dark streaks and blotches and
finely ruffled margins, foetid-smelling,
30–35 mm diameter, each lasting one day.
Habitat: Sandy and shale flats and rock
outcrops.

Moraea tripetala

IRIS FAMILY

Fleur-de-lys moraea (E), blou-uintjie (A)
(Latin *tripetalus,* three-petalled, a reference
to the suppression or loss of three of the
six petals that is characteristic of this species)

Slender cormous perennial, 20–45 cm high.
Leaf solitary, narrow and channelled. Flowers
blue to violet or rarely white or pink, with
three large petals on narrow stalks alternating
with three thread-like petals or these absent,
30–35 mm diameter.
Habitat: Stony sandstone and clay soils in
open scrub.

Moraea serpentina

IRIS FAMILY

Serpentine moraea (E)
(Latin *serpentinus,* snake-like, a reference
to the wavy or coiled leaves)

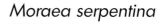

Dwarf cormous perennial, 4–15 cm high, with
branched stems. Leaves mostly two to four,
narrow and channelled and twisted or coiled.
Flowers white and yellow, often flushed violet,
with three larger petals bent sharply downwards alternating with three smaller upright
tepals, 25–35 mm diameter.
Habitat: Dry stony flats.

Moraea ciliata

RIS FAMILY

Velvet-leaved moraea (E)

(Latin *ciliatus*, fringed with fine hairs)

Stemless cormous perennial, 5–10(–20) cm high. Leaves three to five, narrow, usually greyish in colour and sparsely to densely hairy. Flowers blue or yellow, rarely white, spicy-fragrant with the inner three tepals lance-shaped, 30–40 mm diameter.
Habitat: Sandy and clay slopes.

Moraea falcifolia

IRIS FAMILY

Pouooguintjie (A)

(Latin *falcifolius*, sickle-leaved)

Stemless, dwarf cormous perennial to 5 cm high. Leaves narrow and channelled. Flowers white with yellow and lilac to purple markings in the centre, with three larger, spreading petals alternating with three smaller, somewhat upcurved petals, foetid-smelling, lasting a single day, 25–30 mm diameter.
Habitat: Seasonally damp stony clay flats.

Moraea bifida

IRIS FAMILY

(= *Homeria bifida*)

Pink Cape tulip (E), pienktulp (A)

(Latin *bifidus*, two-cleft, referring to the forked style branches)

Cormous perennial to 50 cm high. Leaf solitary, fairly broad below and clasping the lower half of the stem, channelled. Flowers star-shaped, yellow or pink, minutely speckled in the centre, the anthers held at the tip of a bulbous filament column, 25–30 mm diameter.
Habitat: Clay soils in renosterveld.
Notes: Most Cape tulips are poisonous to stock and proliferate in overgrazed veld.

Moraea schlechteri

IRIS FAMILY

(= *Homeria schlechteri*)

Schlechter's homeria (E)

(Named after the German botanist, Rudolf Schlechter, who first collected the species)

Cormous perennial to 60 cm high, the stem usually well-branched. Leaves several, strap-shaped and channelled. Flowers pale yellow with six spreading petals marked with dark blotches at the base, 30–35 mm diameter, each lasting only a single morning and withering at around 1.00 pm.

Habitat: Stony or gravelly flats in open scrub.

Ixia rapunculoides

IRIS FAMILY

Blue ixia (E), bloukalossie (A)

(Resembling a rampion, or campanula, in its flowers)

Slender cormous perennial, 15–70 cm high, often with side branches. Leaves narrowly sword-shaped. Flowers funnel-shaped, blue or mauve, 10–15 mm diameter.

Habitat: Mainly clay soils in renosterveld.

Romulea tortuosa

IRIS FAMILY

Golden romulea (E)

(Latin *tortuosus*, twisted, referring to the leaves)

Cormous perennial to 5 cm high, often in large colonies, the corm flattened and fan-like. Leaves several, needle-like with a narrow groove along the top and twisted or coiled. Flowers cup-shaped, bright yellow with or without dark markings in the throat, lightly scented, 15–25 mm diameter, the floral bracts mostly papery and translucent and the fruits carried on coiled stalks.

Habitat: Seasonally wet gravelly or clay flats or seeps.

Romulea citrina

IRIS FAMILY

Lemon romulea (E)

(Latin *citrinus,* lemon yellow)

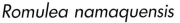

Cormous perennial to 12 cm high, the corm with a fringed U-shaped ridge along the base. Leaves several, needle-like with four narrow grooves along their length. Flowers pale to deep yellow, 20–25 mm diameter, the floral bracts with narrow membranous margins. **Habitat:** Seasonal seeps or washes in gravelly soils.

Romulea namaquensis

IRIS FAMILY

Namaqua romulea (E)

(Latin *namaquensis,* from Namaqualand)

Cormous perennial to 20 cm high, the corm with a fringed U-shaped ridge along the base. Leaves several, needle-like with four narrow grooves along their length. Flowers pink to coppery orange or rarely white and usually with dark markings in the pale greenish throat, 20–30 mm diameter, the floral bracts with narrow membranous margins. **Habitat:** Seasonally moist gravelly seeps on granite outcrops.

Romulea subfistulosa

IRIS FAMILY

Thick-leaved romulea (E)

(Latin *subfistulosus,* somewhat hollow and pipe-like, referring to the spongy leaves)

Cormous perennial to 10 cm high, the corm rounded with curved teeth at the base. Leaves several, curved and somewhat spongy with four broad grooves along their length. Flowers magenta to deep pink with dark blotches around the yellow cup, 20–40 mm diameter, the floral bracts with brown-spotted membranous margins and a prominent membranous tip and the fruits carried on slightly arched stalks. **Habitat:** Seasonally moist dolerite clay soils, often among rocks, near Sutherland.

Romulea sabulosa

IRIS FAMILY

Bokkeveld crocus (E)

(Latin *sabulosus,* sand-loving, a misnomer as the species prefers clay soils)

Cormous perennial to 10 cm high, the corm rounded with curved teeth at the base. Leaves several, needle-like with four narrow grooves along their length. Flowers dark red or rarely pink with black blotches at the edge of a creamy green cup, 30–50 mm diameter, the floral bracts with narrow membranous margins. **Habitat:** Seasonally moist clay flats in open renosterveld.

Notes: *Romulea monadelpha* has black filaments.

Hesperantha cucullata

IRIS FAMILY

Bokkeveld hesperantha (E), bokkeveldaandblom (A)

(Latin *cucullatus,* hooded, a reference to the cupped petals)

Cormous perennial, 15–30 cm high, with a rounded corm. Leaves sword-shaped. Flowers upright with cupped petals, white inside but red to brown on the outside, fragrant, opening in the late afternoon, 18–22 mm diameter. **Habitat:** Mainly seasonally moist shale flats in renosterveld.

Hesperantha bachmannii

IRIS FAMILY

Ballerina hesperantha (E)

(Named after the nineteenth-century German naturalist, Frans Bachmann)

Cormous perennial, 15–30 cm high, with a rounded corm. Leaves narrowly sword-shaped. Flowers nodding on a slender, curved tube with the petals bent backwards, sweetly scented, opening in the late afternoon, 15–20 mm diameter. **Habitat:** Mainly stony clay slopes in renosterveld.

Hesperantha vaginata

RIS FAMILY

Harlequin hesperantha (E), perdeblom (A)

(Latin *vaginatus*, sheathed, referring to the leaves that clasp the stem in the lower part)

Cormous perennial, 12–18 cm high, with a rounded corm. Leaves sword-shaped. Flowers large, cup-shaped, yellow often marked with dark brown, opening in the early afternoon, 25–35 mm diameter.

Habitat: Heavy clay soils usually derived from dolerite.

Hesperantha pauciflora

IRIS FAMILY

Pink hesperantha (E)

(Latin *pauciflorus*, few-flowered)

Cormous perennial to 10 cm high, with corms that have spiny teeth radiating from a flat base. Flowers deep pink to purple, rarely yellow, fragrant, opening in mid-afternoon, 20–25 mm diameter.

Habitat: Seasonally moist clay or gravelly flats in renosterveld.

Geissorhiza splendidissima

IRIS FAMILY

Bokkeveld pride (E)

(Latin *splendidissimus*, most brilliant, referring to the flowers)

Cormous perennial with velvety stems, 8–20 cm high. Leaves narrow and X-shaped in section. Flowers glossy blue-violet with small greenish centres surrounded by prominent black marks and with reddish-brown anthers, 20–25 mm diameter.

Habitat: Stony clay soils in renosterveld.

Notes: Restricted to patches of renosterveld around Nieuwoudtville.

Sparaxis tricolor
IRIS FAMILY

Harlequin flower (E), fluweeltjie (A)

(Latin *tricolor*, three-coloured)

Cormous perennial, 10–30 cm high. Leaves sword-shaped. Flowers orange with a large yellow and black cup and yellow anthers, 35–40 mm diameter.

Habitat: Seasonally moist stony clay flats in renosterveld, often along streams.

Notes: This and the following species, along with *Sparaxis pillansii*, were used in the breeding programmes that have given us the commercially grown sparaxis hybrids. All three of these species are found in the wild only around Nieuwoudtville.

Sparaxis elegans
IRIS FAMILY

Streptanthera, pale harlequin flower (E), spogfluweeltjie (A)

(Latin *elegans*, elegant)

Cormous perennial, 10–20 cm high. Leaves sword-shaped. Flowers salmon pink or white with a purple cup edged in black and yellow and with coiled, purple anthers, 40–50 mm diameter.

Habitat: Clay flats in renosterveld.

Babiana curviscapa
IRIS FAMILY

(Latin *curviscapus*, with a curved flowering stem)

Dwarf cormous perennial to 10 cm high. Leaves lance-shaped and stiffly pleated, velvety. Flowers on short horizontal stems, with a slender tube sharply bent near the top and usually about twice as long as the petals, brilliant purple or cerise with white markings towards the centre, 20–30 mm diameter.

Habitat: Sandy and gravelly flats in open scrub.

Notes: Usually purple-flowered but cerise in colour around Springbok.

Babiana attenuata

IRIS FAMILY

Showy babiana (E)

(Latin *attenuatus,* drawn gradually into a sharp point, referring to the petals)

Dwarf cormous perennial to 10 cm high. Leaves lance-shaped and stiffly pleated, velvety. Flowers on short horizontal stems, with a slender, slightly curved tube usually about as long as the petals, brilliant purple or magenta with white markings towards the centre, fragrant, 30–50 mm diameter. **Habitat:** Seasonally moist sandy and gravelly flats in open scrub.

Babiana vanzyliae

IRIS FAMILY

Yellow babiana (E), stinkbobbejaantjie (A)

(Named after Mrs Van Zyl, who grew the species in her Cape Town garden)

Dwarf cormous perennial to 12 cm high. Leaves lance-shaped and stiffly pleated, velvety. Flowers with a slender tube somewhat longer than the petals, yellow to mauve, fragrant, 30–50 mm diameter. **Habitat:** Stony sandstone in fynbos and renosterveld.

Babiana thunbergii

IRIS FAMILY

(= *Antholyza plicata*)

Cockscomb (E)

(Named after the eminent eighteenth-century Swedish botanist, Carl Peter Thunberg, dubbed the father of South African botany)

Cormous perennial 40–70 cm high, with short, velvety, horizontal branches. Leaves lance-shaped and stiffly pleated, hairless. Flowers bright red with greenish-yellow and black markings on some of the petals, tubular with the tube curved upwards, 25–35 mm long. **Habitat:** Coastal sandy flats and dunes. **Notes:** The curious red flowers are pollinated by sunbirds.

Gladiolus saccatus

IRIS FAMILY

(= *Anomalesia saccata*)

Suikerkannetjie (A)

(Latin *saccatus*, spurred or pouched, a reference to the little spur on the underside of the flowers)

Slender, usually branched cormous perennial, 20–100 cm high, the base of the stems purplish with paler mottling. Leaves narrow and usually with two ribs along their length, often greyish. Flowers facing upwards along the inclined stems, brilliant red with a large, stalked upper petal and five greenish scale-like lower petals, 45–60 mm long.

Habitat: Along shale slopes.

Notes: The curious flowers are adapted to pollination by sunbirds.

Gladiolus scullyi

IRIS FAMILY

Partridge gladiolus (E), patryspypie (A)

(Named after William Scully, Magistrate of Namaqualand in the 1890s)

Cormous perennial, 20–60 cm high. Leaves narrowly sword-shaped. Flowers two-lipped, dull mauve or yellowish grey, strongly scented of violets, 25–30 mm diameter.

Habitat: Stony clay soils in open scrub.

Gladiolus watermeyeri

IRIS FAMILY

Soetkalkoentjie (A)

(Named after Mr E.B. Watermeyer, farmer and surveyor)

Cormous perennial, 10–30 cm high. Leaves narrow and strongly ribbed along their length. Flowers with the upper petal deeply hooded and translucent, the side petals conspicuously veined with brown and the lower tepals yellowish towards the base, strongly scented of violets, 30–40 mm diameter.

Habitat: Rocky sandstone soils in open scrub.

Notes: Marvellously fragrant but very cryptic and more often located first by its smell.

Gladiolus equitans

IRIS FAMILY

amaqua kalkoentjie (E), groot
boikalkoentjie (A)

Latin *equitans,* riding astride, alluding to
he successively overlapping leaves)

Cormous perennial, 15–30 cm high. Leaves
rather broadly oblong and leathery with
thickened reddish margins. Flowers orange to
scarlet with the lower tepals yellowish in the
lower half, the upper petals broadest and the
lower two narrow, 30–35 mm diameter.
Habitat: Granite hills, usually wedged in rock
cracks.

Melasphaerula ramosa

IRIS FAMILY

airybells (E), feëklokkie,
aardmannetjie (A)

Latin *ramosus,* branched)

Cormous perennial, 30–60 cm high. Leaves
sword-shaped and soft-textured. Flowers on
slender, wiry branches, small and two-lipped,
cream to pale yellow with the lower petals
streaked with reddish brown, 10 mm diameter.
Habitat: Rocky slopes, usually sheltered by
rocks or shrubs.

Lapeirousia silenoides

IRIS FAMILY

Springbok painted petals (E), cabong (N)
(Resembling the genus *Silene* in its flowers)

Tufted, dwarf cormous perennial, 5–12 cm high. Leaves narrow and
conspicuously ribbed along their length, the
lowermost longest and arching. Flowers
crowded, with long slender tubes 30–50 mm
long, magenta to cerise with cream-coloured
markings in the centre, 15–20 mm diameter.
Habitat: Seasonally moist gravelly granite-
derived soils.
Notes: This lovely species is particularly common along the roadsides near Kamieskroon.

Lapeirousia arenicola

IRIS FAMILY

(Latin *arenicola,* sand-dwelling, alluding to
its favoured habitat)

Tufted, dwarf cormous perennial, 10–12 cm high. Leaves narrow and
conspicuously ribbed along their length, the
lowermost longest and arching. Flowers
crowded, with slender tubes 10–30 mm long,
cream to pink with red spots at the base of the
lower three petals, 10–15 mm diameter.
Habitat: Deep sandy flats towards the coast.
Notes: Most commonly seen on the sandy flat
north-west of Vanrhynsdorp.

Euphorbia dregeana

EUPHORBIA FAMILY

Dikloot-melkbos (A)

(One of many species commemorating the
plant collector J.F. Drége)

Rounded succulent shrub to 2 m high, with
straight, cane-like branches that are 8–12 mm
diameter, pale greyish with prominent leaf
scars and exuding a milky sap when damaged.
Leaves reduced to scales and soon deciduous.
Flower heads in loose flat-topped clusters at
the branch tips, yellowish, 6–8 mm diameter.
Habitat: Dry rocky slopes.

Euphorbia hamata

EUPHORBIA FAMILY

Beesmelkbos, beeskrag (A)

(Latin *hamatus,* hooked, referring to the
prong-like tubercles on the stems)

Bushy succulent shrublet to 45 cm high, with
somewhat three-angled branches 6–13 mm
diameter, covered with prominent spreading or
curved tubercles, exuding a milky sap when
damaged. Leaves elliptical but soon deciduous.
Flower heads unisexual, solitary at the branch
tips and surrounded by three prominent, often
pinkish leaf-like bracts, yellowish, honey-
scented, 5–7 mm diameter.
Habitat: Dry stony slopes.

Crassula columnaris

RASSULA FAMILY

Chakibutton (E), sentkannetjie,
bergkoesnaatjie (A)

Latin *columnaris*, columnar, alluding to the
shape of the plant)

Dwarf perennial or biennial succulent to
10 cm high, sometimes branched at the base.
Leaves opposite, succulent, scale-like with
minutely hairy margins, closely overlapping in
four rows to form a column. Flowers in a
round head, tubular, white to yellow or tinged
reddish, fragrant, 7–13 mm long.
Habitat: Rock pavements and quartz patches.

Crassula brevifolia

CRASSULA FAMILY

(Latin *brevifolius*, short-leaved)

Twiggy shrublets to 50 cm high.
Leaves opposite, succulent and
clustered towards the ends of the branches,
boat-shaped with hard, translucent margins
and covered with a grey bloom. Flowers in
clusters on slender stalks at the branch tips,
yellowish or white tinged pink, cup-shaped,
3–5 mm diameter.
Habitat: In crevices on granite or quartzite
outcrops.

Tylecodon wallichii

CRASSULA FAMILY

Yellow butterbush (E), kokerbos,
kandelaarbos (A)

(Named after the nineteenth-century
Danish botanist, Nathaniel Wallich)

Succulent shrublet to 1 m high, with fibrous
stems that are covered with short, blunt
protuberances formed from the leaf bases.
Leaves dry or shed at flowering, lance-shaped
to rounded. Flowers in a spreading panicle,
urn-shaped, nodding, greenish yellow,
10–15 mm long.
Habitat: Dry stony soils among scrub.

Tylecodon paniculatus
CRASSULA FAMILY

Common butterbush (E), botterboom (A)

(Latin *paniculatus,* bearing the flowers in a branched raceme or panicle)

Succulent shrublet to 1,5 m high. Leaves deciduous and usually withered at flowering, broadly rounded and fleshy, bright green. Flowers in reddish panicles, nodding and shortly tubular, greenish to orange or red, 20–25 mm long.
Habitat: Dry rocky slopes in scrub.
Notes: Seldom grazed by stock but sometimes eaten in summer, causing cramping or death.

Cotyledon orbiculata
CRASSULA FAMILY

Dog's ears (E), plakkie, hondeoor (A)

(Latin *orbiculatus,* circular, referring to the rounded leaves)

Brittle perennial shrublet to 1 m high, more or less covered with a powdery white bloom. Leaves opposite, succulent and very varied in shape, grey with a red or pale margin. Flowers pendulous, tubular with recurved lobes, red or orange, 25–30 mm long.
Habitat: Widespread in coastal and inland scrub on sandy or stony soils.
Notes: Flower stalks used by early hunters as a flute to mimic the call of a young klipspringer, luring the adults within arrow range.

Tetragonia fruticosa
MESEMB FAMILY

Klimopkinkelbossie, waterslaaibos (A)

(Latin *fruticosus,* shrubby)

Erect or sprawling shrub to 1 m high, often with long trailing branches. Leaves somewhat diamond-shaped, fleshy with the margins rolled under and covered with glistening papillae. Flowers in small groups towards the ends of the branches, yellow, 3–4 mm diameter. Fruits broadly four-winged, with knobs between the wings.
Habitat: Gravelly and sandy soils, especially along the coast.

Mesembryanthemum guerichianum

MESEMB FAMILY

ice plant (E), brakvy (A), kama, nuta (N)

(Named for Georg Gürich, a German geologist, who collected the species)

Trailing or sprawling succulent annual or biennial to 60 cm high with four-angled stems. Leaves in a basal tuft and along the stems, ovate and folded, covered with large, glistening bladder cells and often flushed reddish, to 25 x 10 cm. Flowers in branched clusters, pink with a white or greenish centre, 25–55 mm diameter. Fruits five-segmented.

Habitat: Sandy flats, often along roadsides.

Mesembryanthemum barklyi

MESEMB FAMILY

Giant ice plant, elephant's toilet paper (E), olifantslaai (A), kama, nuta (N)

(Named for Sir H. Barkly, who first collected the species)

Trailing or sprawling succulent annual or biennial to 1 m with four-angled stems. Leaves in a basal tuft and along the stems, ovate, covered with glistening bladder cells, to 40 x 25 cm. Flowers in branched clusters, pink or white, 25–55 mm diameter. Fruits five-segmented.

Habitat: Sandy plains.

Notes: May form large fields.

Cleretum papulosum

MESEMB FAMILY

(Latin *papulosus*, with nipple-like pustules, referring to the leaves)

Tufted annual herb to 5 cm high. Leaves mostly in a basal tuft, elliptical and lightly channelled, covered with large bladder cells. Flowers solitary on short stalks, yellow, 10–40 mm diameter. Fruits five-segmented.

Habitat: Sandy or gravelly flats.

Notes: Occurs in two forms, an early blooming, small-flowered form (subspecies *papulosum*) that is self-fertilised and a later blooming, large-flowered form (subspecies *schlechteri*) that is cross-fertilised.

Dorotheanthus maughanii

MESEMB FAMILY

Karoo snow (E)

(Named after Dr Maughan Brown, resident in Calvinia, who first collected the species)

Tufted annual herb to 5 cm high. Leaves mostly in a basal tuft, spade-shaped, covered with large bladder cells. Flowers solitary on slender stalks, white with a red centre, with prominent, glistening, knob-like stigmas, 50–60 mm diameter. Fruits five-segmented. **Habitat:** Dry gravelly clay in karroid scrub. **Notes:** Common near Calvinia.

Dorotheanthus rourkei

MESEMB FAMILY

(Named after Cape Town botanist, John Rourke)

Tufted annual herb to 5 cm high. Leaves mostly in a basal tuft, narrowly paddle-shaped, covered with large bladder cells. Flowers solitary on slender stalks, white, yellow, orange or pinkish to red, 20–40 mm diameter. Fruits five-segmented. **Habitat:** Deep red sands. **Notes:** Common on the sandy flats north of Vanrhynsdorp.

Aridaria brevicarpa

MESEMB FAMILY

Day-blooming donkeybush (E)

(Greek *brevicarpus*, short-fruited, referring to the almost globular capsules)

Twiggy shrub to 1 m high. Leaves succulent and cylindrical, to 30 x 4 mm. Flowers white to pale pink, closing at dusk, 25 mm diameter. Fruits subglobose, remaining open when dry. **Habitat:** Sandy and gravelly slopes. **Notes:** The flowers of *Aridaria noctiflora* open at dusk and close in the morning.

Lampranthus watermeyeri

MESEMB FAMILY

Watermeyer's lampranthus (E)

(Named after local resident E.B. Watermeyer, who first collected the species)

Rounded succulent shrublet to 30 cm high. Leaves incurved and ± cylindrical, 20–35 x 6 mm. Flowers mostly solitary on long stalks, white or rarely purple, 50–70 mm diameter. Fruits five-segmented.

Habitat: Stony flats in low scrub.

Lampranthus hoerleinianus

MESEMB FAMILY

Hörlein's lampranthus (E)

(Named after a Mr Hörlein, probably of Consolidated Diamond Mines, who facilitated the expedition on which the species was first collected)

Succulent shrublet to 70 cm high. Leaves spreading and ± three-sided, 25–30 x 9 mm. Flowers on very short stalks, purple, 30–40 mm diameter. Fruits five-segmented.

Habitat: Sandy places among rocks.

Ruschia goodiae

MESEMB FAMILY

Namaqua cushion ruschia (E)

(Named for a Mrs Good who first collected the species)

Rounded succulent shrub to 60 cm high, with erect, yellowish branches. Leaves three-angled and succulent. Flowers in clusters, pinkish magenta, 20–25 mm diameter. Fruits five-segmented, top-shaped.

Habitat: Gravelly granite slopes.

Ruschia extensa

MESEMB FAMILY

Namaqua bush ruschia (E)

(Latin *extensus*, stretched out, referring to the long internodes)

Rounded shrub to 1 m high, with spreading, reddish branches. Leaves succulent and almost cylindrical. Flowers in clusters, with a central cone of staminodes, magenta, 15 mm diameter. **Habitat:** Gravelly granite slopes.

Drosanthemum hispidum

MESEMB FAMILY

Roadside dew vygie (E)

(Latin *hispidus*, bristly, referring to the branches)

Erect or spreading shrublet to 60 cm high, with red branches covered in short, stiff hairs. Leaves sausage-shaped, bending downwards, rounded at the tips and densely covered with small bladder cells. Flowers solitary, magenta, 20 mm diameter. Fruits 4–6-segmented. **Habitat:** Pioneer of disturbed, dry flats and roadsides.

Malephora crocea

MESEMB FAMILY

Saffron finger kanna (E), rooivinger-kanna (A)

(Latin *croceus*, saffron yellow)

Erect succulent shrublet to 20 cm high. Leaves crowded on short shoots, finger-like and three-sided. Flowers solitary on short stalks at the branch tips, orange to red, 25–30 mm diameter. Fruits 8–12-segmented. **Habitat:** Dry sandy flats.

Cheiridopsis namaquensis

MESEMB FAMILY

(= *Cheiridopsis cigarettifera*)

Cigarettes (E)

(Latin *namaquensis*, from Namaqualand)

Compact, cushion-forming succulent perennial to 5 cm high. Leaves of two sizes, three-sided and pincer-like, slightly warty on the keels, drying to form a cylindrical papery sheath. Flowers yellow fading red, 30–45 mm diameter. Fruits with ±10 segments.

Habitat: Stony slopes and rock crevices.

Cheiridopsis denticulata

MESEMB FAMILY

T'noutsiama (N)

(Latin *denticulatus*, finely toothed, referring to the leaf keels)

Compact, cushion-forming succulent perennial to 10 cm high. Leaves three-sided, warty and usually with some teeth on the keels, drying to form a cylindrical papery sheath. Flowers cream to yellow and often purplish towards the edges, 60–70 mm diameter. Fruits with 17–19 segments.

Habitat: Sandy and gravelly flats, often in seasonal washes.

Conicosia elongata

MESEMB FAMILY

Goslings (E), gansies, varkslaai (A)

(Latin *elongatus*, elongate, referring to the slender leaves)

Sprawling succulent perennial with a tuber, 10–20 cm high. Leaves slender and tapering, cylindrical to half-cylindrical. Flowers solitary, white or yellow, 50–60 mm diameter. Fruits cone-shaped with 10–25 flaps, opening when dry.

Habitat: Sandy flats, often coastal.

Notes: One of very few mesembs with fruits that open when dry rather than when wet.

Jordaaniella cuprea
MESEMB FAMILY

Copper mat vygie (E)

(Latin *cupreus*, coppery, referring to the flower colour)

Creeping succulent perennial forming compact mats. Leaves finger-shaped, 5–10 cm long. Flowers solitary on short side branches, yellow to salmon-coloured with orange to pink edging, 30–100 mm diameter. Fruits on horizontal stalks, 14–20-segmented.
Habitat: Coastal sands.
Notes: Common near Port Nolloth.

Cephalophyllum pillansii
MESEMB FAMILY

Namaqua creeping vygie (E)

(Named for Cape Town botanist, N.S. Pillans, who first collected the species)

Compact succulent shrublet to 10 cm high, with creeping, annual branches. Leaves erect, cylindrical and succulent, greyish. Flowers solitary on slender stalks, pale yellow with a red centre, 60 mm diameter. Fruits 10–15-segmented.
Habitat: Loamy granite flats, often a pioneer along road banks.

Cephalophyllum spongiosum
MESEMB FAMILY

Giant mat vygie (E), volstruisvygie (A)

(Latin *spongiosus*, spongy and succulent, referring to the leaves)

Sprawling or trailing succulent perennial. Leaves large and finger-shaped, ±10 cm long. Flowers solitary on short side branches, red with an orange centre, 70–100 mm diameter. Fruits on erect stalks, 18–28-segmented.
Habitat: Coastal sands in scrub.

Cephalophyllum spissum

MESEMB FAMILY

(Latin *spissus*, compact, dense, alluding to
the plant form)

Compact, cushion-forming succulent perennial to 10 cm high. Leaves
finger-shaped and three-sided. Flowers solitary
or few on short stalks, purple to pink with a
paler centre, 30–40 mm diameter. Fruits
11–15-segmented.
Habitat: Quartz patches.

Monilaria moniliformis

MESEMB FAMILY

White beaded vygie (E), ertjievygie (A)

(Latin *moniliformis*, like a string of beads,
referring to the curious stems)

Cushion-forming succulent shrublet to 12 cm
high, with the branches pinched like a string of
barrel-shaped beads. Leaves finger-like, fleshy,
covered with glistening bladder cells. Flowers
solitary on long stalks, white, 35–40 mm
diameter. Fruits 5–7-segmented.
Habitat: Quartz patches and stony quartzite
slopes.

Dactylopsis digitata

MESEMB FAMILY

Hitchhiker plant (E),
vingertjie-en-duimpie (A)

(Latin *digitatus*, with the leaves arranged
like fingers)

Compact succulent perennial to 20 cm high.
Leaves very succulent and cylindrical, the first
short and stubby and the second emerging at
an angle and longer, thus resembling a thumb
and finger. Flowers white to cream, 10–20 mm
diameter, remaining open day and night. Fruits
five-segmented.
Habitat: Gravelly quartz patches.

Argyroderma fissum
MESEMB FAMILY

False stoneflower (E)

(Latin *fissus*, cleft or split, referring to the distinct leaf pairs)

Tufted succulent to 15 cm high, usually forming clumps. Leaves reduced to a single pair, finger-like but often flattened on the upper side, firm and highly succulent. Flowers solitary, protruding from between the leaves, purple with a white centre, 30–40 mm diameter. Fruits 14–18-segmented.

Habitat: Patches of gravelly white quartz on the Knersvlakte.

Argyroderma delaetii
MESEMB FAMILY

Silver stoneflower (E), bababoudjies, jakkalsniertjie (A)

(Named after the succulent grower, Mr de Laet-Contich, in whose collection the species was first noticed)

Dwarf succulents to 5 cm high, solitary or forming clumps. Leaves reduced to a single pair, almost globular, smooth, silver-skinned, firm and highly succulent. Flowers solitary, protruding from between the leaves, white to purple or yellow, 30–40 mm diameter. Fruits 14–18-segmented.

Habitat: Patches of gravelly white quartz on the Knersvlakte north of Vanrhynsdorp.

Conophytum subfenestratum
MESEMB FAMILY

Fenestrate coneflower (E)

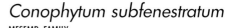

(Latin *sub-*, *fenestratus*, somewhat windowed, referring to the transparent patches on the leaves)

Dwarf succulent perennial to 5 cm high, usually solitary. Leaves reduced to a single pair joined together into a rounded body with more or less transparent patches or windows at the top, 20–25 mm long. Flowers solitary with the petals joined into a slender tube protruding from the mouth of the leaf-body, pink, 15–20 mm diameter.

Habitat: Gravelly quartz fields.

Conophytum minutum
MESEMB FAMILY
Common coneflower (E), toontjies (A)
(Latin *minutus*, very small, minute)

Dwarf succulent perennial to
5 cm high, forming clumps. Leaves reduced to
a single pair joined together into a cone-like
body, spotted, 15–20 mm long. Flowers solitary
with the petals joined into a slender tube
protruding from the mouth of the leaf-body,
magenta to pink, 10–15 mm diameter.
Habitat: Rock sheets or quartzite outcrops.

Oophytum nanum
MESEMB FAMILY
Pebbleflower (E)
(Latin *nanus*, dwarf)

Dwarf succulent perennial to
5 cm high, forming clumps. Leaves reduced to
two pairs joined together into a small globular
body, 10 mm long. Flowers solitary and protruding from the mouth of the leaf-body, pink
with a paler centre, 20–25 mm diameter.
Habitat: Gravelly quartz fields.

Hypertelis salsoloides
MOLLUGO FAMILY
Braksuring (A)
(Resembling the genus *Salsola* or saltwort)

Dwarf, tufted shrublet to 30 cm
high, often much-grazed. Leaves cylindrical
and fleshy, greyish. Flowers in umbels on slender, glandular pedicels which bend down after
flowering, white to pink with the sepals folded
back, 10–12 mm diameter.
Habitat: Dry, often limey or saline soils.

Augea capensis
ZYGOPHYLLUM FAMILY

Elandslaai, boesmandruiwe (A)

(Latin *capensis*, from the Cape)

Brittle succulent annual or short-lived perennial to 40 cm high. Leaves opposite and cylindrical or club-shaped, very succulent. Flowers in small clusters, whitish with the petals three-toothed at the ends, 15 mm diameter. Fruits large and egg-shaped with woolly seeds.
Habitat: Dry sandy flats.

Zygophyllum morgsana
ZYGOPHYLLUM FAMILY

Four-winged twinleaf (E), slaaibos (A)

(Named for the similarity of the leaves to those of a Syrian species, *Z. fabago*, locally known as 'morgsani')

Rounded shrub with grey stems to 1,5 m high. Leaves opposite and shortly stalked, fleshy and divided into two broad leaflets with an unpleasant smell when crushed. Flowers in pairs between the leaves, with four petals that are pale yellow with a purple blotch just above the base, 20 mm diameter. Fruits rounded with four large wings.
Habitat: Sandy flats, often coastal.
Notes: Leaves and seeds are poisonous.

Zygophyllum cordifolium
ZYGOPHYLLUM FAMILY

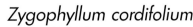

Penny-leaved twinleaf (E), sjielingbos, geldjiesbos (A)

(Latin *cordifolius*, heart-shaped with two lobes, alluding to the paired, rounded leaves)

Greyish shrublet to 70 cm high. Leaves opposite and not stalked, fleshy and almost circular. Flowers in pairs between the leaves with five petals that are pale yellow with a prominent red blotch near the base, 20 mm diameter. Fruits egg-shaped with five narrow wings.
Habitat: Sandy or gravelly flats, often coastal.

Tribulus cristatus
ZYGOPHYLLUM FAMILY

(Latin *cristatus*, crested, referring to the winged fruits)

Prostrate annual with stems radiating from a crown. Leaves opposite and unequal in size, divided into numerous oblong, silky leaflets. Flowers solitary in the leaf axils, bright yellow, 20 mm diameter. Fruits with four crested wings.

Habitat: Sandy flats and roadsides.

Notes: A similar species, *Z. zeyheri*, has small, spiny fruits that fragment into four segments.

Grielum humifusum
DUIKER-ROOT FAMILY

White-eyed duiker-root (E), duikerwortel (A), t'koeibee (N)

(Latin *humifusus*, spreading on the ground)

Prostrate, thinly white-woolly annual often forming mats. Leaves lobed to deeply divided into flat segments that are rounded at the tips and nearly hairless above. Flowers yellow, usually with a pale eye, 20–30 mm.

Habitat: Sandy lower slopes and flats.

Notes: Fleshy roots are edible although slimy. Common along roadsides and in fallow lands.

Grielum grandiflorum
DUIKER-ROOT FAMILY

Green-eyed duiker-root (E), platdoring (A)

(Latin *grandiflorus*, large-flowered)

Sprawling white-woolly perennial forming mats. Leaves deeply divided into narrow to thread-like segments, each with a small pointed tip and covered with silvery hairs. Flowers yellow, usually greenish in the centre, 35–50 mm diameter.

Habitat: Sandy and stony coastal flats.

Monsonia parvifolia

GERANIUM FAMILY

Desert parasol-flower (E)

(Latin *parvifolius*, small-leaved)

Mat-forming perennial to 1 m diameter with the branches covered in glandular hairs. Leaves broadly ovate with irregularly toothed margins. Flowers few on slender stalks in the leaf axils, yellow or white to pink, 25–35 mm diameter. **Habitat:** Dry sandy flats.

Monsonia crassicaule

GERANIUM FAMILY

(= *Sarcocaulon crassicaule*)

Bushman's candle (E), boesmanskers (A), noerap (N)

(Latin *crassicaulus*, thick-stemmed)

Spiny shrublet to 50 cm high, with succulent branches thicker than 10 mm diameter. Leaves ovate and irregularly divided with the margins toothed, usually hairy. Flowers pale to bright yellow, to 55 mm diameter with the sepals each bearing a sharp point at the tips longer than 2 mm.

Habitat: Dry rocky or stony slopes.

Notes: *Monsonia ciliata* has the petals fringed with fine hairs. *Monsonia spinosa* has notched leaves with smooth margins.

Pelargonium echinatum

GERANIUM FAMILY

Hedgehog stork's bill (E), krimpvarkmalva (A)

(Latin *echinatus*, armed with prickles or spines like a hedgehog)

Fleshy shrublet to 50 cm high, with gnarled, dark grey, prickly stems. Leaves rounded and shallowly three- to seven-lobed, grey-powdery beneath. Flowers in clusters on prominent stalks, white or pale pink to brilliant magenta with dark red streaks and blotches on the upper petals, 18–25 mm diameter. **Habitat:** Rocky slopes in scrub.

Pelargonium crithmifolium

GERANIUM FAMILY

Dikbasmalva (A)

(Latin *crithmifolium*, with leaves like a
Crithmum or samphire)

Fleshy shrublet to 1 m high, with smooth,
swollen, pale greenish stems. Leaves fleshy
and deeply divided into narrow, toothed lobes.
Flowers in branched clusters, pale pink with
reddish flecks on the upper petals, 15–20 mm
diameter, the old pedicels becoming stiff and
thorny.
Habitat: Dry stony soils.

Pelargonium sericifolium

GERANIUM FAMILY

Silver-leaved stork's bill (E)

(Latin *sericifolium*, leaves with silky hairs
pressed to the surface)

Closely branched shrublet to 20 cm high, with
the remains of the leaf bases persisting on the
branches. Leaves deeply divided into narrow
segments covered with silvery silky hairs.
Flowers in pairs at the branch tips on slender
pedicels, brilliant magenta with darker streaks
on the three lower petals, 20 mm diameter.
Habitat: Rocky or stony granite slopes near
Springbok.

Pelargonium incrassatum

GERANIUM FAMILY

T'neitjie (N)

(Latin *incrassatus*, thickened, a mistaken
reference to the leaves which are not
evidently leathery or succulent)

Tufted tuberous perennial to 50 cm high, with
a large tuber covered with flaking brown bark.
Leaves in a tuft, irregularly lobed and soft and
silky with a silvery sheen. Flowers in dense
rounded clusters on long stalks, brilliant
magenta with the three lower petals very much
smaller than the upper, 15 mm diameter.
Habitat: Gravelly soils.
Notes: Easily the most outstanding pelargonium in Namaqualand. The tubers were a
traditional food source.

Pelargonium praemorsum
GERANIUM FAMILY
Engeltjiemalva (A)
(Latin *praemorsus*, much bitten, alluding to the distinctly toothed leaves that appear to have been bitten off at the ends)
Twiggy shrublet to 1 m high, with jointed, brown stems. Leaves fleshy and deeply divided with five toothed lobes. Flowers mostly solitary, white with red veining on the two upper petals and with only two, smaller lower petals, 25–35 mm diameter.
Habitat: Rocky slopes in open scrub.

Montinia caryophyllacea
MONTINIA FAMILY
Peperbos (A), t'iena (N)
(Latin *caryophyllaceus*, resembling certain members of the carnation family Caryophyllaceae in its flowers)
Erect greyish shrub to 1,5 m high. Leaves elliptical, leathery and sometimes in tufts. Flowers at the branch tips with the sexes on separate plants, the male flowers in small clusters and the female flowers solitary or in pairs, white, 8 mm diameter.
Habitat: Stony or rocky slopes in scrub.
Notes: The hard stems were used by the Khoisan as digging sticks.

Solanum giftbergense
POTATO FAMILY
Gifappeltjie (A)
(Latin *giftbergensis*, from the Gifberg near Klawer)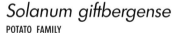
Shrub to 1,5 m high, with mealy stems armed with slender, yellow or reddish-brown spines to 12 mm long. Leaves ovate and conspicuously lobed, spiny on the veins. Flowers in clusters of one to four, mauve to purple, to 10 mm diameter. Berries orange to red and 10 mm diameter.
Habitat: Rocky slopes.
Notes: The berries of all solanums should be regarded as poisonous.

Gomphocarpus cancellatus

MILKWEED FAMILY

(= *Asclepias cancellata*)

Milkweed (E), katoenbos (A)

(Latin *cancellatus*, latticed, alluding to the lacy appearance of the flower heads)

Shrub to 1,5 m high, with hairy branches oozing a milky sap when damaged. Leaves opposite, elliptical and leathery with wavy margins. Flowers cream-coloured and green, 10 mm diameter. Fruits swollen and teardrop-shaped with fleshy spines.

Habitat: Stony slopes.

Notes: All milkweeds should be regarded as toxic. Powdered roots used as a snuff.

Hoodia gordonii

MILKWEED FAMILY

Hoodia (E), wolweghaap (A), ghaap (N)

(Commemorates Col. Robert Gordon, commander of the garrison at the Cape, who collected the species in 1779)

Leafless succulent producing clumps of 11–17-ridged stems closely covered with spine-tipped warts. Flowers saucer-shaped, pinkish to maroon and foul-smelling, 40–100 mm diameter.

Habitat: Dry stony slopes and flats.

Notes: Used traditionally by the San as an appetite suppressant.

Pachypodium namaquanum

MILKWEED FAMILY

Halfmens (A)

(Latin *namaquensis*, from Namaqualand)

Usually single-stemmed succulent trees to 3 m high, with a tapering, swollen stem covered with spine-tipped warts. Leaves elliptical and densely velvety with wavy margins. Flowers clustered among the leaves, tubular, yellowish green outside and reddish inside, c.50 mm long.

Habitat: Very arid rocky slopes.

Notes: Stems tilted towards the north, probably as protection from overheating in the summer sun.

Oxalis comosa

OXALIS FAMILY

Rock sorrel (E)

(Latin *comosus*, bearing a tuft of leaves)

Erect and often branched cormous perennial to 80 cm high. Leaves crowded at the tips of the stems and branches, divided into three triangular leaflets that are deeply notched at the tips and either hairless or sparsely hairy beneath. Flowers solitary on slender stalks from the leaf clusters, pale pink with a yellow cup, 15 mm diameter.

Habitat: Rocky granite outcrops, often in the shade of boulders.

Notes: Common in the Kamiesberg.

Oxalis namaquana

OXALIS FAMILY

Namaqua sorrel (E), namakwasuring (A)

(Latin *namaquensis*, from Namaqualand)

Tufted cormous perennial to 10 cm high. Leaves divided into three hairless oblong leaflets that are shortly notched at the tips. Flowers solitary on slender stalks, bright yellow, 20 mm diameter.

Habitat: Along seasonal streams and in seeps on granite outcrops.

Oxalis obtusa

OXALIS FAMILY

Yellow-eyed sorrel (E), geeloogsuring (A)

(Latin *obtusus*, blunt, referring to the leaflets)

Tufted cormous perennial to 10 cm high. Leaves divided into three broad, hairy or hairless leaflets that are deeply notched at the tips. Flowers solitary on slender stalks that bear a pair of minute scales at a joint near the middle, pink, brick-red or pale yellow with a yellow eye and usually with reddish veining on the petals, 20 mm diameter.

Habitat: Common and widespread on sandy, gravelly or clay soils, often in the shelter of rocks.

Oxalis callosa

OXALIS FAMILY

Red-eyed sorrel (E)

(Latin *callosus*, bearing a callus or wart, a reference to the orange calli on the sepals, a common feature in oxalis)

Small cormous perennial to 10 cm high. Leaves on hairy petioles and divided into three elliptical leaflets that are lightly notched at the tips and hairy beneath. Flowers solitary on slender hairy stalks, pink with a yellow tube ringed with purple at the mouth, 20 mm across.
Habitat: Clay flats.
Notes: Common between Nieuwoudtville and Calvinia.

Oxalis pulchella

OXALIS FAMILY

Large sorrel (E), grootsuring (A)

(Latin *pulchellus*, beautiful and little)

Tufted cormous perennial to 15 cm high. Leaves divided into three oblong leaflets that are shortly notched at the tips and sparsely hairy beneath. Flowers solitary on slender stalks, pale lilac with a broad yellow cup, 20–30 mm diameter.
Habitat: Sheltered spots on granite outcrops.

Wahlenbergia annularis

BELLFLOWER FAMILY

Greater bellflower (E), pronkblouklokkie (A)

(Latin *annularis*, ring-shaped, referring to the often ring-shaped gland below the stigma)

Tufted annual herb to 40 cm high. Leaves mostly in a basal tuft, elliptical and roughly hairy with wavy margins. Flowers on long slender stalks, bowl-shaped, white to pale blue, 15–20 mm diameter.
Habitat: Sandy flats and lower slopes.
Notes: Similar to *W. androsacea*, which has smaller, deeper flowers.

Heliophila coronopifolia
CABBAGE FAMILY

Showy sunflax (E), sporrie (A)

(Latin *coronopifolius*, with leaves like swine-cress, *Coronopus*)

Annual herb to 60 cm high with the stem roughly hairy below. Leaves narrow but sometimes lobed. Flowers blue with a white or greenish centre, 15 mm diameter. Fruits slender and beaded, 30–90 mm long.
Habitat: Gravelly and sandy flats and lower slopes.

Heliophila variabilis
CABBAGE FAMILY

Sporrie (A)

(Latin *variabilis,* varying in colour, a reference to the flowers which open white but turn pink with age)

Erect or spreading annual herb to 35 cm high, with minutely hairy stems and leaves. Leaves divided into three to seven thread-like segments. Flowers white turning pinkish with age, 10 mm diameter. Fruits narrow and weakly beaded, 20–40 mm long.
Habitat: Dry sandy or gravelly flats.

Pharnaceum aurantium
MOLLUGO FAMILY

Karoosneeuvygie (A)

(Latin *aurantius,* orange, referring to the colour of the flowers in the original specimens seen)

Sprawling or erect shrublet to 80 cm high. Leaves scattered along the stems, small and needle-like with membranous, fringed stipules at the base. Flowers on long wiry pedicels that flex down in fruit, white to yellow or rarely orange, 5 mm diameter.
Habitat: Stony or gravelly slopes in open scrub.
Notes: Flowers are usually white but populations near Garies have wonderful orange flowers.

Hermannia trifurca

MALLOW FAMILY
Koerhassie, koerasie (N)
(Latin *trifurcatus,* three-forked, alluding to
the leaves)

Twiggy shrublet to 1 m high. Leaves oblong,
often blunt and three-toothed at the tips,
leathery with a greyish powdery surface.
Flowers nodding on slender, arching, one-sided
racemes, pinkish mauve, slightly sour smelling,
10–12 mm long.
Habitat: Rocky slopes in scrub.

Hermannia stricta

MALLOW FAMILY
Desert rose (E)
(Latin *strictus,* very straight, referring to the
stiffly upright branches)

Twiggy shrublet with stiffly erect branches to
1 m high. Leaves oblong and narrowed below,
blunt and coarsely toothed in the upper part,
thinly mealy on both surfaces. Flowers
nodding on slender stalks, pink to apricot,
15–25 mm diameter.
Habitat: Dry stony slopes.
Notes: May become covered in charming,
lantern-shaped flowers.

Hermannia disermifolia

MALLOW FAMILY
Jeukbos (A)
(Greek, origin obscure, possibly suggesting
with leaves like *Salvia disermas*)

Twiggy shrublet to 1 m high, with mealy
branches. Leaves oblong and stiffly leathery
with crisped margins, densely mealy on both
surfaces. Flowers nodding on slender stalks,
yellow, 10 mm diameter.
Habitat: Granite outcrops.

Melianthus pectinatus
MELIANTHUS FAMILY
Namaqua turkeybush (E)
(Latin *pectinatus*, with narrow divisions like
a comb, referring to the leaves)

Shrub to 2 m high. Leaves divided into narrow,
often toothed leaflets with the margins rolled
under, hairless above but hairy beneath.
Flowers in whorls of two to four in erect
racemes among the leaves, with red petals in
bud that turn brown at maturity, 20–25 mm
long. Fruits with four large wings.
Habitat: Rocky granite outcrops.
Notes: The curiously shaped flowers, that
appear withered when they are in fact in full
bloom, are pollinated by nectar-feeding birds.

Lebeckia sericea
PEA FAMILY
Silver ganna (E), blou fluitjiebos (A),
t'aibie (N)
(Latin *sericeus*, covered with silky hairs
pressed flat against the surface)
Shrub to 1,5 m high. Leaves divided into three
narrow leaflets thinly or more thickly covered
with silvery silky hairs. Flowers in dense or
open racemes, cream to bright yellow, 10 mm
diameter.
Habitat: Gravelly slopes, often along roadsides.

Lessertia brachypus
PEA FAMILY
Namaqualand balloon pea (E)
(Greek *brachypus*, short-footed, alluding to
the very shortly stalked racemes)
Erect shrublet to 60 cm high. Leaves divided
into several elliptical leaflets. Flowers in very
short racemes that are much shorter than the
leaves, purplish, 6 mm diameter. Pods swollen
and balloon-like with smooth papery walls.
Habitat: Gravelly slopes.

Lessertia frutescens

PEA FAMILY

(= *Sutherlandia frutescens*)

Scarlet balloon pea (E), kankerbos, kalkoentjiebos (A)

(Latin *frutescens*, becoming shrubby)

Erect or sprawling shrublet to 1 m high. Leaves divided into many small oblong leaflets that are rounded at the tips, greyish green and mostly thinly hairy above. Flowers in short racemes, bright red, 20–40 mm long. Pods large and balloon-like with smooth papery walls.
Habitat: Widespread on a variety of soils but usually along roads.
Notes: Very variable in stature and in the size of its flowers and fruit. It is palatable to stock and although it enjoys high repute for the treatment of cancer there is no evidence in support of this belief.

Dyerophytum africanum

PLUMBAGO FAMILY

(Latin *africanus*, from Africa)

Straggling shrub to 1 m high, with slender greyish branches.
Leaves leathery and broadly spoon-shaped with a pointed tip, covered with mealy granules. Flowers crowded in narrow spikes, with the calyx papery and apparently five-winged, creamy with pink tinges, 8–10 mm long.
Habitat: Dry stony slopes.
Notes: Very palatable to stock.

Codon royenii

FORGET-ME-NOT FAMILY

Suikerkelk (A)

(Named after the eighteenth-century Dutch botanist, Adriaan van Royen)

Roughly hairy shrublet to 1,5 m high, covered with white prickles. Leaves elliptical and covered with straight white prickles. Flowers large and bell-shaped, cream to yellow with purple stripes, 25 mm long.
Habitat: Dry stony slopes.

Peliostomum virgatum
SNAPDRAGON FAMILY

(Latin *virgatus*, with slender rod-like stems)
Loosely branched shrublet to 30 cm high, with slender wand-like branches. Leaves elliptical and covered with glandular hairs. Flowers violet with purple and white marks in the throat, 20 mm long.
Habitat: Stony slopes and flats.

Aptosimum indivisum
SNAPDRAGON FAMILY

Karoo violet (E), karooviooltjie (A)
(Latin *indivisus*, undivided, referring to the leaves)
Cushion-forming dwarf shrublet to 7 cm high, with a woody taproot. Leaves spatula-shaped and leathery. Flowers violet with purple marks around the white throat, 15 mm diameter.
Habitat: Rocky flats in open scrub.

Jamesbrittenia fruticosa
SNAPDRAGON FAMILY

(= *Sutera fruticosa*)
(Latin *fruticosus*, shrubby)
Aromatic, twiggy shrublet to 1 m high, with glandular hairs on the new growth. Leaves elliptical and sparsely hairy. Flowers crowded towards the tips of the branches, mauve to purple with a dark purple eye, 15–20 mm diameter with a tube 16–26 mm long.
Habitat: Sandy and stony flats in open scrub.
Notes: Often along roads and at the base of rock outcrops.

Jamesbrittenia racemosa

SNAPDRAGON FAMILY

(= *Sutera tomentosa*)

(Latin *racemosus*, with the flowers in a raceme)

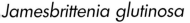

Aromatic annual herb to 50 cm high, covered with glandular hairs. Leaves ovate and coarsely toothed. Flowers in the axils of the upper leaves, white to pale lilac with a star-like purple eye and notched petals, 12–24 mm diameter with a tube 15–18 mm long.
Habitat: Usually granite outcrops in the shelter of boulders or crevices but also gravelly watercourses.

Jamesbrittenia glutinosa

SNAPDRAGON FAMILY

(= *Sutera glutinosa*)

(Latin *glutinosus*, glutinous or gooey)

Aromatic annual or possibly short-lived perennial herb to 50 cm high, covered with glandular hairs. Leaves ovate with toothed margins, covered with glistening glandular hairs. Flowers in the axils of the leaves almost from the base, mauve to lilac with a pale yellow eye, 15–18 mm diameter with a tube 16–24 mm long.
Habitat: Usually granite outcrops in the shelter of boulders or crevices but also gravelly watercourses.

Zaluzianskya affinis

SNAPDRAGON FAMILY

Purple drumstick-flower (E)

(Latin *affinis*, related to, alluding to its close resemblance to *Z. villosa*)

Hairy annual herb to 30 cm high. Leaves more or less elliptical and sparsely hairy. Flowers in crowded spikes that elongate in fruit, white to mauve with a yellow or reddish eye and Y-shaped petals, 10 mm diameter with a slender tube 10–25 mm long.
Habitat: Sandy flats and slopes, often along the coast.
Notes: Replaced in the south by the more hairy *Zaluzianskya villosa*.

Manulea silenoides
SNAPDRAGON FAMILY

Mauve fingerphlox (E)

(Resembling the genus *Silene* in its flowers)

Annual herb branching from the base, to 15 cm high. Leaves in a basal tuft, more or less elliptical and sparsely hairy. Flowers in crowded spikes, mauve with a yellow eye and Y-shaped petals, 6–12 mm diameter with a tube 3,5–5,5 mm long. **Habitat:** Sandy granite soils.

Manulea altissima
SNAPDRAGON FAMILY

Keyhole fingerphlox (E), vingertjies (A)

(Latin *altissimus*, tallest, alluding to the unusually long flowering stalks)

Short-lived perennial herb to 1 m high, covered with foetid glandular hairs. Leaves in a basal tuft, elliptical and obscurely toothed. Flowers crowded in head-like racemes on slender stalks, with the mouth of the floral tube keyhole-shaped, white to pale yellow with a dark yellowish centre, scented, 10 mm diameter. **Habitat:** Deep sandy soils, mainly coastal.

Colpias mollis
SNAPDRAGON FAMILY

Rock snapdragon (E), klipblom (A)

(Latin *mollis*, soft, alluding to the soft hairs)

Tufted shrublet to 20 cm high, usually softly hairy but sometimes hairless. Leaves ovate with toothed margins. Flowers on slender stalks in the leaf axils, funnel-shaped with a pair of small pouches beneath, yellow to white, scented, 20–30 mm diameter. **Habitat:** Shaded, south-facing rock crevices, mostly in granite.

Nemesia leipoldtii

SNAPDRAGON FAMILY

Karoo nemesia (E), karooleeubekkie (A)

(Named after the famous South African poet
and naturalist, C.L. Leipoldt)

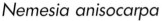

Annual herb to 30 cm high. Leaves opposite,
ovate with toothed margins. Flowers in
racemes, two-lipped and white to mauve with a
yellow patch on the lower lip, the upper four
petals oblong and the lower lip pouched
beneath.
Habitat: Clay flats in open scrub, often along
roadsides.

Nemesia anisocarpa

SNAPDRAGON FAMILY

Namaqua nemesia (E), geelbekkie (A)

(Greek, anisocarpus, unequal fruit, a
misnomer based on malformed fruit)

Annual herb to 20 cm high. Leaves opposite,
elliptical with lightly toothed margins. Flowers
in racemes, two-lipped with a white upper lip
and a yellow lower lip, the upper four petals
oblong and the lower lip with a straight spur
3–5 mm long.
Habitat: Mainly sandy flats and lower slopes.

Nemesia affinis

SNAPDRAGON FAMILY

Sandveld nemesia (E),
sandveldleeubekkie (A)

(Latin affinis, related to, alluding to its
close resemblance to some other species)

Annual herb to 30 cm high. Leaves opposite,
lance-shaped and toothed. Flowers in racemes,
usually yellow but sometimes white or blue,
15 mm diameter, the upper four petals oblong
and the lower lip bulging with two velvety
bumps in the mouth and a spur 3–5 mm long.
Habitat: Sandy and granite slopes and flats.

Hemimeris racemosa
SNAPDRAGON FAMILY

Common yellowfaces (E), bobbejaangesiggies (A)

(Latin *racemosus*, with the flowers in a
raceme)

Annual herb, 3,5–40 cm high. Leaves opposite,
ovate with the margins toothed or lobed.
Flowers on slender pedicels in the upper leaf
axils, yellow, *c.* 7,5–13 mm long with two spurs
1,5–3 mm long.
Habitat: Shaded and moist places, often
among rocks.

Diascia rudolphii
SNAPDRAGON FAMILY

Schlechter's diascia (E)

(Named after the German botanist,
Rudolph Schlechter)

Annual herb, 5–50 cm high. Leaves mostly
basal, elliptical with toothed or scalloped
margins. Flowers solitary on long, slender
pedicels, orange to salmon with a yellow cup
edged with maroon, bowl-shaped with two
shallow pockets, 15–20 mm diameter.
Habitat: Seasonally moist gravelly soils, often
in the shelter of boulders or along stream lines.

Diascia tanyceras
SNAPDRAGON FAMILY

Long-horned diascia (E), bokhorinkies (A)

(Greek *tanyceras*, long-horned, alluding to
the long spurs on the flowers)

Annual herb, 10–50 cm high. Leaves mostly
basal, elliptical with toothed or deeply lobed
margins. Flowers solitary on long stalks, reddish purple with a pair of elliptical spots at
the base of each of the upper two petals,
two-lipped, 15 mm diameter with a pair of
spreading spurs ± 20 mm long.
Habitat: Gravelly loam soils, often in fallow
lands.
Notes: *D. namaquensis* has a single large
yellow spot stretching from the base of each
upper petal onto the base of the adjacent side
petal.

Acanthopsis disperma

ACANTHUS FAMILY

(Greek *dispermus*, two-seeded, alluding to the generic character of only one or two seeds per ovary chamber)

Spiny dwarf perennial to 10 cm high. Leaves in a basal tuft, narrowly elliptical with coarsely toothed and spiny margins. Flowers in dense spikes among spiny bracts, one-lipped, blue or rarely white, 20 mm long.

Habitat: Dry stony slopes and flats.

Paranomus bracteolaris

PROTEA FAMILY

Bokkeveldpoppiesbos (A)

(Latin *bracteolaris*, with small bracts)

Single-stemmed shrub to 2 m high. Leaves finely divided into needle-like segments, hairy when young. Flowers in small clusters arranged in spikes at the branch tips, purple-pink, lightly scented, 20–25 mm long.

Habitat: Drier sandstone slopes.

Vexatorella alpina

PROTEA FAMILY

Kamiesberg vexatorella (E)

(Latin *alpinus*, literally growing in the alpine zone but in this case in the mountains)

Dense shrub to 2 m high, forming large stands. Leaves narrowly elliptical, leathery and greyish green. Flowers in rounded heads 20–25 mm diameter, cream-coloured and fragrant.

Habitat: Granite soils at high altitude.

Notes: Restricted to the upper slopes in the Kamiesberg.

Male

Female

Leucadendron remotum

PROTEA FAMILY

Bokkeveld conebush (E)

(Latin *remotus,* scattered or remote, an allusion to the fact that this species occurs at the extremity of the range of the genus) Single-stemmed, densely leafy shrub to 1,5 m high, branching from near the base. Leaves narrowly elliptical and rounded at the tips, greyish and thinly silky when young. Flowers very small, in rounded heads 15–20 mm across

that are surrounded by dark brown bracts; the sexes are on separate plants, with the male flower heads in clusters at the branch tips and the female flower heads solitary and nested in the upper leaves.

Habitat: Sandy soils on sandstone in dry fynbos.

Notes: Common on the Bokkeveld escarpment near Nieuwoudtville.

Protea glabra

PROTEA FAMILY

Chestnut protea (E), kaiingbos (A)

(Latin *glabrus,* hairless, referring to the leaves or bracts)

Small tree to 5 m high, branching from the base. Leaves elliptical, leathery and grey. Flowers crowded in pincushion-like heads surrounded by spreading, brown bracts, the heads 70–90 mm diameter.

Habitat: Dry sandstone slopes and plateaus in arid fynbos.

Pteronia incana

DAISY FAMILY

Karoo gumbush (E), gombos (A),
t'kaibe (N)
(Latin *incanus,* hoary, alluding to the
grey-woolly leaves)

Stiffly branched, grey-leaved shrub to 1 m high.
Leaves narrow, opposite, grey-woolly. Flower
heads solitary at the branch tips, without ray
florets, yellow, surrounded by several series of
hairless bracts.
Habitat: Dry stony places on sand or clay.

Eriocephalus punctulatus

DAISY FAMILY

Kapokbossie (A)
(Latin *punctulatus,* minutely dotted, referring
to the oil glands on the leaves)

Greyish shrublet to 1 m high. Leaves in
clusters on short side branches, leathery and
needle-like. Flower heads in small clusters
above the leaves, purple with a few white ray
florets, 6–8 mm diameter, surrounded by four
or five elliptical bracts with membranous
margins. Seeds silky.
Habitat: Rocky slopes in scrub.

Pentzia incana

DAISY FAMILY

Skaapkaroo, alsbossie (A)
(Latin *incanus,* hoary, alluding to the
grey-woolly leaves)

Aromatic, twiggy shrub to 1 m high, with
white-woolly stems. Leaves divided into
narrow or thread-like lobes, grey-woolly.
Flower heads solitary on long, sometimes leafy
stalks, without ray florets, yellow, 7–10 mm
diameter, surrounded by several rows of blunt
bracts with membranous margins.
Habitat: Dry stony flats in scrub.

Cotula leptalea

DAISY FAMILY

Namaqua buttons (E),
namakwaganskos (A)

(Greek *leptaleus*, also slender, alluding
to the resemblance to other species)

Slender annual herb to 15 cm high. Leaves
mostly towards the base of the stem, finely
once- or twice-divided and silky. Flower heads
solitary on wiry stalks, without ray florets,
yellow with the outermost florets female,
5–10 mm diameter, surrounded by two series
of elliptical bracts with brown-edged
membranous margins.
Habitat: Gravelly slopes.

Cotula barbata

DAISY FAMILY

Buttons (E), kleinganskos (A)

(Latin *barbatus*, bearded, alluding to the
hairy leaves)

Slender annual herb to 15 cm high. Leaves
crowded in a basal tuft, finely once- or twice-
divided and softly hairy. Flower heads solitary
on wiry stalks, without ray florets, yellow or
white with all the florets bisexual, 10 mm
diameter, surrounded by two series of almost
round bracts with membranous margins.
Habitat: Gravelly slopes.

Felicia brevifolia

DAISY FAMILY

Grey-leaved felicia (E)

(Latin *brevifolius*, short-leaved)

Well-branched shrub to 1 m
high. Leaves variously toothed or lobed, greyish. Flower heads solitary on short stalks, yellow with blue
to mauve ray florets, 15–30 mm diameter,
surrounded by three series of narrow, pointed
bracts.
Habitat: Stony flats and slopes in scrub.

Felicia filifolia

DAISY FAMILY

Needle-leaved felicia, fine-leaved felicia (E), draaibos (A)

(Latin *filifolius*, thread-leaved)

Well-branched shrub to 1 m high. Leaves in tufts, needle-like, lightly dotted with glands. Flower heads solitary on slender stalks, yellow with blue to mauve ray florets, 15–20 mm diameter, surrounded by three series of narrow, pointed bracts.

Habitat: Stony flats and slopes in scrub.

Felicia merxmuelleri

DAISY FAMILY

Namaqualand felicia (E), Namakwa-sambreeltjies (A)

(Honouring German botanist, Hermann Merxmüller)

Shortly hairy annual herb to 25 cm high. Leaves spatula-shaped and covered with short, coarse hairs. Flower heads solitary on slender stalks, yellow with blue ray florets, 15–30 mm diameter, the ray florets without bristles, surrounded by two series of narrow, pointed bracts.

Habitat: Granite outcrops and gravelly slopes.

Felicia australis

DAISY FAMILY

Common felicia (E), sambreeltjies (A)

(Latin *australis*, southern)

Thinly hairy, sprawling annual herb, 5–25 cm high. Leaves very narrow and sometimes lightly toothed with hairs along the margins. Flower heads solitary on slender stalks, yellow with blue to mauve ray florets, 15–18 mm diameter, surrounded by three series of narrow, pointed bracts.

Habitat: Sandy or clay flats.

Senecio cakilefolius

DAISY FAMILY

Namakwahongerblom (A)

(Latin *cakilefolius*, with leaves like the sea rocket, *Cakile maritima*)

Completely hairless annual herb, 15–40 cm high. Leaves elliptical with the margins lightly rolled under and toothed or lobed. Flower heads, several in branched clusters, yellow with mauve or sometimes white ray flowers, 15–18 mm diameter, surrounded by a single series of narrow bracts.

Habitat: Stony slopes, mostly on clay.

Senecio cardaminifolius

DAISY FAMILY

Namaqua groundsel (E)

(Latin *cardaminifolius*, with leaves like bitter-cress, *Cardamine*)

Hairless annual herb, 15–40 cm high. Leaves more or less deeply lobed. Flower heads several in branched clusters, yellow with yellow ray florets, 10–15 mm diameter, surrounded by a single series of narrow bracts.

Habitat: Gravelly and sandy slopes, often in disturbed places.

Senecio erosus

DAISY FAMILY

Sticky-leaved groundsel (E)

(Latin *erosus*, with the margins irregularly toothed as if gnawed)

Tufted perennial to 60 cm high, with smooth or roughly hairy stems issuing from a woolly crown. Leaves mostly in a basal tuft, petiolate and narrowly elliptical with irregularly toothed or lobed margins. Flower heads solitary or few on sparsely leafy stems, yellow with yellow ray florets, 18–20 mm diameter, surrounded by a single series of narrow bracts.

Habitat: Seasonally moist gravelly or clay flats.

Senecio junceus

DAISY FAMILY

Sjambokbos (A)

(Latin *junceus*, rush-like, alluding to the rod-like stems)

Apparently leafless, succulent-stemmed shrub to 90 cm high, with rod-like stems from a woody rootstock. Leaves scale-like, dry. Flower heads in clusters at the branch tips, yellow with ± five short yellow ray florets, 10 mm diameter, surrounded by a single series of narrow bracts.

Habitat: Dry rocky lower slopes.

Senecio corymbiferus

DAISY FAMILY

Grey-leaved bush senecio (E)

(Latin *corymbiferus*, bearing the flower heads in flat-topped clusters known as corymbs)

Succulent shrublet with smooth, greyish stems to 60 cm high. Leaves clustered near the tips, succulent and finger-like with a grey bloom and tapering, pointed tips. Flower heads in clusters at the branch tips, yellow with yellow ray florets, 10 mm diameter, surrounded by a single series of narrow bracts.

Habitat: Dry rocky slopes.

Othonna cylindrica

DAISY FAMILY

Common babooncress (E),

ossierapuisbos (A)

(Latin *cylindricus*, cylindrical, referring to the leaves)

Succulent shrub to 1 m high, with pale grey, brittle stems. Leaves clustered at the branch tips, cylindrical and succulent and covered with a white bloom. Flower heads few in open, branched clusters on long stalks, yellow with yellow ray florets, 15–20 mm diameter, surrounded by a single series of smooth, broad bracts.

Habitat: Sandy and stony flats and rocks, often coastal.

Othonna sedifolia

DAISY FAMILY

Namaqua babooncress (E), karoorapuis (A)
(Latin *sedifolius*, with leaves like a house-leek, *Sedum*)

Succulent shrublet to 60 cm high, with pale grey, brittle stems. Leaves clustered at the branch tips, ovoid or spherical and succulent and covered with a white bloom. Flower heads one to few on long stalks, yellow with yellow ray florets, 15–20 mm diameter, surrounded by a single series of smooth, broad bracts.
Habitat: Stony slopes and banks.

Leysera tenella

DAISY FAMILY

Common wireweed (E), skilpadteebossie (A)
(Latin *tenellus*, delicate)

Annual herb to 20 cm high, branching from the base. Leaves grey and hairy, narrow and thread-like. Flower heads loosely clustered at the ends of the branches, yellow with yellow rays, 15–18 mm diameter, surrounded by several series of stiff bracts that are papery at the tips.
Habitat: Sandy flats.
Notes: *Leysera gnaphalodes* (page 246) is similar but is a shrublet to 40 cm high and the bristles on the seeds are feathery from the base rather than just in the upper part.

Rhynchopsidium pumilum

DAISY FAMILY

Yellow snow (E), geelsneeu (A)
(Latin *pumilus*, dwarf, alluding to the small stature)

Spreading, thinly cobwebby annual herb to 10 cm high, often forming carpets. Leaves narrow or thread-like and hairy. Flower heads solitary on short, slender stalks, yellow with yellow ray florets, 12–15 mm diameter, surrounded by several rows of firm bracts with papery tips.
Habitat: Sandy or gravelly flats.

Dimorphotheca cuneata

DAISY FAMILY

Bosmagriet (A)

(Latin *cuneatus*, wedge-shaped, referring
to the leaves)

Rounded, glandular-hairy and sticky shrublet
to 50 cm high. Leaves elliptical and toothed
to lobed. Flower heads on short peduncles,
yellow with white, salmon or orange ray florets
that are purplish beneath, 40–50 mm diameter,
surrounded by two series of narrow bracts.
Habitat: Stony and shale ridges and flats.
Notes: When in bloom may give the landscape
the appearance of a snow-covered field.

Dimorphotheca tragus

DAISY FAMILY

(= *Castalis tragus*)

Geelmagriet, jakkalsbos (A)

(Latin *tragus*, the goat-like smell of the
armpits, a picturesque but obscure reference)

Cushion-like, tufted perennial to 25 cm high,
sprouting from a woody base. Leaves narrow
and coarsely toothed, rough. Flower heads on
long peduncles, blackish with orange to
salmon-coloured ray florets, 40–50 mm diameter, surrounded by two series of narrow bracts,
nodding in seed. Seeds disc-like and papery.
Habitat: Stony or rocky places in scrub.

Dimorphotheca sinuata

DAISY FAMILY

Namaqualand daisy (E),

Namakwalandmadeliefie, jakkalsblom (A)

(Latin *sinuatus*, sinuate or strongly waved,
referring to the leaf margins)

Sprawling, roughly hairy annual herb to 30 cm
high. Leaves narrowly elliptical and shallowly
lobed or toothed. Flower heads on elongate
peduncles, black with pale orange to biscuit-
coloured ray florets, 40–50 mm diameter,
surrounded by one series of narrow bracts.
Seeds disc-like and papery.
Habitat: Sandy and gravelly slopes.

327

Tripteris microcarpa

DAISY FAMILY

(= *Osteospermum microcarpum*)

(Greek *microcarpus*, small-fruited)

Glandular-hairy, sticky annual or short-lived perennial to 60 cm high. Leaves glandular-hairy and deeply lobed. Flower heads on slender stalks, yellow with yellow ray florets, 15–20 mm diameter surrounded by ± one series of narrow bracts.

Habitat: Arid sandy or gravelly flats, often along seasonal washes.

Tripteris sinuata

DAISY FAMILY

(= *Osteospermum sinuatum*)

Golden windowseed (E), skaapbos (A)

(Latin *sinuatus*, waved, referring to the toothed leaves)

Rounded, brittle-stemmed shrub to 60 cm high, foetid-smelling. Leaves opposite, narrow and conspicuously toothed, leathery with a grey bloom. Flower heads several on branching stems, yellow with golden yellow ray florets, 30–40 mm diameter, drooping in seed, surrounded by two series of narrow bracts. Seeds three-winged, translucent and papery.

Habitat: Dry sandstone or granite outcrops among rocks.

Tripteris oppositifolia

DAISY FAMILY

(= *Osteospermum oppositifolium*)

Dark-eyed windowseed (E), stinkskaapbos (A)

(Latin *oppositifolius*, opposite-leaved)

Rounded, brittle-stemmed shrub to 1 m high, foetid-smelling. Leaves opposite, narrow and obscurely toothed, leathery with a grey bloom. Flower heads several on branching stems, black with pale to golden yellow ray florets, 30–40 mm diameter, drooping in seed, surrounded by two series of narrow bracts. Seeds three-winged, translucent and papery.

Habitat: Dry sandstone or granite outcrops among rocks.

Tripteris amplectens

DAISY FAMILY

(= *Osteospermum amplectens*)

Springbok windowseed (E),

dassiegousblom (A)

(Latin *amplectens*, clasping, alluding to the leaf bases)
Glandular-hairy, aromatic annual herb to 50 cm
high. Leaves elliptical and irregularly toothed.
Flower heads dark purplish with yellow ray
florets, 30–40 mm diameter, surrounded by two
series of narrow bracts with membranous margins narrower than the central green portion,
nodding in seed. Seeds three-winged,
4–5 mm long.
Habitat: Rock outcrops and gravelly flats,
often along roadsides.
Notes: Common around Springbok.

Tripteris hyoseroides

DAISY FAMILY

(= *Osteospermum hyoseroides*)

Namaqua windowseed (E),

dassiegousblom (A)

(Resembling the Mediterranean daisy, *Hyoseris*)
Glandular-hairy, aromatic annual herb to 50 cm
high. Leaves elliptical and irregularly toothed.
Flower heads dark purplish with orange ray
florets, 30–50 mm diameter, surrounded by two
series of bracts with membranous margins
broader than the central green portion, nodding in seed. Seeds three-winged, 7–8 mm long.
Habitat: Stony flats.

Osteospermum pinnatum

DAISY FAMILY

Satin boneseed (E), jakkalsbos (A)

(Latin *pinnatus*, divided into narrow segments like a feather, referring to the leaves)

Sprawling, hairy annual herb to 5 cm high.
Leaves divided to the base into narrow or
thread-like lobes. Flower heads orange with
glistening cream to biscuit ray florets that
are dark at the base, 40–50 mm diameter,
surrounded by one series of narrow bracts.
Seeds warty.
Habitat: Dry gravelly or sandy slopes and flats.

Ursinia calenduliflora
DAISY FAMILY

Namaqua parachute-daisy (E),
berggousblom (A)

(Latin *calenduliflorus*, with flowers like a
Calendula)

Annual herb to 35 cm high. Leaves divided into
narrow lobes. Flower heads dull black with
orange ray florets that have a dark band at the
base, 30–60 mm diameter, surrounded by many
series of overlapping bracts, the innermost
with large, papery tips. Seeds with five white,
papery scale-like wings.
Habitat: Gravelly slopes and flats.

Ursinia chrysanthemoides
DAISY FAMILY

Red parachute-daisy (E), rooibergmagriet (A)

(Resembling a chrysanthemum)

Sprawling annual or perennial
herb to 45 cm high with the stems more or less
woody below. Leaves mostly twice-divided into
narrow lobes. Flower heads glossy black with
orange to reddish ray florets with dark reverse,
35–50 mm diameter, surrounded by many
series of overlapping bracts, the innermost
with large, papery tips. Seeds with five white,
papery scale-like wings plus five whiskers.
Habitat: Gravelly slopes and flats.

Hirpicium alienatum
DAISY FAMILY

Haarbos (A)

(Latin *alienus*, incongruous or foreign, a
reference to its anomalous appearance
when it was first described in the genus *Oedera*)

Twiggy shrub to 1 m high, with stiff blackish
branchlets. Leaves in tufts, narrow with the
margins rolled under, bristly above and white-
felted beneath. Flower heads yellow with pale
or deep yellow ray florets, 20–30 mm diameter,
surrounded by several series of spreading,
spine-like bracts that are joined at the base.
Habitat: Stony shale slopes in scrub.

Berkheya fruticosa

DAISY FAMILY

Large wild thistle (E), vaaldissel (A)

(Latin *fruticosus*, shrubby or bushy)

Shrub with white-woolly stems
to 1,5 m high. Leaves elliptical and lightly
toothed with spiny margins, dark green and
± hairless above but white-woolly beneath.
Flower heads in clusters at the branch tips,
yellow with yellow ray florets, 40–50 mm
diameter, surrounded by several series of
spine-tipped bracts.

Habitat: Dry rocky slopes in scrub.

Didelta spinosa

DAISY FAMILY

Namaqua salad thistle (E), slaaibos (A)

(Latin *spinosus*, spiny, referring to the
leaves)

Shrub to 2 m high. Leaves opposite, glossy,
elliptical and spine-tipped, lobed at the base
with the margins lightly rolled under and
sometimes prickly. Flower heads solitary,
yellow with yellow ray florets, 40–50 mm
diameter, surrounded by two rows of bracts,
the outer four bracts large and leafy and the
inner narrow with prickly teeth.

Habitat: Dry granite and sandstone slopes.

Notes: Highly palatable, especially the dry
leaves in summer.

Didelta carnosa

DAISY FAMILY

Dune salad thistle (E), kusslaaibos (A)

(Latin *carnosus*, fleshy, referring to the
leaves)

Rounded shrublet to 1 m high. Leaves fleshy
and lance-shaped with the margins usually
rolled under, thinly or densely cobwebby.
Flower heads yellow with yellow ray florets,
40–50 mm diameter, surrounded by two rows
of bracts, the outer four bracts large and leafy
and the inner narrow with prickly teeth.

Habitat: Coastal dunes and sandy flats.

Gorteria diffusa

DAISY FAMILY

Beetle daisy (E)

(Latin *diffusus*, diffuse or loosely branched)

Sprawling annual herb to 10 cm high. Leaves narrowly elliptical and sometimes lobed with the margins rolled under, roughly hairy above and white-felted beneath. Flower heads black with orange ray florets, some or all with beetle-like markings at the base, 25–35 mm diameter, surrounded by several series of spine-like bracts.

Habitat: Stony clay or gravelly granitic flats.

Gazania lichtensteinii

DAISY FAMILY

Yellow gazania (E), geelgazania, kougoed (A)

(Named after the nineteenth-century German doctor and naturalist, Martin Lichtenstein)

Annual herb to 20 cm high. Leaves elliptical and toothed with the margins lightly rolled under, leathery and ± hairless above but woolly beneath. Flower heads yellow with yellow to orange ray florets that are marked with small green blotches at the base, 25–35 mm diameter, the bracts joined into a smooth cup that is pushed in at the bottom like a champagne bottle.

Habitat: Arid gravelly and sandy flats, often in washes.

Gazania rigida

DAISY FAMILY

Karoo gazania (E), karoogazania (A)

(Latin *rigidus*, rigid or stiff, alluding to the rather firm-textured leaves)

Tufted stemless perennial herb to 25 cm high. Leaves usually deeply lobed, rarely strap-like with the margins rolled under, thinly hairy above and white-woolly beneath. Flower heads yellow with yellow or orange ray florets usually banded with dark marks at the base, 50–60 mm diameter, the bracts joined into a roughly hairy cup that is rounded at the base.

Habitat: Stony flats and lower slopes.

Gazania krebsiana

DAISY FAMILY

Red gazania (E), rooigazania (A)
(Named after an eighteenth-century
Eastern Cape farmer, George Krebs)

Tufted stemless perennial herb to 20 cm high.
Leaves strap-like or lobed with margins rolled
under, thinly hairy above and white-felted
beneath. Flower heads yellow with yellow to
orange ray florets variously marked at the
base, 50–60 mm diameter, the bracts joined
into a smooth cup that is rounded at the base.
Habitat: Stony flats, often along roadsides.

Arctotheca calendula

DAISY FAMILY

Cape weed (E)
(Named for the purported resemblance to
the marigold genus, *Calendula*)

Tufted to sprawling annual herb to 20 cm high.
Leaves mostly in a basal tuft, paddle-shaped to
deeply lobed or even twice-lobed, roughly
hairy above and white-woolly beneath. Flower
heads black with yellow ray florets that are
paler towards the base or marked with a dark
band, 30–40 mm diameter, surrounded by
several series of bracts, the outer with their
tips bent back. Seeds woolly.
Habitat: Coastal sands and disturbed places
along roads or in lands.

Arctotis fastuosa

DAISY FAMILY

Namaqualand arctotis (E), namakwa-
gousblom (A)
(Latin *fastuosus*, proud or haughty)

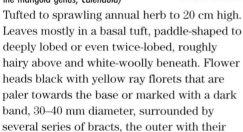

Slightly fleshy, often robust annual herb to
45 cm high. Leaves elliptical and deeply lobed,
often eared at the base and softly white-woolly.
Flower heads solitary, blackish with orange ray
florets that are marked with a dark band at the
base, 60–80 mm diameter, surrounded by
several series of bracts, the outer with short
tails and the inner with rounded, papery tips.
Habitat: Sandy and gravel slopes in drier
areas, often along washes.

Arctotis campanulata

DAISY FAMILY

Kamiesberg arctotis (E)

(Latin *campanulatus*, bell-shaped, referring to the flower heads)

Stemless perennial to 40 cm high. Leaves divided into elliptical lobes with crisped margins, thickly silvery-cobwebby on both sides. Flower heads black with orange ray florets that are marked with a dark band at the base, 50–70 mm diameter, surrounded by several series of bracts, the outer with slender woolly tips and the inner with rounded, papery tips.

Habitat: Seasonally damp granitic flats.

Arctotis acaulis

DAISY FAMILY

Tufted arctotis (E), renostergousblom (A)

(Latin *acaulis*, stemless)

Stemless perennial to 40 cm high. Leaves lanceolate to paddle-shaped and often lobed with obscurely toothed margins, roughly hairy above and grey-felted beneath. Flower heads black with orange, yellow or cream-coloured ray florets that are marked with dark bands at the base, 50–70 mm diameter, surrounded by several series of bracts, the outer with slender woolly tips and the inner with rounded, papery tips.

Habitat: Clay, granitic or limestone flats.

Arctotis scullyi

DAISY FAMILY

(= *Arctotis merxmuelleri*)

Wit-soê (A), soê (N)

(Named after William Charles Scully, Magistrate of Namaqualand in the 1890s)

Perennial herb to 40 cm high. Leaves lance-shaped and shallowly lobed or toothed, very roughly hairy. Flowers black with white ray florets that are banded with black at the base, 40–60 mm diameter, surrounded by several series of bracts, the outer with long dark tails and the inner with rounded, papery tips.

Habitat: Coastal sands in scrub.

A

actinomorphic: radially symmetrical, divisible into equal halves in 2 or more planes

alternate: applied to leaves when they are arranged on the stem such that each one is inserted between the place of insertion of two on the opposite side of the stem

annuals: plants which complete their lifecycle, from seed germination to flowering and seed production, within a year and then die

anther: the fertile part of one of the male organs, comprising the pollen sacs and the connective but excluding the stalk or filament

anthesis: the stage of floral development at which the pollen is shed, usually coinciding with the full opening of the flower

axillary: arising along the stem in the angle formed by a leaf or bract and the stem

B

beak: sterile portion at the tip of an organ, especially the fruit in Geraniaceae and some Brassicaceae

berry: fleshy, indehiscent, many-seeded fruit containing no hard parts except the seeds

bract: leaf-like appendage at the base of the pedicel in most flowers, the flower arising from the angle between the bract and the stem

bulb: underground or surface organ formed by the much swollen leaf-bases of the plant attached to a small disc-like stem from which the roots issue, the organ not renewed totally each year

C

capsule: a dry, non-fleshy fruit comprising more than 1 carpel, usually dehiscent

calyx: collective term for all the sepals, particularly when they are more or less joined together

carpel: a unit of the gynoecium (female part of the flower) when this is compound and the units are fused together

cladode: flattened, leaf-like branch or stem

compressed: flattened from the sides

connective: sterile tissue connecting the pollen sacs of an anther

corm: subterranean organ formed by a much abbreviated and much swollen rhizome which is renewed annually and which is covered by dry leaf bases

corolla: collective term for all the petals, particularly when they are more or less joined together

corymb: racemose inflorescence in which the lower flowers have longer pedicels than the upper

D

deciduous: falling in season

dehiscent: bursting or splitting open at maturity, used of fruits that shed their seeds and of anthers that rupture to shed their pollen

dioecious: of species in which flowers of separate sexes are borne on different individuals

disc: specialized part of the receptacle, usually producing nectar, within the calyx or corolla and stamens; the central part of the flower head or capitulum in Asteraceae as opposed to the rays

discolorous: with the upper and lower surfaces distinctly differently coloured

E

exserted: of stamens which protude beyond the mouth of the corolla

F

filament: the stalk of an anther, usually thread-like

floret: small flower, especially the flower of daisies; **disc florets:** the central florets of a daisy, having 5 small equal petals each; **ray florets:** the outer florets of a daisy, having a single very large strap-shaped petal-like lobe each

G

globose: nearly spherical

H

herbaceous: soft and not woody (of plants); green and leaf-like (of sepals)

I

included: of stamens which are completely enclosed within the corolla

inferior: applied to the ovary when the other floral organs are inserted above it

internode: the part of the stem between the sites of leaf insertions

involucre: a ring of bracts, usually surrounding a cluster of flowers

M

monoecious: of species in which flowers of separate sexes are borne on the same individual

N

node: the part of the stem at which a leaf is inserted

nut: a hard and indehiscent one-seeded fruit

nutlet: a dry and indehiscent one-seeded fruit or part of a compound fruit

O

opposite: applied to leaves when they are arranged on the stem such that each one is inserted opposite another on the other side of the stem

ovary: part of the female organ consisting of one or more chambers containing the ovules

P

palmate: shaped like a hand, thus lobed or divided from a common point

panicle: a branched inflorescence in which each branch ends in a flower, the youngest flowers in the centre and the oldest having been produced beneath these

pedicel: stalk of an individual flower

peduncle: stalk of a group of flowers or an inflorescence

perianth: the sepals and petals together, particularly when they are similar

persistent: not falling or decaying in time

petiole: the stalk of a leaf

plumose: feather-like

R

raceme: an unbranched inflorescence in which the flowers are stalked or pedicellate, the oldest at the bottom and the youngest at the top

receptacle: the portion of the axis on which the parts of the flower are inserted

rhizome: underground stem producing rootlets and the apex bearing stems or leaves

S

sessile: attached directly to the stem without an intervening stalk

shrub: a woody plant smaller than a tree and without a single trunk but with several main stems from the base.

spathulate: spoon-shaped with a narrow claw and expanded blade

spike: an unbranched inflorescence in which the flowers are sessile, the oldest at the bottom and the youngest at the top

spathe: large bract enclosing a flower cluster

stamen: one of the male parts of the flower, comprising an anther and its filament

staminodes: rudimentary stamen producing no pollen but often functioning as a petal or nectary

stigma: tip of the style or style branches which pick up the pollen grains during pollination

style: the thread-like stalk connecting the ovary with the stigma

stipule: a leaf-like or linear appendage, usually in pairs, at or near the base of the petiole in some plants, sometimes transformed into spines

succulents: plants which store water in their swollen stems or leaves and which can survive periods of drought by drawing on these water reserves

superior: applied to the ovary when the other floral organs are inserted below it

T

tepal: sepal or petal when no distinction is made between them

tuber: a much swollen root or part of a root

U

umbel: an unbranched inflorescence in which the flowers are stalked or pedicellate and arise from the same point at the tip of the peduncle, the oldest on the periphery and the youngest at the centre

W

whorled: applied to leaves when they are arranged on the stem such that three or more are inserted in a ring

Z

zygomorphic: bilaterally symmetrical, divisible into equal halves in 1 plane only